MOLDS, YEASTS, and ACTINOMYCETES

Henrici's

MOLDS, YEASTS, and

ACTINOMYCETES

A Handbook for Students of Bacteriology

Henrici, Arthur Trautwein [handwritten]

SECOND EDITION

By

CHARLES E. SKINNER, Ph.D.

Assistant Professor of Bacteriology
University of Minnesota, Minneapolis, Minnesota

CHESTER W. EMMONS, Ph.D.

Principal Mycologist, Division of Infectious Diseases
National Institute of Health, Bethesda, Maryland

HENRY M. TSUCHIYA, Ph.D.

Research Associate, Division of Microbiology
Hormel Institute, University of Minnesota
Austin, Minnesota

New York: JOHN WILEY & SONS, Inc.
London: CHAPMAN & HALL, Limited

PREFACE TO THE SECOND EDITION

Molds, Yeasts, and Actinomycetes by Henrici, published in 1930, has been out of date for a number of years. The late author made a start on a revision but had to abandon the task because of failing health. We undertook the revision very largely out of respect and regard for Dr. Henrici. We were aided by beginnings of a revision, which, however, were entirely concerned with the first three chapters. Chapter II was prepared by Henrici and is inserted almost exactly as he wrote it. However, scattered notes in his personal marked copy and especially the memory of many conversations indicated the general nature of the revision which he hoped to make.

Mere verbal changes, a modernization of nomenclature, a few deletions and insertions of new material were found insufficient. A complete rewriting was essential, and a considerable change in arrangement of topics seemed advisable. Two entirely new chapters dealing with material scarcely mentioned in the first edition have been added. Some deletions of portions of the old book, which experience had shown were of limited value, were made. In spite of all this, however, we have attempted to produce a book in the spirit of the original book—namely a discussion of molds, yeasts, and actinomycetes for students of bacteriology. Like Henrici, we include in the term students many individuals who have completed their formal education. It was for such students that Henrici called his first edition a handbook.

Dr. Henrici was very insistent that, for their own good, bacteriologists would do well to have some working knowledge of mycology. Inasmuch as most books on fungi are written for the botanist, the agriculturist, the phytopathologist, and others, the emphasis, in general, is often on those forms of least interest to the bacteriologist, and the forms of greatest interest to him are likely to be ignored or merely mentioned. Here the emphasis is reversed. The stress on medical and industrial applications of mycology has been retained in this edition and has been intensified. Moreover, Henrici was of the opinion that bacteriologists, whatever their special field, should have some knowledge of the morphology of fungi—classification, cytology, genetics, life cycles, and so on—so that they might better

v

understand and more intelligently discuss the many problems of the morphology of bacteria. He also maintained that an elementary knowledge of mycology, including a vocabulary, should be a special requisite for writers on variation and so-called life cycles in bacteria. He frequently predicted that, if and when sexuality in bacteria was demonstrated and proved, the persons responsible would be individuals with some knowledge of modern mycology. We, therefore, have not cut the discussions of life cycles in Chapter I and "sexuality" of yeasts in a later chapter. Rather we have, as Henrici explicitly intended, expanded them considerably. The increased knowledge in recent years in the very things of greatest importance to the bacteriologist, namely, "sexuality" in fungi and medical and industrial applications of mycology, has necessitated a larger book. This was foreseen by Henrici who at one time considered the advisability of two separate volumes.

Unfortunately, information on certain subjects was unavailable to us because of its restricted or confidential nature or because certain published materials were not available in the United States during the war period in which the manuscript was prepared. We should like to ask the indulgence of our readers on such matters and we hope that it will be possible to rectify these omissions later.

Although separated by half a continent, we have kept in touch with one another by correspondence and most parts of the text have been read and approved by the other two authors. Troublesome points in nomenclature and other slight differences of opinion were resolved by copious use of the mails. Although many suggestions from the other two authors were incorporated, in general Chapter I was prepared by Skinner from Henrici's notes; Chapter II is Henrici's own; Chapter III was prepared by Skinner from Henrici's notes, and many additions, deletions, and rearrangements were made by Emmons; Chapters IV, V, IX, and XII were prepared by Skinner; Chapters VI, VII, X, and XIII by Emmons; and Chapters VIII, XI, and XIV by Tsuchiya. We hope that those who use the book will make comments and criticisms and write their suggestions for improvement.

We wish to express thanks to various individuals who have assisted us: to Dr. Louise Dosdall who read the rough draft of Chapter I and made many suggestions for materials to be included; to Dr. B. O. Dodge who read the same chapter in its nearly final form; to Dr. J. J. Christensen who went over the discussion on the Basidiomycetes; to Dr. Charles Thom who made many suggestions for the revision of Dr. Henrici's chapter on Fungi Imperfecti, and to Dr.

Rhoderick Sprague who read the rough draft after revision; to Dr. L. L. Ashburn who read Chapters VI and VII; to Dr. H. Koepsell who read portions of Chapter XI; and to Dr. S. A. Waksman and Dr. Charles Drake who read Chapter XIII. Thanks are due Dr. L. G. Romell, Experimentalfältet, Sweden, who in the face of great difficulties got through to us much information on Björkman's theory of mycorrhiza, and to Dr. W. P. Larson, "Chief" to Dr. Henrici and to two of us, who suggested the revision and encouraged its completion. We wish to thank Dr. Sprague, Dr. N. H. Huff, Dr. Kenneth Raper, and Miss Hazel Jean Henrici for original drawings and photographs; also the following holders of copyrighted figures and tables, each of which is credited to the author in the text: Macmillan and Company, Ltd., Dr. Fred J. Seaver, *Phytopathology*, Williams and Wilkins Co., Minnesota Agricultural Experiment Station, American Medical Association, New York Botanical Garden, W. B. Saunders Co., United States Department of Agriculture, Dr. S. A. Waksman, Dr. R. L. Starkey, and Dr. J. R. Porter.

C. E. SKINNER
C. W. EMMONS
H. M. TSUCHIYA

August, 1945

PREFACE TO THE FIRST EDITION

The bacteriologist is continually confronted with molds, yeasts, and Actinomycetes, no matter what may be the particular field of application of the science in which he is engaged. Many of these are but contaminants, as Thom says, "noxious weeds" which plague him by overgrowing his cultures of bacteria. But an ever-increasing number of fungi are found to be causes of disease processes in man and animals, while in the chemical transformations of the soil and spoilage of foods and other organic products of industry they are of equal importance with the bacteria. The industrial uses of these microorganisms have been known to a limited extent for some time, but promise to undergo extensive development in the near future. These fungi cannot, then, be ignored by the bacteriologist.

The lower fungi are of interest, however, not alone because of their practical importance. Very significant and interesting facts are being discovered concerning their complicated life-cycles, particularly with regard to the behavior of the nuclei, and their sexual relations, which will have an important bearing upon problems of variation and evolution in this group. Since it is becoming daily more clearly evident that at least some of the bacteria belong to the fungi, and there is a well-defined movement to trace similar cycles and relationships in the bacteria, it behooves the bacteriologist to make himself acquainted with at least the essentials of this newer knowledge.

This book will, it is hoped, help fill the gap existing between the brief and inadequate discussions of the fungi found in current textbooks of bacteriology and the extensive monographs and technical articles which treat of particular groups. The latter are too extensive to be easily used, too technical to be easily understood by the student of bacteriology who generally has no foundation in mycology.

In this work I have tried to present sufficient information about fungi in general, and about those forms of importance to the bacteriologist in particular, so that the student will be prepared to use the more technical literature; to present such description and keys that will enable him with confidence to identify some of the commoner

ix

or more important species, and at least approximately place the others within their proper family and genus; and to furnish references to general works or specific monographs where detailed information on particular forms may be found.

The book has grown out of a lecture course which has been offered for some years to advanced students in that ever-growing group that have planned their college work with the definite idea of becoming bacteriologists. It is therefore a sort of textbook. But it will also, I hope, find a field of usefulness as a handbook to be kept in the clinical or technical laboratory for reference when problems involving yeasts, molds, or Actinomycetes are encountered. I feel strongly that bacteriology has distinctly suffered from a too sharp division of the science into categories according to particular fields of application. I have therefore attempted to deal equally with the medical and industrial applications of the subject. If the book seems to be somewhat overbalanced on the medical side, this is due to the richer literature available in that field.

No claims are made for the work on the grounds of completeness or originality. It has been my task to select, condense, and where possible simplify, from the extensive available literature, such information as seemed important enough to be necessary, tangible enough to be useful, to the student of microbiology. The subject has been plagued by a tendency of its workers to create new species on the slightest provocation, to classify and reclassify, until a bewildering number of synonymous names are in use. My approach to the subject has been purely pragmatic. I have avoided discussion of debated problems of taxonomy except where such is necessary for an intelligent understanding of the literature. I have felt that to be useful the book must be kept within the scope of a small handbook, and must be made as simple as the subject matter will allow. I have therefore omitted discussions of numerous species and genera which are of no practical importance, or which are so uncommon that they are not likely to be encountered in routine bacteriological work.

The literature cited includes, for the most part, only works of a general character or specific monographs in which extensive bibliographies may be found, save that more recent contributions not found in such works have been included. I have as far as possible provided original illustrations. It has been necessary, however, to borrow illustrations of material that was not available to me. . . . Department of Plant Pathology of this institution. Dr. H. E. Michelson of the Division of Dermatology . . . Dr. J. C. McKinley of the Division of Neurology . . . Dr. F. W. Tanner . . . Dr. P.

Tate . . . Dr. Aldo Castellani . . . Dr. W. J. MacNeal . . . Dr. A. H. Sanford . . . Dr. Lendner . . . Dr. Thom . . . and Dr. Waksman. . . . I am indebted to my colleagues in the Department of Bacteriology for many helpful suggestions, and in particular to Dr. H. O. Halvorson for his cooperation in preparing the section on alcoholic fermentation. To all of these I make grateful acknowledgment.

ARTHUR T. HENRICI

The University of Minnesota
April 1, 1930

CONTENTS

CHAPTER I

THE STRUCTURE AND CLASSIFICATION OF THE FUNGI

The molds, yeasts, and actinomycetes are Fungi, a subdivision of the Thallophyta, one of the four divisions of the plant kingdom. A division in botany corresponds to a phylum in zoology. The Thallophytes are characterized by their growth in irregular plant masses not differentiated into roots, stems, and leaves like higher plants. Such a mass of plant tissue is called a thallus. The Thallophytes comprise the Algae and the Fungi. The former, being provided with chlorophyll, are capable of synthesizing their food from inorganic compounds by the energy of sunlight; the latter, being devoid of chlorophyll, must depend for their food upon organic matter synthesized by other organisms, growing as either saprophytes or parasites. The lichens (Lichenes) have been considered a third subdivision of the Thallophytes, because they are peculiar plants composed of algae and fungi growing together in symbiosis. Most modern authors classify them with the Fungi.

The fungi are subdivided into the true fungi or Eumycetes, the bacteria or Schizomycetes, and the slime-molds or Myxomycetes. The relationships of the last group are not clearly understood; in fact some biologists believe that they should be classified with the protozoa in the animal kingdom. The relationships of the bacteria are also in some doubt, but the actinomycetes seem clearly to represent a transition between them and the molds. The molds and yeasts belong to the Eumycetes. In this work where the word "fungi" is used without qualification, it will refer only to the Eumycetes.

The fungi may be unicellular or multicellular. In some, as the true yeasts, the organism is ordinarily one-celled, though a few cells may be temporarily attached in irregular clusters when actively growing. Other fungi, however, may grow as one-celled organisms for a time, or in a particular environment, and become multicellular later or under changed conditions. Many of the fungi parasitic for man and animals show this dimorphism, growing in one form in the body, in another form on artificial culture media.

Mycelium. The multicellular fungi are composed of cells arranged end-to-end to form filaments or hyphae. These filaments branch

1

and rebranch and intertwine, sometimes even uniting or anastomosing, to form a structure called mycelium. This mycelium may form a loose meshwork as in the molds or a compact tissue as in the mushrooms. Thus, although fundamentally the same in their finer structure, fungi may show extreme variations in their external appearance, due simply to the degree of compactness of the mycelium.

Such variations in external appearance have to some extent been used in the past as a basis for classification, but they are not always correlated with other characters and are unreliable. The same organism may form a loose mold-like mycelium in some circumstances, and a fleshy solid tissue in others. The true relationships of the fungi are indicated by minute cell characters, and more especially by their modes of reproduction.

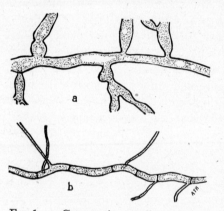

FIG. 1. *a,* Coenocytic mycelium; *b,* septate mycelium.

In some fungus tissues, however, the cells are not arranged in filaments, but form compact masses of round or polygonal cells like those of higher plants. Such a tissue is called a pseudoparenchyma; its cells have their origin in mycelium. Sometimes such masses of fleshy tissue become quite dry and firm, developing thick, hard walls, and may have the property of maintaining vitality in a dormant state for long periods.

In some fungi the mycelium is not divided into individual cells by crosswalls or septa. The entire mass of mycelium forms one large cell containing many nuclei. This absence of septa makes possible a flowing of protoplasm. Such a structure (described as being coenocytic) also occurs in the filaments of certain green algae, and has been considered (together with other evidence) to indicate a relationship between these algae and those fungi which possess it. Consequently the latter have been called Phycomycetes, or alga-like fungi. The other fungi possess a septate mycelium. In these, each cell, separated from the others by crosswalls, may contain one or more nuclei. In some of the Basidiomycetes and Ascomycetes the mycelium at certain stages of its development is made up of cells, each with two nuclei. Streaming of protoplasm has been shown by Buller and others to occur in septate hyphae through central pores of the septa. Slow motion pictures of growing septate mycelia, however, show that the streaming is very much cut down as soon as the septa are formed.

Thus the three main classes of fungi may be recognized, in part at least, by the character of their mycelium: the Phycomycetes possess non-septate or coenocytic mycelium (Fig. 1); the Ascomycetes and Basidiomycetes septate mycelium. These characters, however, are not the main ones upon which the classification of fungi is based, and are not absolutely constant, for the mycelium of both Ascomycetes and Basidiomycetes may be non-septate when the plant is very young, and the mycelium of Phycomycetes will develop septa in certain conditions, as for separating off spores.

Cells of Fungi. The cells of fungi are much like those of higher organisms in their general characters. They possess a cell wall which is frequently of appreciable thickness. This was formerly thought to be composed of a substance similar to cellulose, though it does not give the microchemical reactions of cellulose, and was called "fungus-cellulose"; but more recent investigations indicate that it is chitin, or a mixture or compound of chitin and cellulose.

Within the cell wall is the cell proper, or protoplast. It contains one or more nuclei, as indicated above. These are very small and not easily demonstrated, special complicated staining methods being required. The cytoplasm generally presents a granular or foamy appearance due to the accumulation within it of various reserve substances in the form of granules or vacuoles. These may be of various kinds—fat, carbohydrate, and protein. The amount of this reserve material varies with the age of the mycelium; in old portions of the thallus it may nearly fill the cell. Fat appears in the form of very highly refractile globules; it may be identified by staining with Sudan III. Carbohydrate is stored as glycogen as in animals, not as starch as in green plants. Protein is apparently stored in several forms. A noteworthy reserve substance almost peculiar to fungi is known as volutin or metachromatic material. It is identical with the material found in some bacteria designated in them, metachromatic granules or polar bodies. It may appear either as granules or as vacuoles, the former sometimes floating in the latter. It is probably a colloid which may exist in either the sol or the gel state. There has been considerable discussion regarding its true nature and function, which will be gone into in further detail in connection with the yeasts. It is generally considered a reserve material and recent studies indicate that it is a free nucleic acid differing slightly from the thymonucleic acid found characteristically in the nucleus itself. It is easily demonstrated by vital staining with neutral red.

Growth and Differentiation of Mycelium. Although in many cases any part of a thallus may grow and give rise to a new individual if artificially transferred to a new medium, normally fungi are reproduced by specialized cells called spores. These spores give rise to a new mycelium by germination, i.e., the protoplasm within the spore absorbs water and swells when in a favorable environment, bursts through the spore wall, and extends outward as a long filamentous process called a germ tube. Several of these may be formed from one spore. Growth is mainly at the apex of this germ tube. At first the mycelium is non-septate, but after it reaches a certain size, septa are formed in those varieties which possess them, beginning in the oldest part of the mycelium and proceeding toward the periphery. Thus in a mold which is still growing there may be no septa at the tips of the filaments of mycelium. Several stages of spore germination are shown in Fig. 2.

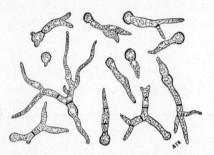

FIG. 2. Germination of spores (conidia) of a species of Aspergillus.

With most multicellular fungi there can be seen a differentiation of the mycelium into two parts: a vegetative portion which burrows into the substrate, digests and absorbs it, and a reproductive portion which usually extends into the air and forms and discharges the reproductive bodies or spores. The reproductive mycelium and its spores are widely diverse in different kinds of fungi and serve to classify and identify them. Not infrequently one finds molds growing on artificial culture media which do not form any reproductive bodies. They can develop only imperfectly on such a medium. Such molds are called *Mycelia sterila,* and usually cannot be identified with any degree of satisfaction.

Oidia and Yeast-like Cells. In addition to reproduction by specialized bodies or spores, many species of fungi can also propagate by the separation of cells from any part of the mycelium, including the vegetative. Such methods, however, are not peculiar to any class of fungi and do not serve to classify. The same type may be formed by widely diverse species. But in some species they occur so regularly or are so prominent that they may be of great value in identification.

These free cells may be formed by a segmentation of the mycelium into its component cells by a split through the septa. The resulting cells may be cylindrical in form (Fig. 119) as in *Geotrichum candidum*, or may become rounded as in *Mucor racemosus* (Fig. 36). Free cells formed in this way are known as oidia. They may give rise to new free cells by division or by budding, or may give rise to mycelium. Free cells may also arise from the mycelium by either lateral or terminal budding, as also occurs with *M. racemosus* (Fig. 37) and with the various species of Candida (Fig. 116). These may also form either new free cells (by budding) or mycelium, depending upon their environment.

Such free cells differ from spores in that they are not equipped for maintaining life in a dormant condition for long periods of time. They do serve, however, to multiply rapidly and disseminate the species, especially in liquid media. They are to be looked upon as "growth forms" rather then specialized reproductive bodies. The conditions which determine their appearance are quite diverse for different species. Thus in Mucors they are formed only under semi-anaerobic conditions, whereas in Candida they are predominant in aerobic cultures in sugar media.

These oidia or free cells bear a great resemblance to and may be readily mistaken for true yeasts, especially when they multiply by budding. In fact, as will be shown later, yeasts are probably descended from more complexly organized fungi, which have permanently lost the power to produce mycelium and maintain only the one-celled growth form. But, as pointed out above, yeast-like cells may be formed under certain circumstances by representatives of all the great classes of fungi, Phycomycetes, Ascomycetes, and Basidiomycetes. Similarly we may trace, with the true yeasts, evidences (in their spores) of relationships to at least two of these classes, Ascomycetes and Basidiomycetes. Yeasts, then, are a heterogeneous group of fungi which maintain a unicellular growth form, and are not an independent class of organisms. Their classification together is only for convenience and does not imply a true systematic relationship.

Chlamydospores. With many species of fungi we may find a cell here and there in the mycelium (including the submersed or vegetative portion) which becomes differentiated from the others by increased size, due to the storage of much reserve foodstuff, and by a markedly thickened cell wall. These are known as chlamydospores. They are particularly adapted for maintaining vitality through long periods of dormancy. They remain intact and viable after the remainder of the mycelium has died and disintegrated (see Fig. 36).

Like the oidia and the yeast-like cells, chlamydospores are not peculiar to any class of fungi, but may be formed by quite diverse species. Moreover, they are particularly likely to develop in just those species that frequently form free vegetative cells, and one may often find all transitions between the actively vegetative yeast-like cells and the dormant chlamydospores. Similarly, one may find all transitions between the vegetative oidia formed in the submersed mycelium of an organism and the conidia or true spores formed by its aerial mycelium. These transitions have led to much confusion in classification and nomenclature. These transitional types of growth or reproduction are particularly frequent in many of the lower forms of fungi important to the bacteriologist.

Spores. The spores proper are very constant in their characters and mode of formation and are therefore largely relied upon for classification and identification. They may be either sexual, i.e., formed either directly or indirectly after the fusion of nuclei from two similar or dissimilar cells, or asexual, i.e., by the division of a single cell without fusion of nuclei. Some fungi reproduce by only one method, some by both, the latter forming non-sexual spores at one stage of their life history and sexual ones at another stage. In some parasitic fungi, the rusts, two different hosts may be necessary for the life cycle, and several kinds of spores may be produced in succession in each host, so that the cycle becomes complicated.

Asexual Spores. Asexual spores are usually formed in great abundance, are ordinarily capable of dormancy, and serve to disseminate the species. At times they are enclosed in a slimy fluid, which may attract insects that carry them to a new habitat. More often they are dry and, being of light weight and small size, may be spread widely by the wind. Mold spores are abundant in the atmosphere. Asexual spores may be divided into two groups according to their mode of formation: endogenous and exogenous.

In one large class of fungi, the Phycomycetes, the asexual spores are surrounded by a membrane during their formation. A cell at the tip of a filament of mycelium is cut off from the rest of the filament by a crosswall. The multinucleate protoplasm in this cell now separates into a number of small portions each of which develops a membrane. These small bodies are sporangiospores and the original cell wall forms a sac, the sporangium, to contain them. The filament which bears this sporangium is a sporangiophore. When the sporangiospores are mature, the sporangium either ruptures from internal pressure or it is dissolved by secreted enzymes, and so the sporangio-spores are set free. If sporangiospores are ciliated they are called zoospores. See Figs. 23 and 31.

Exogenous spores, either unicellular or multicellular, may be formed from the mycelium in several ways, but in all cases they are born free, not contained within membranes. Collectively they are called conidia and the stalks of mycelium which bear them are conidiophores. The term sporophore means a differentiated portion of mycelium which bears spores. It is a more general term than sporangiophore, conidiophore, etc. In recent years many mycologists have distinguished more carefully between the different sorts of conidia, especially in the class of Fungi Imperfecti. Such distinctions were first clearly made by Vuillemin, who introduced new names to indicate the various sorts.

Vuillemin divided exogenous spores into two main divisions, thallospores and "conidia vera." The true conidia, in contrast to the thallospores, are produced by an abstriction of the hyphae. The thallospores are further divided into arthrospores, produced by the disarticulation of a filament of septate mycelium into its component cells, and blastospores which are produced by budding from the ends or sides of the filaments of mycelium (Fig. 118). These two sorts of thallospores thus correspond to the two sorts of unicellular growth forms previously described as oidia and yeast-like cells. The distinction between thallospores and unicellular growth forms is not clear, but in general the spores are formed on aerial mycelium, are dry, and are capable of remaining dormant and of being distributed by the wind, whereas the unicellular growth forms are produced by the submerged mycelium, are moist, and are capable of continued growth as unicellular bodies. But one may find in a single culture of, for instance, *Geotrichum candidum* all transitions from submerged oidia to aerial arthrospores, and recent authors have tended to avoid such distinctions, referring for example to the yeast-like growth forms of *Candida albicans* as blastospores and all the reproductive bodies of Geotrichum as arthrospores or oidia. We shall, in general, follow this usage.

True conidia were subdivided by Vuillemin according to whether they were borne on what he interpreted as undifferentiated hyphae as in Sporotrichum, or on well-defined conidiophores as in most Fungi Imperfecti. See Figs. 45 and 52. Among the latter he distinguished those which were borne on terminal, differentiated, bottle-shaped cells of the conidiophores, the phialides or sterigmata. Conidia borne on phialides have occasionally been called phialospores. See Fig. 52.

Vuillemin recognized two further types of conidia. Hemispores were considered to be transitional between arthrospores and true conidia. Aleuriospores (in French, "aleuries") were differentiated from true conidia by the fact that they are not set free when mature, but are only liberated upon the disintegration of the mycelium that forms them. They are analogous to lateral chlamydospores. Recent workers have not recognized either of these as valid distinctions from true conidia.

Fungi may form more than one type of conidium from a single thallus. Thus in the dermatophytes some species form small unicellular conidia of the type which Vuillemin called aleuriospores, and large multicellular fusiform conidia which have been called spindle-spores. See Fig. 79. Certain other fungi may produce apparently the same kinds of conidia from different types of conidiophores. Some of the fungi isolated from cases of chromoblastomycosis have been found to form conidia from such different types of conidiophores. See Fig. 103. Since the classification of the molds is largely dependent upon the characters of the sporophores and the spores, such multiple types of conidia and conidiophores lead to a great deal of confusion.

In recent literature dealing with fungi which produce two sorts of conidia, they have often been classified according to size, as microconidia and macroconidia. Thus the bodies formerly referred to as aleuriospores in the dermatophytes are now often called microconidia or simply conidia; the spindle-spores are referred to as macroconidia. In some fungi it has been shown that the microconidia are sex cells or spermatia, but this is not generally true. There are also so-called "conidia" which are actually sporangia containing one or only a few sporangiospores. They are seen singly or in chains and resemble closely true exogenous conidia. Actually their method of formation and the fact that the spores themselves, or small groups of them, are surrounded each by a membrane, show their true nature of sporangia. They are usually called conidia but sporangiola is a better term for them (Fig. 42).

Sexual Spores. Spores resulting from the fusion of nuclei and subsequent reduction division are produced in most of the lower fungi less frequently and less abundantly than are the asexual spores. Here the functions of sex, concerned with heredity and variation, are to some extent separated from the functions of multiplication and distribution of the species, which is carried on mainly by the conidia or sporangiospores. Often these "sexual spores" may be produced only in some particular habitat, or in the presence of some environmental factor which is not at all necessary for asexual reproduction.

Sexual spores result from the fusion of two nuclei containing chromosomes in the haploid, or 1x number. The fusion of the gametes, followed by a fusion of the nuclei, leads to the diploid, or 2x chromosome number. Immediately after fusion of cells or at some later stage in the life history of the organism, a reduction division leads to a segregation of the "sexes" and to the haploid state of the nucleus. In all this the fungi behave in many respects like other plants and animals that reproduce sexually. Some of the fungi, however, exhibit certain special features.

In some cases fusion of the gametangia, that is, the structures which contain the gametes, is not followed by an immediate fusion of the nuclei. From the fused cells there may arise an extensive mycelium with binucleate cells. The paired nuclei divide simultaneously and one nucleus from each parent remains in the old cell and one of each goes into the new cell. This is known as conjugate nuclear division. In some cases the pairs of nuclei are not separated by septa until just before maturity. The nuclei, however, continue to divide separately and are found in pairs, each nucleus of the pair being of opposite "sex" to the other. The mycelium with paired nuclei of opposite "sex" which divides conjugately is known as the dikaryon or is described as dikaryotic. A mycelium such as fused to produce this dikaryon is often called the haploid mycelium. A haploid mycelium consists of uninucleate or multinucleate cells, all nuclei in the mycelium being haploid and identical genetically. All the nuclei were derived ultimately from the same uninucleate haploid spore. This dikaryon may give rise to binucleate spores which, when they germinate on the proper substrate, give rise to mycelium with paired nuclei again. Eventually the nuclei fuse in special organs and this fusion is followed immediately or after a period of dormancy by a reduction division. In many yeasts this diploid cell proliferates for a time before reduction division. Tracing the nuclear fusions and segregations, the diploid or the dikaryotic and the haploid stages of the fungus through its life history, has become an important part of modern mycology. It would take us too far afield to discuss this in detail. The reader is referred to monographs of Gäumann and of Kniep and to current botanical journals for further information.

Homothallism and Heterothallism. In some fungi the gametes may arise from the same thallus or plant mass and are said to be homothallic. In many cases the cells which fuse must be derived from separate thalli, usually not of the same sex, and the process is called one of heterothallic conjugation. Heterothallism was first discovered in fungi by Blakeslee. It is widespread among the fungi and has been important in studying their life cycles, heredity, and variations since it makes it possible to carry, in many cases, the sexes in separate pure cultures and to make crosses at will. Hybrids may frequently be formed and certain fungi are being used by geneticists. Their rapid growth and fructification and the fact that they can so readily be grown in absolutely pure culture, under conditions controlled at will, give fungi a decided advantage over seed plants, fruit flies, etc.

Heterogamy and Isogamy. In some cases the cells which fuse are morphologically differentiated into male and female elements. In some primitive forms, a passive egg cell may be fertilized by a motile sperm cell. In higher forms the smaller or male cell is designated an antheridium, the larger or female cell an oogonium. In many fungi, however, the gametangia are not morphologically distinguishable. Being exactly alike in appearance, they cannot be called male and female, but are designated + and −. Where the sex cells are differentiated, reproduction is said to be heterogamous; when they are alike the process is isogamous. Isogamy is often associated with heterothallism, in which case the whole thallus is + or −. Instead of the term sex, sign is sometimes used where there is no morphological differentiation into oogonia and antheridia.

Multipolar Sexuality. Sex in the fungi is still further complicated by the occurrence in some species of more than two "sexes." In some of the Basidiomycetes one may find that of the four basidiospores, the nuclei of the mycelium from one may pair with the nuclei in the mycelium from only one of the other three; thus mycelium from basidiospore 1 may conjugate with 2 but not with 3 or 4, while 3 will conjugate with 4 but not with 1 or 2. Here there are obviously not two but four "sexes." However, in some species only two types of spores are produced from a single basidium. Mycelium from spore 1 or 2 will mate with mycelium from spore 3 or 4, however the hyphae may anastamose from any mycelium of the same species: 1 and 1, 1 and 2, 3, or 4, etc., but the nuclei will pair and divide conjugately only when the proper "sexes" come together. The mycelium from a single spore in some species may fuse and divide conjugately with mycelia from any one of the four spores from another individual of the same species collected from some distant area. By matching spores from many collections, a large number of races or strains capable of fertile conjugation may be obtained. A somewhat similar situation is found in some of the ciliated protozoa. Such a condition, where apparently more than two "sexes" occur, has been designated multipolar sexuality, and the different strains capable of conjugation have been called mating types rather than sexes. The term mating type has come, to a considerable extent, to replace the term sex in discussions of the Basidiomycetes.

Classes of Fungi. Instead of recognizing only one class of true fungi, the Eumycetes, most mycologists recognize four classes, which together with the Schizomycetes and the Myxomycetes make up the subdivision Fungi. They are Basidiomycetes, Ascomycetes, Phycomycetes, and Fungi Imperfecti. This last is an artificial class created to include the fungi whose perfect stage, that is, the stage involving sexual reproduction, has not been observed. The first three classes are divided upon the basis of their sexual reproduction. In the Basidiomycetes the sexual spores, basidiospores, are exogenous and typically four in number. In the Ascomycetes the sexual ascospores are endogenous and typically eight in number. The Phycomycetes form sexual spores which are in some cases single and in others multiple. There are also other differences between these three classes. Many modern mycologists divide the Phycomycetes into two or three classes, each of equal rank with the other three classes.

Basidiomycetes. The class Basidiomycetes comprises in part the large, fleshy fungi, as the mushrooms, the puffballs, and the bracket fungi which grow upon trees. These are the Homobasidiomycetes. Some species are known to form oidia in cultures, and some form conidia on either the mononucleate or binucleate mycelium or both, but mostly they reproduce by only one type of spore, the basidiospore. What we call a mushroom consists of only the spore-forming or reproductive part of the plant. There is an extensive vegetative mycelium penetrating the substrate.

Life Cycle of a Gilled Mushroom. The stalk of a mushroom is composed of numerous filaments of mycelium arranged in a compact bundle. These terminate in the gills in the form of swollen or pear-shaped tips, the basidia. In most species each basidium gives rise to four basidiospores attached each to a minute stalk, the sterigma (Fig. 3). When these basidiospores germinate they give rise to a haploid mycelium which sooner or later becomes uninucleate, i.e., divided by septa into cells with but one nucleus each. In heterothallic species, if mycelia from two mating types come in contact the hyphae may anastamose and the nuclei pair. From this point on, the paired nuclei divide conjugately and an extensive binucleate mycelium, in many species with clamp connections at the septa, is formed (Fig. 4a). Progeny of the original paired nuclei, many nuclear generations removed, fuse in the basidia.

Conjugate nuclear division of many species of Basidiomycetes is accomplished by the formation of clamp connections. From the terminal binucleate cell, a hook bends back (Fig. 4b), each nucleus divides (Fig. 4c), and two septa are formed, one cutting off a single nucleus in the hook and the other cutting off another nucleus of opposite mating type in the penultimate cell, but leaving one of each mating type in the terminal cell (Fig. 4d). The hook and the penultimate cell then anastamose and each cell now has two nuclei of

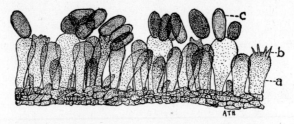

FIG. 3. Section through the margin of a gill of a mushroom (*Coprinus* sp.) showing: *a*, basidia; *b*, sterigmata; *c*, basidiospores.

opposite mating type (Fig. 4e). This continues throughout the binucleate stage of the organism. Eventually nuclei in the terminal cells fuse and so form a diploid nucleus (Fig. 4g). This nucleus undergoes a reduction division and divides again (Fig. 4h). The four nuclei, now again haploid, migrate through projections (sterigmata) of the now swollen tip cell (basidium) and are cut off to become the four haploid basidiospores (Fig. 4i). These basidiospores usually are mononucleate and haploid, of different mating types and, when mature, are forcibly discharged and are capable of germinating to form the haploid mycelium again. Only haploid mycelium is produced unless mycelia of opposite mating type come in contact, in which case cells may fuse to produce the binucleate mycelium again (Fig. 4a).

The presence of clamp connections is thus an outward sign that the mycelium is binucleate and has arisen from the fused mycelium derived from two different spores (Fig. 4a). Thus the sexual act in such fungi is divided into two phases, a fusion of cells from mycelium arising from different spores early in the growth of the mushroom, and a fusion of the nuclei at a much later stage, when the plant is mature.

This separation of the phases of sexual reproduction with a di-karyotic mycelium interpolated between the fusion of cells and the fusion of nuclei is characteristic of the Basidiomycetes. The Basidio-

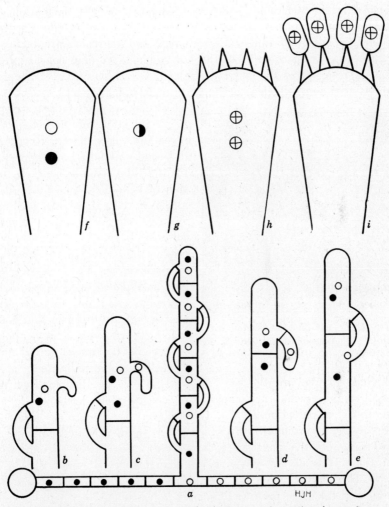

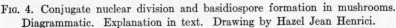

FIG. 4. Conjugate nuclear division and basidiospore formation in mushrooms. Diagrammatic. Explanation in text. Drawing by Hazel Jean Henrici.

mycetes are isogamous and in many cases heterothallic in origin. In homothallic species paired nuclei appear to arise spontaneously in the mycelium from a single basidiospore and conjugate nuclear divi-sion may be accompanied with or without the formation of clamp connections. It is much more difficult to establish sexual relation in these species.

In addition to the large, fleshy mushrooms and their allies (the subclass Homobasidiomycetes) certain more minute forms are included in the Basidiomycetes because of the mode of formation of their basidiospores. These Heterobasidiomycetes include largely plant parasites, the smuts (Ustilaginales) and the rusts (Uredinales).

Smuts. As an example of the Ustilaginales we may consider the causative agent of the corn (maize) smut, *Ustilago Zeae*. When a smut sporidium, which is uninucleate and haploid, comes in contact

FIG. 5. An ear of corn affected with smut. Photographed by Dr. N. F. Huff.

with the corn plant only a superficial infection of fine haploid mycelium takes place. If mycelia from two sporidia of opposite mating type come in contact, fusion of cells may take place and a heavy and extensive mycelium with paired nuclei which divide conjugately results. This dikaryotic mycelium eventually matures in special galls. Many of the cells become rounded, rough and dark in color, and in these cells, morphologically chlamydospores (each at first with a single pair of nuclei), the nuclei unite and the cells become uninucleate and diploid. These are the smut spores. They are disseminated in great numbers and are capable of considerable dormancy. On germination, reduction division takes place. Then septa are formed, dividing the promycelium, which is a short germination hypha growing from the smut spore, into three or four cells. From each of these cells of the promycelium, daughter cells repeatedly bud off. These are the haploid uninucleate sporidia mentioned above. (See Fig. 6.) The promycelium may be considered a basidium and the sporidia basidiospores. These sporidia are capable of multiplying by budding and can be cultured on nutrient media. They have a superficial resemblance to yeasts.

It will be noted that both the mushroom and the corn smut have haploid uninucleate basidiospores which germinate to form a haploid mycelium. In both, mycelium of opposite mating type may fuse to produce a mycelium with paired nuclei, the dikaryon. After ex-

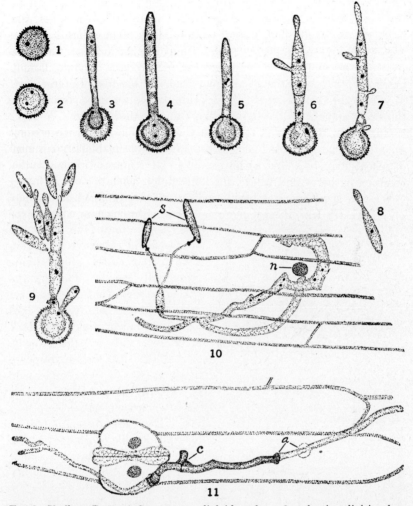

Fig. 6. *Ustilago Zeae.* 1, Smut spore, diploid nucleus; 2, reduction division has taken place; 3, promycelium formed; 4, one daughter nucleus divided; 5, other nucleus dividing; 6, septa and sporidia are forming; 7, all four cells of basidium separated and sporidia forming from each; 8, sporidium budding; 9, many sporidia formed; 10, two sporidia (*s*) on surface of corn plant have produced mycelia which penetrated plant; hyphae united to form mycelium with paired nuclei (*n* = nucleus of plant cell); 11, mycelium in plant came to surface of plant at *a*, and reentered at stomatal opening (clamp-connection at *c*). From W. F. Hanna, *Phytopathology*, **19**, 415 (1929).

tensive proliferation by conjugate nuclear division the pairs of **nuclei**, each pair in a separate cell, unite to form the only diploid cell in the life history. After reduction division in this cell (in both), the haploid uninucleate basidiospores are set free. These basidiospores are of different mating types (two to four to a basidium). The close relationships of the corn smut and the mushroom, so very different in gross appearance, is clear from their cytological life histories. Moreover in certain smuts the sporidia are discharged forcibly in the same manner as the basidiospores of the mushrooms.

Rusts. In the rusts (Uredinales) the life cycle is still more complicated. The fungus (*Puccinia graminis*) causing black stem rust of wheat may be taken as an example. It requires two hosts, the common barberry and wheat, for its complete cycle.

When a sporidium (or basidiospore), which is uninucleate, lodges on a barberry leaf, it may give rise to haploid mycelium. Such my-

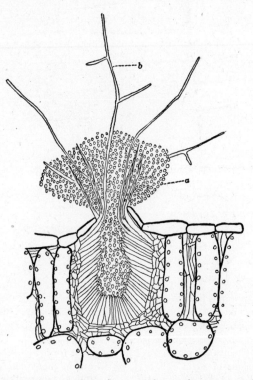

FIG. 7. Section through a portion of a pustule on the upper surface of a barberry leaf infected with *Puccinia graminis* showing pycnium, pycniospores (*a*), and receptive hyphae (*b*). Redrawn from figure of A. H. R. Buller, *Nature*, **141**, 33 (1938).

celium may eventually form a spore-forming structure, the pycnium, on the upper surface of the barberry leaf (Fig. 7). In this structure stalks of mycelium cut off uninucleate spores, the pycniospores (spermatia, pycnidiospores). These are accompanied by a secretion which attracts insects, the latter serving to transfer the pycniospores to new barberry plants which, as will be shown, they cannot infect directly. The sporidium is uninucleate and the mycelium and the pycniospores derived from it are haploid. *P. graminis* is heterothallic.

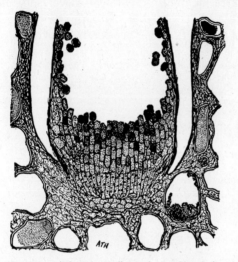

Fig. 8. Section through a "cluster cup" on the under surface of a barberry leaf infected with *Puccinia graminis* showing the formation of aeciospores.

If two sporidia of opposite mating type infect the same barberry leaf near enough to each other to enable their mycelia to fuse, "cluster cups" or aecia form on the under side of the barberry leaf. The chains of aeciospores (aecidiospores) borne in these cluster cups are binucleate. As with the mushrooms and the smuts, cellular fusion without nuclear fusion has taken place. If only one sporidium falls on a barberry leaf the haploid mycelium produces only pycnia and pycniospores. The pycniospores themselves cannot infect the barberry, but if pycniospores of mating type opposite to that of the haploid mycelium already growing in a barberry leaf are carried to that leaf in an infected area, these pycniospores fuse with the haploid receptive hyphae protruding from the pycnia and their paired nuclei are thought to migrate through the mycelium. Aecia and binucleate aeciospores (Fig. 8) are known to form as a result of such a union of pycniospores and receptive hyphae.

The aeciospores can infect only wheat, barley, oats, rye, and certain wild grasses. They do not infect barberry. They give rise to a mycelium with paired nuclei, the dikaryon, which eventually forms

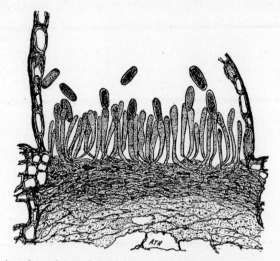

FIG. 9. Section through a red pustule on wheat affected with *Puccinia graminis* showing the formation of urediospores.

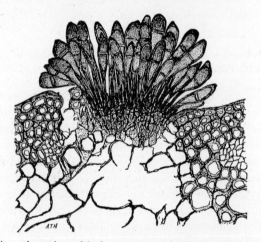

FIG. 10. Section through a black pustule on wheat affected with *Puccinia graminis* showing the formation of teliospores.

another kind of spore, the urediospore (uredospore, urediniospore). These are produced singly on the sporophore, and are binucleate. They are reddish in color and form the red pustules on wheat leaves and stems, the red rust. The urediospores can also infect only the wheat, not the barberry, and they spread the disease rapidly.

Toward the end of the summer the host plant matures and the infection tends to develop more abundantly on the stems and from the mycelium on the stems there arises a fifth type of spore, the teliospore (teleutospore). The teliospores are surrounded by a thick dark-colored cell wall and are formed in the black pustules on the stems, the black rust. They are two-celled, each spore consisting of two separate protoplasts, each in its own compartment (Fig. 10). Each cell is at first binucleate but, in the teliospore, the nuclei fuse and the uninucleate, diploid stage is found.

The teliospores remain dormant over winter. In the process of germination the fusion nucleus undergoes reduction division as in the smut spores. The four nuclei become separated by crosswalls in

FIG. 11. Germination of a teliospore of *Puccinia graminis* showing the formation of promycelium and basidiospores.

the promycelium so that we have a four-celled basidium as in some of the smuts (Fig. 11). From each of these four cells a sporidium, which may be considered a basidiospore, is formed, each with but one haploid nucleus. These spores are capable of infecting the barberry but not the wheat.

This complex life cycle on two hosts is not a special case but is typical of many of the rusts. Resemblances to the cycle of the mushrooms and smuts can be seen. The complete cycle is known for a large number of rusts including many of great economic importance. Sometimes the greater economic loss is in the alternate host, that is, the host which corresponds to the barberry in the disease just considered, and in which cell union but not nuclear fusion takes place. Many of the species of rusts complete their life cycle on a single host, and are said to be autoecious. Many, however, like *P. graminis* do require two different hosts. These are heteroecious. The two host plants required for heteroecious rusts are themselves not closely related, as for instance wheat and barberry, the hosts of the stem rust of wheat, currants and white pine, the hosts of the white pine blister rust, cedars and apple trees, the hosts of the cedar rust of apples. It might be of interest to bacteriologists that the necessity of two different hosts for *P. graminis* to complete the sexual cycle and the various stages in the life cycle were known in essential details by 1865, largely as a result of the work of the Tulasne brothers and DeBary. It was not until Theobald Smith, twenty-eight years later, had worked out the cycle of the protozoan parasite of Texas tick fever that such a life cycle was known in animal pathology. The alternate method of fertilization, that is, the pairing of the nuclei from the receptive hyphae and from pycniospores of opposite mating type, was discovered only fairly recently by Craigie in Canada.

Physiologic Races. Although the smuts may be cultivated on artificial media, growth in a host plant is usually necessary for the development of the diploid smut spores. The rusts are obligate parasites, which have not been grown in artificial cultures. In both of these groups, host specificity has developed to a very high degree, most species of smuts being capable of infecting but a single kind of plant, whereas with the rusts, each species of the parasite requires one or two unrelated host plants. But it is known that there occurs a still higher degree of host specificity, for within the species of the parasite there are found different races or strains, morphologically identical, but capable of infecting only certain varieties or "lines" of the host species. These races or strains of parasitic fungi apparently arise by mutation and hybridization. Such divisions of a species, capable of infecting only certain lines of the host species, are known as physiologic races, and the phenomenon is referred to as physiologic specialization.

Ascomycetes. The Ascomycetes are the largest and perhaps the most important class of the fungi, including such widely different types as the large fleshy morels and the minute one-celled yeasts. Many important plant pathogens are Ascomycetes, and some of the molds important to the bacteriologist also belong to this class. It is characterized by the formation of spores, called ascospores, contained within a membrane or sac called an ascus. There are generally eight ascospores in an ascus, but many asci may be formed by one thallus. Although there is a wide diversity in gross characters and external appearances between the various groups of Ascomycetes, the mode of formation of the ascospores is fairly uniform and indicates the homogeneity of the class.

Ascospores. The formation of the ascospores is a result of sexual fusion of nuclei. The mechanism of their production is simplest in the yeasts. Different stages in the formation of the ascospores of a yeast, Schizosaccharomyces, are shown in Fig. 12. Two contiguous yeasts cells send out minute tube-like processes which meet and fuse; their nuclei come together and unite, the single nucleus resulting undergoes division three times to form eight daughter nuclei. Each of these becomes surrounded by a certain amount of reserve material, and a spore wall is formed. The cell containing these spores (usually four or eight) is the ascus. The ascus is formed less directly in many other yeasts. In these the haploid ascospores fuse in the ascus two by two, or the haploid cells which develop from the ascospores fuse

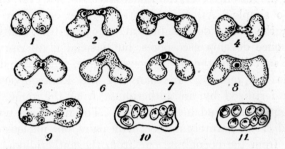

FIG. 12. Various stages in the formation of ascospores in a yeast, *Schizosaccharomyces octosporus*. After Guilliermond.

with each other or with an unfertilized ascospore. These fused cells then develop into the ordinary yeast cell which is generally supposed to have a single diploid nucleus. After considerable proliferation by budding, some of these cells may undergo reduction division, form-

FIG. 13. Various stages in the development of ascospores: *A, Eremascus fertilis; B, Endomycopsis fibuliger*. After Guilliermond.

ing the ascospores, usually four in number. This process will be elaborated in Chapter X.

In the genus Endomycopsis and related fungi, a group of molds closely related to and often classified with the yeasts, the formation of ascospores is equally simple. Two contiguous cells in a filament of mycelium send out bud-like processes. Sometimes one of these is larger than the other, i.e., there may be a differentiation into an antheridium and oogonium. These unite, their nuclei fuse, and spores are formed immediately as in some of the yeasts. Various stages are shown in Fig. 13.

In most of the Ascomycetes, the Euascomycetes, however, the process is not so simple. After fertilization of the oogonium by the antheridium, the nuclei do not fuse at once and the resulting cell does not at once develop ascospores, but instead gives rise to new filaments of mycelium, the ascogenous hyphae, with paired nuclei which divide conjugately. In many of the Euascomycetes the oogonium is fertilized by an antheridium from the same thallus. They are homothallic and heterogamous. The nuclei do not unite at once but divide separately and occur in pairs, one nucleus of each pair derived from the oogonium, one from the antheridium. These ascogenous hypha is often at first without crosswalls but eventually septa are formed across at least the end cells. These form their sexual spores and in some species proliferate in a manner which has many analogies with the conjugate nuclear division and basidiospore formation of the Basidiomycetes.

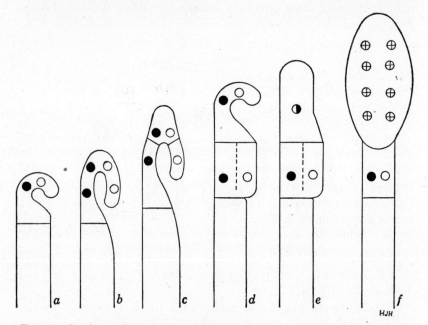

HJH

FIG. 14. Crozier and ascospore production in Ascomycetes. Diagrammatic. Explanation in text. Drawing by Hazel Jean Henrici.

The paired nuclei come to lie side by side in the terminal cell (Fig. 14a) which bends to form a crozier (Fig. 14a). Each nucleus divides (Fig. 14b) and two septa are formed, one isolating a single nucleus in the crozier, now the terminal cell, and one nucleus of opposite sex in the antepenultimate cell (Fig. 14c). The penultimate cell still has two nuclei, one of each sex. The crozier cell and the antepenultimate cell now anastamose and simultaneously the penultimate cell either forms another crozier (Fig. 14d) or else the nuclei fuse (Fig.

FIG. 15. Apothecia of *Peziza sylvestris*. From F. J. Seaver, *The North American Cup-Fungi*, 1928.

14e). If the former happens we may have several croziers being formed at the same time, for the cell formed by the union of crozier and antepenultimate cells, as well as the penultimate cell, now the new terminal cell, may form a crozier, and thus we may have a complicated system of ascogenous hyphae. Eventually, however, the nuclei fuse in the penultimate cells (Fig. 14e) of the ascogenous hyphae. This diploid nucleus undergoes reduction division, and each cell divides twice again (Fig. 14f) and the eight haploid ascospores are produced in this cell which becomes enlarged to form an ascus. While the ascogenous hyphae are thus proliferating, the mononucleate or multinucleate mycelium arising from the cells which bore the oogonium and antheridium may form a complicated network of mycelium to cover the ascogenous hyphae. This becomes the ascocarp. There are many modifications of the above process.

By far the greatest number of the species of Ascomycetes have eight ascospores per ascus. Whereas in the lower Ascomycetes the ascospores may be formed on any part of the mycelium, in the higher forms they are developed in particular areas and become surrounded and protected by a dense mass of tissue, thus forming a special fruit-

ing organ (the ascocarp). This may be arranged as a hollow sphere (the perithecium) or as a cup-like structure (the apothecium). The fruiting bodies of the cup fungi (Fig. 15) are apothecia. Their inner walls are lined by the asci in a continuous layer, the hymenium which appears in section in Fig. 16.

In addition to the ascospores, many Ascomycetes also multiply by the production of exogenous asexual spores, the conidia. These are formed in great abundance when conditions are favorable for rapid multiplication of the species, whereas ascospores are often formed only sparsely or under exceptional circumstances.

FIG. 16. Section through an apothecium of Peziza showing asci. Some are undeveloped. Two contain the full complement of eight ascospores.

Life Cycle of Ergot. The parasite (*Claviceps purpurea*) producing a disease of grains, especially rye, and grasses known as ergot may be taken as an example to illustrate the life history of a typical Ascomycete. This organism is of some importance in medicine, since it produces in the infected grains a substance which produces contractions of involuntary muscles. It has produced poisoning both in man and domestic animals, producing abortion by inducing contractions of the uterus, and gangrene by causing constriction of blood vessels. It is also used as a drug to produce a firm contraction of the uterus after childbirth.

The fungus grows in the seeds, which, as they develop, become much larger than the healthy grains. The tissue of the grain is gradually replaced by mycelium. During this period the fungus reproduces by the non-sexual conidia (Fig. 17) formed on the surface of the grain. These are accompanied by a secretion of "honeydew" which attracts insects. They carry the conidia to the flowers of other plants, which thus become infected. As the grain ripens, those seeds which are infected are completely replaced by the mycelium, which now dries out and forms a dense, hard, black mass, the sclerotium. This retains the general form of the seed but is larger and projects considerably from the

FIG. 17. Formation of conidia by *Claviceps purpurea*. Stained section of a grain affected with ergot. Only a portion of the fungus on the surface is shown.

head of grain (Fig. 18). It is these ergot grains which contain the poison.

These ergot grains fall to the ground and remain dormant over winter. In the spring, they revive and sprout a number of little stalks which develop rounded masses of tissue at their tips (Fig. 19). These are called stromata. In each stroma a number of pear-shaped areas, the perithecia, are formed (Fig. 20). One of these is shown in section in Fig. 21. Each perithecium contains a number of asci, and each ascus contains eight needle-like ascospores. When mature, these are forcibly discharged into the air and carried by the wind. If they lodge on grain they germinate, forming a mycelium which invades the growing grain and starts the cycle over again.

Subclasses of Ascomycetes. The Ascomycetes are subdivided into two main series according to the way in which they are borne in the ascocarp. The first series, the subclass Protoascomycetes, contains the more primitive forms, in which the ascogenous hyphae are lacking. In Endomycopsis and the yeasts like Schizosaccharomyces mentioned above, the fusion cells give rise to asci at once and hence ascogenous hyphae are lacking. In many of the yeasts, after fusion of two cells, and presumably also of nuclei, the resulting diploidal cell proliferates by budding. Here also there are no ascogenous hyphae. In the second series, the Euascomycetes, the fusion

Fig. 18. A head of grain affected with ergot showing a sclerotium.

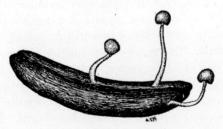

Fig. 19. "Germination" of a sclerotium of *Claviceps purpurea* showing the formation of stromata.

cell gives rise to ascogenous hyphae which are now usually thought to have paired nuclei. By far the greatest number of species falls into this group which is often given the rank of subclass. It is sometimes divided into three more or less well defined subclasses. In the first, the Plectomycetes, the asci are scattered on the ascogenous hyphae and are consequently distributed irregularly inside the perithecium, like Aspergillus (Eurotium). See Fig. 48. In the second subclass, the Discomycetes, the asci are borne in palisades, a hymenium, in an open cup or plate-like apothecium, like in Peziza (Fig. 15). In the third or Pyrenomycetes the asci are contained in a hymenium in perithecia as in Claviceps (Fig. 21). See page 33 for key to subclasses of Ascomycetes.

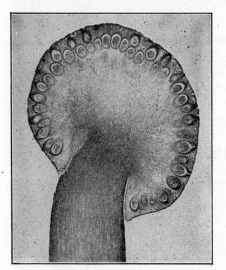

FIG. 20. Stained section of a stroma of *Claviceps purpurea* showing numerous perithecia at the periphery.

It must be emphasized that there are literally hundreds of species and scores of genera of Ascomycetes the life cycles of which for the most part have not been worked out. The cycles of some of them, however, have been worked out as completely as that of *Claviceps purpurea*, which has been taken as an example. One may find excellent material for microscopic wet mount study of ascospores in the common saprophyte Peziza in the spring, or powdery mildews of a number of plants, e.g., lilac, late in the summer or early autumn. Dried material of either will yield very satisfactory preparations when wetted. The ascospores of yeasts, Aspergillus, and other forms of special interest to the bacteriologist will be considered later.

Fungi Imperfecti. There are many fungi which possess the characteristic mycelium of Ascomycetes, which reproduce by conidia similar to those formed by known Ascomycetes, yet which do not form ascospores, or whose ascospores have not yet been discovered. These are designated imperfect fungi, or Fungi Imperfecti. It must be confessed that probably in many cases the imperfection lies in our knowledge of the organism rather than in the organism itself. They must be classified and identified by their conidia. Although the Fungi Imperfecti have been established as a class equal in rank to the Basidiomycetes, Ascomycetes, and Phycomycetes, it should be recognized that an attempt is continually being made to classify the latter three classes in a natural system which expresses their phylogenetic relationship, whereas the class Fungi Imperfecti is, to some extent at least, an artificial classification of conidial stages of natural groups. They consist of "form species," "form genera," "form families," "form orders." From time to time the perfect forms of these are discovered and then the species are removed from the class of Fungi Imperfecti and placed in their proper place in the Ascomycetes. This leads to some confusion.

Thus the large genus Aspergillus is placed in the Fungi Imperfecti because most of the known species do not form ascospores; but such sexual spores have been found in some species, which are therefore included by some authors in another genus, Eurotium, of the Ascomycetes. It might be argued that finding ascospores in one species of a genus of imperfect fungi would warrant transferring the whole genus to the Ascomycetes. But this cannot be safely done, since the genera of Fungi Imperfecti are based upon the mode of formation of their conidia and it is known that diverse types of Ascomycetes may produce the same sorts of conidia. In a few instances, fungi formerly classified in the Fungi Imperfecti were found on further study to belong in the Basidiomycetes or

FIG. 21. Stained section through a perithecium of *Claviceps purpurea* showing the elongated asci. Each of these contains eight needle-like ascospores.

Phycomycetes. It is probable, however, that most of the Fungi Imperfecti are conidial stages of Ascomycetes. See page 94. Unfortunately, it is the imperfect fungi which are of least interest to the mycologist and have therefore had, in general, less intensive study, and at the same time they are of most interest to the practical bacteriologist. Most of the fungi pathogenic for man must be placed in this group, and likewise most industrial molds (not yeasts) belong to the Fungi Imperfecti.

Phycomycetes. The Phycomycetes are the most primitive class of the fungi. Some of them reproduce by both sexual spores and nonsexual spores. There are three subclasses which are so diverse that the class can best be described by considering each subclass separately. Indeed, as stated above, many mycologists consider them so diverse that they divide the Phycomycetes into two or three classes, each equal in rank to the other two classes of perfect fungi.

The Archimycetes are primitive forms, mainly aquatic and parasitic on water plants and animals, though some are important causes of disease of land plants. They are characterized by the absence of mycelium, the thallus being a single cell or an irregular mass, though a rudimentary mycelium is formed by some. They reproduce mainly by motile, flagellated spores called zoospores. In some, sexuality is very primitive. In others, well-defined gametes, oogonia, and antheridia, are formed. There are no forms of importance to the bacteriologist.

The Oomycetes are also mostly aquatic forms; some are parasitic on land plants, and some live in soil. They reproduce by sexual spores called oospores and non-sexual zoospores which in many forms are motile.

Life Cycle of Saprolegnia. The common water molds of the genus Saprolegnia may be considered to illustrate the life history of an Oomycete. They are found especially on dead animal matter sub-

Fig. 22. A minnow infected with Saprolegnia.

merged in water, as insects and fish. Some are parasitic on fish. The scum which develops frequently on goldfish in aquaria or minnows kept in bait-pails is due to the growth of this mold. They are especially prone to develop on fish after the latter have been handled or bruised (Fig. 22).

The non-sexual spores are formed at the tips of filaments of mycelium projecting into the water. The terminal portion of the filament becomes separated from the rest by a crosswall. The cell so cut off contains many nuclei. Vacuoles appear in various parts of this cell and by growing and coalescing they gradually cut up the enclosed protoplasm into a number of small cells, which develop cell walls and finally two flagella each. They are the zoospores, and

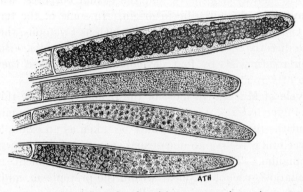

FIG. 23. Sporangia of Saprolegnia with zoospores in various stages of development.

the cell in which they are formed is a zoosporangium (Fig. 23). The zoospores are pear-shaped, with the two flagella inserted at the apex. After swimming about for a time they come to rest, lose their flagella, and become rounded. After a resting period, these rounded cells give rise to a new sort of zoospore, bean-shaped, with the two flagella inserted on the side. These then swim about and, if they reach a suitable substrate, come to rest and germinate, forming the coeno-cytic mycelium.

Sexual spores are not formed so fre-quently. They are produced by the con-jugation of two morphologically unlike cells, a large oogonium and one or more small tube-like antheridia. These gen-erally develop from neighboring branches of the same filament. Both the oogonium and the antheridium are at first multi-nucleate like the coenocytic mycelium

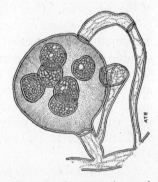

FIG. 24. An oogonium of Saprolegnia. It has been fertilized by two antheridia and contains six oospores.

from which they are derived. They become separated from this my-celium by crosswalls. The protoplasm of the oogonium becomes divided into cells containing each a single nucleus. The antheridia penetrate the oogonium and their nuclei fuse two by two with those of the cells of the oogonium. These fertilized cells then become the oospores, by enlarging and developing a thick membrane. They are capable of remaining dormant for considerable periods of time.

Thus in Saprolegnia two types of spores are formed, the endogenous motile asexual zoospores and the sexual oospores, which are heterogamous and homothallic in origin. In some of the terrestrial forms of Oomycetes parasitic on plants, such as Cystopus, the spores germinate directly by a germ tube and simulate conidia. But these show their relationship by first developing flagella when they lodge in a drop of water and later developing mycelium.

Life Cycle of Mucor. In most of the Zygomycetes, the third subclass of Phycomycetes, the multinucleate character is maintained throughout the life cycle. Mucor may be taken as an example. The aerial mycelium gives rise to non-sexual spores in a sac or membrane, the sporangium. The terminal portion of the filament becomes greatly enlarged, vacuoles appear within the protoplasm, and by enlarging and coalescing these gradually separate the protoplasm into individual cells. Each of the spores so formed contains several nuclei. They mature by developing a spore wall. The inflated tip of the sporangiophore, which projects into the sporangium, is the columella. When the spores are mature the sporangial membrane dissolves away, liberating the spores, which are distributed by the wind. A portion of the sporangial wall remains attached to the base of the columella. (See Fig. 34.)

The sexual spores of the Zygomycetes are called zygospores. They are usually isogamous and heterothallic in origin. When two hyphae capable of conjugating come together, their terminal portions become separated by crosswalls. Their cell walls dissolve where they touch, and the two multinucleated masses of protoplasm run together, the nuclei proceeding to unite two by two. The cell develops a thick wall with generally warty or spiny projections from its surface. Various stages in the formation of a zygospore are illustrated in Fig. 25.

Zygospores, like oospores, generally remain dormant for considerable periods. When they revive, they may germinate by putting forth a single filament which at once forms a sporangium and sporangiospores or they may produce a more or less extensive mycelium. Further discussion of morphology of Zygomycetes is given in Chapter IV.

Although there is no morphologically distinguishable differentiation into two sexes in most of the Zygomycetes, it can be shown with the heterothallic species that there is a physiological differentiation.

By inoculating spores from different thalli on the two halves of a Petri plate culture, it will be found that in some cases where the two thalli come together the filaments will fail to fuse and form

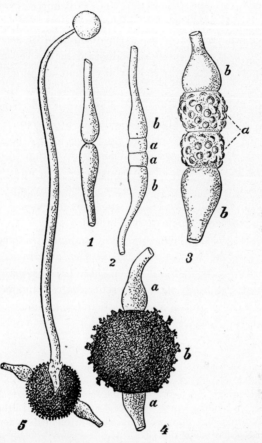

FIG. 25. *Mucor Mucedo.* Zygospores: 1, two hyphae in terminal contact; 2, articulation into gametangia *a* and suspensors *b;* 3, fusion of gametangia; 4, mature zygospore supported by suspensors; 5, germination of zygospore. After Bredfeld.

zygospores, whereas with other combinations they will fuse. By repeating this experiment with many strains one can demonstrate that two sexes really exist, though they cannot be distinguished by their appearance. These "sexes" are referred to as plus and minus strains.

Origin and Evolution of the Fungi. Certain of the Oomycetes, like Saprolegnia, show resemblances to certain of the green algae, like Vaucheria. This resemblance consists of the coenocytic character of the protoplasm, in the mode or formation of the oospores and the production of motile, endogenous asexual spores. It was therefore believed for some time that the Phycomycetes had been derived from green algae which had become saprophytic. Similarly a resemblance was traced between the formation of ascospores in the Ascomycetes and the sexual reproduction in the red algae, and the Basidiomycetes were supposed to have had an independent origin.

More recently, however, many mycologists have thought of fungi as a group which has evolved as a separate line from a primitive unicellular form, probably a flagellated protozoan. Some of the Archimycetes show resemblances to the colorless flagellates. It is believed that there has been a continuous evolution from such simple forms to the higher types of Phycomycetes. In addition, the origin of the Ascomycetes has been sought in the Phycomycetes and the origin of the Basidiomycetes in the Ascomycetes. The alternate mononucleate or multinucleate and binucleate mycelium of the Basidiomycetes and Ascomycetes and the analogies between the clamp connections of the former and the crozier apparatus of the latter point to a close relationship between these two classes. It is thought by some that the fungi thus represent a single independent line of descent from the protozoa and that their resemblance to algae is circumstantial.

LITERATURE

For the bacteriologist whose interest in the Eumycetes has been aroused by the preceding chapter, or who feels a compulsion out of a sense of duty to make a further study of the true fungi, the following suggestions are made. In the first place, mycology is a science that had advanced further, in many respects, by the time that Pasteur and Koch had founded bacteriology, in 1900, than bacteriology has advanced today. Also there are probably at least as many individuals doing research today on pure and applied mycology as are working on problems in bacteriology. Thus there is a larger literature and more facts are known. But this does not make the subject more difficult; rather the contrary, since monographic treatments have to a great extent combined and systematized what has been discovered and, in spite of the seemingly unnecessarily large vocabulary, the covering up a lack of knowledge by vocabulary is, in general, a thing of the past as far as mycology is concerned. We bacteriologists (including immunologists) can decide for ourselves whether or not this is true in our own science. In general, many of the doubtful points in pure mycology have been confirmed or rejected, whereas in bacteriology, corresponding features are a subject of investigation, polemics, or conjecture. This does not mean that all is known. Perusal of current botanical journals

KEY TO THE CLASSES AND SUBCLASSES OF PERFECT FUNGI

I. Mycelium coenocytic if present, if absent not reproducing by budding or fission.   Class *PHYCOMYCETES*

II. Mycelium septate if present, if absent reproducing by budding or fission.
  - A. Sexual spores exogenous.   Class *BASIDIOMYCETES*
  - B. Sexual spores endogenous.   Class *ASCOMYCETES*
  - C. Sexual spores unknown.   Class *FUNGI IMPERFECTI*

Subclasses of Phycomycetes

I. Mycelium absent or rudimentary.   Subclass *ARCHIMYCETES*

II. Mycelium well developed.
  - A. Sexual reproduction heterogamous; non-sexual spores motile or developing motility.   Subclass *OOMYCETES*
  - B. Sexual reproduction in most cases isogamous; non-sexual spores non-motile.   Subclass *ZYGOMYCETES*

Subclasses of Ascomycetes

I. Asci produced from oogonium directly, or after multiplication by budding of diploid cells.   Subclass *PROTOASCOMYCETES*

II. Asci borne on ascogenous hyphae.   (Euascomycetes)
  - A. Asci distributed irregularly in a closed perithecium.   Subclass *PLECTOMYCETES*
  - B. Asci arranged in a hymenium.
    1. Hymenium in an apothecium.   Subclass *DISCOMYCETES*
    2. Hymenium in a perithecium.   Subclass *PYRENOMYCETES*

Subclasses and Orders of Basidiomycetes

I. Basidia always simple; basidiospores on germinating producing mycelium directly.   Subclass *HOMOBASIDIOMYCETES*
     (Mushroom and allies)

II. Basidia septate or deeply divided or arising from a teliospore or probasidium.   Subclass *HETEROBASIDIOMYCETES*
  - A. Basidiocarp well developed; usually saprophytic.   Order *TREMALLALES*
  - B. Basidiocarp represented by a mass of probasidia, often compound (teliospore); always parasitic on vascular plants.
    1. Basidiospores borne on sterigmata, never reproducing by budding.   Order *UREDINALES*
       (Rusts)
    2. Basidiospores sessile on epibasidia, usually capable of reproducing by budding.   Order *USTILAGINALES*
       (Smuts)

will show how much fundamental work is being done. Either of the following two texts is good for the serious beginner.

Bessey, E. A., *A Textbook of Mycology*, Blakiston, Philadelphia, 1935.

Smith, G. M., *Cryptogamic Botany, Vol. I, Algae and Fungi*, McGraw-Hill, New York, 1938.

For a discussion of the morphology and cytology of fungi and the basis of classification, the following two monographs are suggested. The second is difficult!

Gwynne-Vaughn, H. C. I., and B. Barnes, *The Structure and Development of the Fungi*, Cambridge Press, Cambridge, 2nd ed., 1937.

Gäumann, E. A., *Comparative Morphology of the Fungi*, translated by C. W. Dodge, McGraw-Hill, New York, 1928.

For a discussion of the sexuality of fungi, Gäumann's monograph or the following is suggested.

Kniep, H., *Die Sexualität der niederen Pflanzen*, Fischer, Jena, 1928.

For a very readable, popular, but truly excellent discussion of an important field of applied mycology, with considerable pure mycology painlessly applied, the following book by an English novelist is highly recommended.

Large, E. C., *The Advance of the Fungi*, Holt, New York, 1940.

A valuable pamphlet giving very full keys through the families, with representative genera, several sketches, and an excellent glossary, will be found in the following.

Martin, G. W., *Outline of the Fungi*, University of Iowa Studies in Natural History, Vol. 18, Supplement, 1941.

CHAPTER II

VARIATIONS IN THE LOWER FUNGI *

Fungi, like other living things, are subject to variations in form and function. Some of these are but temporary or reversible changes, others are permanent; some occur spontaneously, others result from the action of known environmental factors; some result from changes in the hereditary constitution of a single cell, i.e., they are mutations, whereas others result from an interbreeding of two races or species, i.e., they are hybrids. But it is often difficult or impossible to determine in a given instance whether the observed change is temporary or permanent, spontaneous or induced, mutant or hybrid. These variations are important in explaining the origin and evolution of new races and species, but as they occur in the laboratory they are often very annoying, since they lead to a loss or alteration of specific characters that are being studied, and lead to a great deal of confusion in classification and nomenclature.

Pleomorphism. If one sends to a type culture collection for cultures of several species of dermatophytes, he is likely to receive several tubes bearing different labels, but which contain molds looking very much alike—an abundance of white woolly aerial mycelium, with few or no conidia or other diagnostic characters. These molds were quite different when first isolated—some powdery, some velvety, some white, some colored, and with different types of spores. But after long-continued cultivation they have gradually lost their distinguishing characters, becoming more and more woolly in character and producing more and more sterile aerial mycelium. Pigment production is usually the first character to go. These variations have been described in detail by Grigoraki.[15]

Dermatologists, following the usage of Sabouraud, call such changes pleomorphism. But this word was first used by DeBary to designate the series of changes observed in rust fungi as these appear on their different host plants, a phenomenon quite distinct from that which we have under discussion. German mycologists have used a better word, degeneration, and they have designated the change just

---

* This chapter has been used as it was written by Dr. Henrici, with the exception of some minor editorial changes.

described as woolly degeneration. This woolly degeneration occurs not only with the ringworm fungi, but also with a variety of molds, such as *Aspergillus nidulans,* which loses first the ability to form perithecia, and then forms fewer and fewer conidia and more and more sterile mycelium. It is most likely to occur when cultures are frequently transferred on highly favorable media. This fact was recognized long ago by Sabouraud who devised a conservation medium, rich in peptone and poor in sugar, on which stock cultures were maintained. These should be transferred only at long intervals.

Another type of change observed in cultures of fungi has been called faviform degeneration by Alexander.[1] In ringworm fungi it usually follows a stage of woolly degeneration. The mold now grows as a low, flat, wrinkled, waxy-looking mass of mycelium, without any aerial mycelium or conidia, firmly adherent to the agar. This is the normal appearance of the fungus of favus, hence the name. Although less frequently observed than woolly degeneration, it is seen in a variety of molds, and occurs very constantly with the organism of North American blastomycosis, a fungus which normally grows with an abundance of sterile woolly aerial mycelium.

Still another type of change may be observed in certain fungi which normally do not produce any aerial mycelium, but grow as a moist mat on the surface of the agar. Such fungi are *Candida Krusei, Sporotrichum Schenckii,* and *Pullularia pullulans.* I have observed with all of these, after long-continued cultivation on Sabouraud agar, the development of dry aerial mycelium, with conidia in the last two.

Finally, one may observe changes in yeasts after long-continued cultivation. Normally forming no mycelium, they may develop first elongated cells, then pseudomycelium, and finally some filaments of true, septate, branched mycelium. An extension of this phenomenon is observed in organisms like *C. albicans,* which on Sabouraud agar normally form an abundance of yeast cells and little mycelium, but which on long-continued cultivation gradually produce more and more mycelium and fewer yeast cells, so that eventually they come to look like *C. Krusei.*

Microbic Dissociation in Fungi. It may be observed that all these variations form a continuous series which may be indicated thus:

Yeast → Submerged → Aerial   → Sterile   → Faviform
        mycelium   mycelium   woolly   growth
                with   aerial
                spores   mycelium

So far as I know, no single fungus has ever been observed to go through all these changes, unless possibly *Blastomyces dermatitidis.*

But if the fungus changes on long-continued cultivation, it usually changes in the direction indicated by the arrows. The so-called black yeasts may go through the first three stages, finally appearing as a mold of the genus Cladosporium. See page 111. Ringworm fungi may pass through the last three stages. Although transformations in the direction of the arrows are seen far more frequently than in the reverse direction, these variations are not entirely irreversible.

Punkari and Henrici,[25] studying variations in the yeast *Cryptococcus pulcherrimus,* called attention to the similarities between the variations and those exhibited by bacteria as they change from smooth to rough forms. As the yeast develops into rudimentary mycelium, the colonies become rough and wrinkled. Negroni [24] made a similar comparison in the case of *Candida albicans.* Since the basic mechanisms are unknown in both cases, no definite statement can be made, but one is justified in assuming that the common variations in fungi, as indicated in the diagram above, are of the same general character as the variations commonly observed in colonies of bacteria and usually designated microbic dissociation.

Sectors and Secondary Colonies. These variations have been described as appearing rather gradually in the cultures, but it seems probable that what actually occurs is a rather sudden change in a cell here and there, and then a gradually developing dominance of these new types over the normal types as the strain is continued in further subcultures. Exactly similar transformations may be observed to occur rather suddenly in portions of a single culture. As with bacteria, such changes are best seen in colonies, especially giant colonies, i.e., a single large colony allowed to grow for a long time on a Petri plate or in a flask of agar. The occurrence of variation in these giant colonies is usually manifested by the occurrence of sectors, wedge-shaped areas differing in color or texture from the body of the colony. Such sectors represent the growth of the fungus from a cell which has undergone a transformation. As the colony spreads, the growth from this cell differs in appearance from that of other cells at the periphery of the colony. Sometimes little tufts of mycelium or little papillae of yeast cells will occur in an older part of the colony, which are different in character from the rest of the colony. These tufts or papillae correspond to the secondary colonies of bacteria.

Spontaneous Variations. Little is known regarding the mechanisms involved in these variations, but it seems likely that both internal and external factors are involved, and that external agencies merely increase the rate of a change that tends to occur spontaneously. Variations are much more likely to occur in old laboratory strains than in recently isolated cultures. Although it is true that instability is more likely to appear in a strain which has been frequently transferred than in one which has been subcultured only at long intervals, it is also true that, once instability occurs, the degree of variation is increased if the culture is allowed to grow for a long time in a single culture, as in giant colonies. Thus staling of the medium and aging of the organism appear to be potent factors. Variants have been described more frequently in parasitic species than in saprophytic ones, but this may be due merely to the fact that mycologists have been more interested in pathogenic species.

Induced Variations. Little work has been done on the deliberate production of variants in fungi by the action of external agents. Barnes [2] reported the development of variants of *Thamnidium elegans, Botrytis cinerea,* and *Eurotium herbarium* (resulting from the application of heat to the spores). Dickson,[10] working with species of Chaetomium, and Nadson and Philippov [23] with Mucorales, obtained variants from the action of x-rays. Haenicke [16] obtained variants of Penicillium species by adding poisons to the medium. Emmons and Hollaender [13] reported very precise experiments upon the production of mutants of *Trichophyton metagrophytes (T. gypseum)* by the action of ultraviolet light. They found that the mutants observed were similar to those that occur spontaneously, and stated that the ultraviolet light accelerates the rate of mutation. They found that the percentage of mutants among the progeny of the surviving conidia increased with the duration of exposure up to a certain point (at which only about 8 per cent of the spores were still alive); with longer exposures and lower survivals, the proportion of mutants decreased. Negroni [24] produced rough type colonies of *Candida albicans* by the use of immune serum, a procedure which has been very fruitful in inducing the S → R transformation in bacteria.

Variations in Infection. There is some evidence that variations may occur in the tissues in fungus diseases. Thus Weidmann [29] reported a case of trichophytosis of the feet. Cultures were taken over a period of years. At first an organism downy in appearance, and identified as *Trichophyton interdigitale,* was obtained regularly in cultures. But after five years a flat powdery type of colony, *T. mentagrophytes,* appeared. I have been greatly impressed by observations which I have made on organisms isolated from two cases of moniliasis. In one case, an adult, a chronic pulmonary infection was followed by multiple abscesses through the body. From the sputum during life, and from the bronchi post-mortem, a typical *Candida albicans* was isolated. But from abscesses in the kidneys and other viscera, there was obtained a yeast which had the same fermentation reactions, but which failed completely to form mycelium under any conditions. The second case was a child which had suffered for some years from oral and intestinal moniliasis, with repeated attacks of moniliid. From the mouth and feces again *C. albicans* was isolated repeatedly. At autopsy caseous nodules were found in the peribronchial glands and in the lungs near the hilus. From these were obtained pure cultures of *C. Krusei*, non-virulent and non-fermentative. It seems very unreasonable to suppose that a simultaneous infection with two closely related species occurred in each of these three cases. It seems much more likely that in all of them the original fungus had undergone a variation within the infected tissues.

Variations in Different Characters. The variations considered so far have concerned mainly the texture of the colony, which is determined largely by the morphology of the fungus. Variations have been observed in a variety of other characters, as pigmentation, virulence, and biochemical activities. It would require too much space adequately to review all the growing literature on variations in fungi. A few papers will be cited, from which further references may be obtained.

Chodat[6] made extensive studies of variants of *Aspergillus ochraceous* and *Phoma alternariaceum*, the latter giving rise to five distinct races. Both morphological and physiological characters varied. Some of the new races were permanent, others reverted. Dodge[11] obtained an albino race of the red mold, *Neurospora sitophila*. Emmons[12] described variations in color and texture of the colonies of *Microsporum gypseum*. Biltris[3] also described variations of a dermatophyte, *Trichophyton mentagrophytes*. Wiltshire[30] found sectors in cultures of Alternaria which gave rise to conidia of the Stemphyllium type. Fabian and McCullough[14] described variations in yeasts, Mackinnon[22] in *Candida albicans*. There have been some studies of variations in virulence and host-specificity, but these have been confined to the plant pathogens, especially to smuts and rusts.

The intrinsic mechanisms which give rise to variations in fungi are undoubtedly very complex, and far from being fully known. It now seems probable that there occur all the mechanisms known to occur in higher organisms, involving on the one hand the variations caused by a loss or alteration or instability of genes, which are called mutations, and on the other hand those due to the combinations and segregations of genes involved in sexual reproduction, which result in hybrids.

Ever-sporting Races. Once a culture begins to throw variants, it usually becomes continuously unstable, an ever-sporting race. While the parent strain is thus continuously varying, the variants are usually more stable, sometimes apparently permanent. Occasionally variants revert immediately to the parent type. But once a culture of a dermatophyte has become woolly, it is practically impossible to get it to change back to its typical form. Occurring frequently in vegetative mycelium, or in imperfect fungi where sexual reproduction is absent, tending to occur constantly in one direction and often apparently irreversible, such variations seem to show the characteristics of gene mutations, and especially those attributed to unstable genes (see Demerec [9]).

Reversible Variations. But in many cases variants which seemed for a long time to be permanent have eventually reverted to the parent type. Thus some of the white variants of the red yeast *Cryptococcus pulcherrimus* described by Punkari and Henrici [25] appeared to be permanent but one of these kept by me turned red again after more than a year of continued subcultivation. Negroni [24] obtained a partial reversion of the R variant of *Candida albicans* by growing it in a sterilized culture of the S type to which anti-R type serum was added. Burkholder [5] described a woolly change in the normally slimy fungus, *Fusarium Martii* var. *Phaseoli*. When inoculated on beans, the normal host plant, this variant reverted to the normal type.

Mutant or Hybrid. The fact that the observed variations are so frequently reversible led Brierley [4] to doubt that they are true mutations. He believed that they result rather from a recombination of characters already present in the hereditary constitution of the organism. Such a theory implies that in all cases there occurs something of the nature of sexual reproduction, nuclear fusions and segregations. Since most of the fungi exhibit sexual reproduction, and many of them complex life cycles in which the various combinations and segregations are often obscure, this seems to be a reasonable theory.

There are, however, certain data which indicate that variations may occur without any cell fusions. Thus Punkari and Henrici [25] emphasized the complete absence of spores in the yeast *Cryptococcus pulcherrimus* which they studied, since so far as was known sexual fusion in yeasts always results in the formation of spores.

This may be questioned in view of the recent demonstration by Winge and Laustsen [31] that many yeasts are normally diploid, and that sexual fusions actually occur in yeasts formerly believed to be parthenogenetic. More convincing as examples of true mutation are the observations of Hanna,[17] and of Stakman [28] and Christensen [7] on the occurrence of mutations in cultures of *Ustilago Zeae* derived from single spores known to be haploid. Undoubtedly these examples could be multiplied.

Genetics of Fungi. Within the past decade there has grown an extensive literature on the genetics of fungi. This work had its origin in the discovery of heterothallism by Blakeslee. Heterothallism makes it possible to cultivate the sexes of a fungus separately, each in the haploid state, which in turn makes it possible to study the effect of single genes, rather than the complicated condition of pairs of genes which occur in diploid cells. Unisexual cultures may then be crossed at will to produce new combinations. The discovery of heterothallism by Shear and Dodge [26] in the pink mold *Neurospora sitophila* led Dodge [11] to an extensive study of the genetics of this and related fungi. The discovery of an albinistic mutant of this species made possible a series of hybridization experiments. These studies, continued by Lindegren [21] and others, bid fair to make Neurospora as famous an organism as Drosophila in the history of genetics. Similar studies are being made with other heterothallic fungi, notably the smuts and rusts. More recently Winge and Laustsen [31] have extensively investigated the genetics of yeasts, using the micromanipulator for the isolation of spores from an ascus, and have conducted hybridization experiments with these microorganisms.

It would take us too far afield to review this extensive and complicated literature, references to which will be found at the end of the chapter. Dodge has recently summarized it as follows: "We know now that new races of fungi are arising through natural hybridization. Hybrid structures have been obtained showing dominance and Mendelian segregations with crossing-over at reduction which is such an important feature in favoring evolution. We also find in the fungi mutants, lethal factors, deficient chromosomes, sex-chromosomes, sex-linked characters and other genetic features. . . . The fungi in their reproduction and inheritance follow exactly the same laws that govern these activities in higher plants and animals."

Hyphal Fusions. When heterothallic fungi conjugate, hyphae derived from two spores of different sex fuse. This hyphal fusion results, in the Basidiomycetes, in a new type of mycelium, binucleate, with two haploid nuclei in each cell. Such a dikaryophyte presents special problems in genetics peculiar to the fungi. Eventually in some of these binucleate cells the nuclei fuse, and the resulting diploid nucleus divides to give rise to the haploid basidiospores or sporidia. Hyphal fusions are not, however, confined to the Basidiomycetes. They have been observed to occur in a variety of fungi. Vegetative anastomoses occur between neighboring filaments of a single plant, and between neighboring colonies of imperfect fungi. Such fusions do not result in sexual spores. Laibach[20] and Köhler[19] have called attention to the morphologic and physiologic similarity between these vegetative anastomoses and hyphal fusions in the smuts.

The genetic significance of such hyphal fusions is not yet clear. Hansen and Smith[18] noted the occurrence of hyphal fusions between different single-spore races of *Botrytis cinerea,* and believed that they resulted in mycelia containing nuclei from both of the parent strains. In this species, as in numerous other imperfect fungi, the conidia as well as the hyphal cells are multinucleate and these authors state that "a multinuclear spore is, therefore, not an individual but, in reality, a colony, and it can, therefore, not give rise to a genetically pure culture unless all of its nuclei are genetically identical." They observed variants in the offspring of cultures derived from hyphal fusions occurring between two different races, and suggested that such strains owe their instability not to mutation but to nuclear heterogeneity. In later work they "crossed" two species, *B. Allii* and *B. Ricini,* and obtained three types which they considered to be new varieties or new species. Davidson, Dowding, and Buller[8] observed the occurrence of hyphal fusions in several species of dermatophytes (*Microsporum Audouini, M. Canis, Trichophyton mentagrophytes*). They found that fusions occurred readily between different strains of the same species, but not between different species, and suggested this as a criterion for species identification. They did not observe variants, and Emmons also failed to observe any evidence of hybridization when different variants of *M. gypseum* were seeded together. It should be noted here that Spring[27] failed to find any evidence of heterothallism in dermatophytes.

Practical Considerations. What does all this signify to the practicing bacteriologist? It need not disturb his routine work very much. It is not intended to give the impression that *all* fungi will transform into new types on continued cultivation. This is a tendency which has been observed in many species of the lower fungi studied by medical and industrial mycologists. But, as with the bacteria, many species, and some strains of nearly all species, will "stay put" almost indefinitely in artificial cultures. Strains recently isolated from their natural habitat are likely to be very stable, and if old laboratory strains "go pleomorphic," they can usually be readily replaced. Spontaneous variations are of course of importance in explaining the occurrence of new races or physiological types of pathogenic fungi, especially in the plant parasites, and the possibility of developing new industrial yeasts and molds by induced mutations or by hybridization is an attractive field for investigation. But the phenomena of variation in fungi are probably most important from the standpoint of classification and nomenclature. Some of the variants which have been observed differ so much from the parent culture that one might be justified in calling them new species. And some of the variants, particularly those described by Emmons on his studies of dermatophytes, are apparently identical with species already known in nature.

Taxonomy. Throughout nature individuals exist in infinite variety, and when we group them into species we draw artificial lines which do not actually exist. This has led, throughout the history of biology, to a conflict between the "splitters" who would make a new species of every new individual, and the "lumpers" who recognize only the grossest of differences. "The 'lumper' is the horror of the 'splitter,' the 'splitter' is anathema to the 'lumper'; both are the source of genuine grief and much hardship to conscientious men, who are possessors of normally constituted minds and truly scientific habits." † Conscientious men with normal minds and scientific habits will recognize the modal types about which individuals fluctuate, and designate these as species. They will recognize the normal limits of variation within these species.

Unfortunately in the study of the lower fungi we have suffered from a plethora of splitters and a dearth of lumpers. This is due, in part, to the failure of most workers to take into account the frequent occurrence of slight and often transient variations. Thus we have in the literature of medical mycology probably two or three hundred species names and combinations which differ mainly in slight variations in form, color, or texture of the colonies—characters which are almost never constant. Similar conditions obtain in many other genera of the lower fungi. As our investigations of variation continue, many of these species will necessarily be reduced to synonymy.

† W. J. Holland in *The Moth Book.*

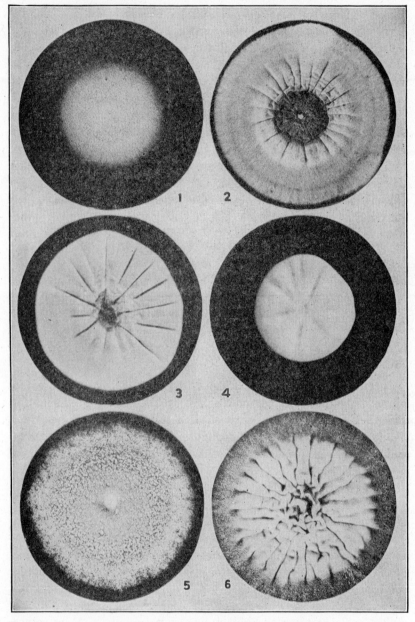

Fig 26. Spontaneous variation in a dermatophyte, *Trichophyton mentagro-phytes:* 1, an original strain; 2, 3, and 4, variants derived from it; 5, another strain; 6, variant derived from it. From C. W. Emmons, *Arch. Dermatol. Syphilol.* (*Chicago*), **25**, 987 (1932).

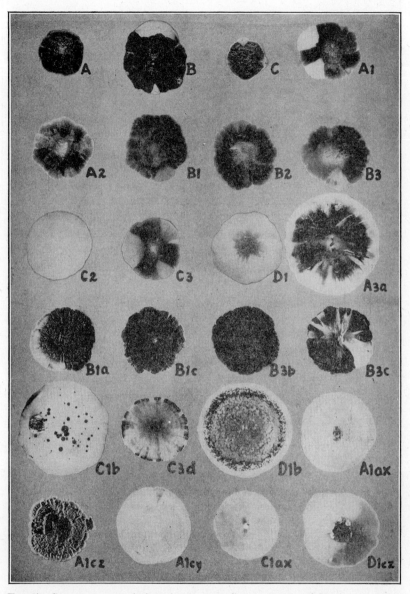

Fig. 27. Spontaneous variations in a yeast, *Cryptococcus pulcherrimus*. Giant colonies derived from a single cell. The original strain was smooth and red. Rough and white variants were obtained. Sectors and secondary colonies may be seen. From L. Punkari and A. T. Henrici, *J. Bact.*, **26**, 125 (1933).

Fig. 28. Hybrid fungi. Giant colonies from eight different sporidia of *Ustilago Zeae* obtained from smut spores resulting from a crossing of two strains of corn smut parasites. From J. J. Christensen, *Minn. Agr. Exp. Sta. (St. Paul)*, *Tech. Bull. 65* (1929).

LITERATURE

1. ALEXANDER, A., Ueber die faviforme Degeneration resp. Unwandlung unserer Dermatophyten, *Dermatol. Z.*, **56**, 225 (1929).

2. BARNES, B., Variations in *Eurotium herbariorum (Wigg.) Link.* induced by the action of high temperatures, *Ann. Botany*, **42**, 783 (1928); Variations in *Botrytis cinerea* induced by the action of high temperatures, *Ann. Botany*, **44**, 825 (1930); Induced variation, *Trans. Brit. Mycol. Soc.*, **20**, 17 (1935).

3. BILTRIS, R., Sur la variabilité des caractères de l'espèce chez les dermatophytes, *Ann. inst. Pasteur*, **43**, 281 (1929).

4. BRIERLEY, W. B., Variation in fungi and bacteria, *Proc. Intern. Congr. Plant Sci., Ithaca*, **2**, 1629 (1929).

5. BURKHOLDER, W. H., Variations in a member of the genus Fusarium grown in culture for a period of five years, *Am. J. Botany*, **12**, 245 (1925).

6. CHODAT, F., Recherches expérimentales sur la mutation chez les champignons, *Bull. soc. bot. Genève, Ser. 2*, **18**, 41 (1926).

7. CHRISTENSEN, J. J., Mutation and hybridization in *Ustilago zeae, Minn. Agr. Exp. Sta. Tech. Bull. 65* (1929); Studies on the genetics of *Ustilago zeae, Phytopath. Z.*, **4**, 129 (1931).

8. DAVIDSON, A. M., E. S. DOWDING, and A. H. R. BULLER, Hyphal fusions in dermatophytes, *Can. J. Research*, **6**, 1 (1932).

9. DEMEREC, M., Unstable genes, *Botan. Rev.* **1**, 233 (1935).

10. DICKSON, H., The effects of x-rays, ultraviolet light and heat in producing saltants in *Chaetomium cochliodes* and other fungi, *Ann. Botany*, **46**, 389 (1932); Saltation induced by x-rays in seven species of Chaetomium, *Ann. Botany*, **47**, 735 (1933).

11. DODGE, B. O., Nuclear phenomena associated with heterothallism and homothallism in the Ascomycete Neurospora, *J. Agr. Research*, **35,** 289 (1927); Unisexual conidia from bisexual mycelia, *Mycologia*, **20,** 226 (1928); Breeding albinistic strains of the Monilia bread mold, *Mycologia*, **22,** 9, (1930); Reproduction and inheritance in Ascomycetes, *Science*, **83,** 169 (1936); Some problems in the genetics of the fungi, *Science*, **90,** 379 (1939).

12. EMMONS, C. W., Pleomorphism and variation in the dermatophytes, *Arch. Dermatol. Syphilol. (Chicago)*, **25,** 987 (1932).

13. EMMONS, C. W., and A. HOLLAENDER, The influence of monochromatic ultraviolet radiation on the rate of variant production in *Trichophyton mentagrophytes, Genetics*, **24,** 70 (1939); The action of ultraviolet radiation on dermatophytes, II. Mutations induced in cultures of dermatophytes by exposure of spores to monochromatic ultraviolet radiation, *Am. J. Botany*, **26,** 467 (1939).

14. FABIAN, F. W., and N. B. McCULLOUGH, Dissociation in yeasts, *J. Bact.*, **27,** 583 (1934).

15. GRIGORAKI, L., Recherches cytologiques et taxonomiques sur les dermatophytes, *Ann. sci. nat. Botan.*, **7,** 165 (1925).

16. HAENICKE, A., Vererbungsphysiologische Untersuchungen an Arten von Penicillium und Aspergillus, *Z. Botan.*, **8,** 225 (1916).

17. HANNA, W. F., Studies in the physiology and cytology of *Ustilago zeae* and *Sorosporium reilianum, Phytopathology*, **19,** 415 (1929).

18. HANSEN, H. N., and R. E. SMITH, The mechanism of variation in imperfect fungi: *Botrytis cinerea, Phytopathology*, **22,** 953 (1932); The origin of new types of imperfect fungi from interspecific co-cultures, *Zentr. Bakt., Parisitenk., II,* **92,** 272 (1935).

19. KÖHLER, E., Beiträge zur Kenntnis der vegetativen Anastomosen der Pilze, *Planta*, **8,** 140 (1929).

20. LAIBACH, F., Über Zellfusionen bei Pilzen, *Planta*, **5,** 340 (1928).

21. LINDEGREN, C. C., The genetics of Neurospora, I. The inheritance of response to heat-treatment, *Bull. Torrey Botan. Club*, **59,** 85 (1932); II. Segregation of the sex factors in the asci of *N. crassa, N. sitophila* and *N. tetrasperma, Bull. Torrey Botan. Club*, **59,** 119 (1932); III. Pure bred stocks and crossing-over in *N. crassa, Bull. Torrey Botan. Club*, **60,** 133 (1933); IV. The inheritance of tan vs. normal, *Am. J. Botany*, **21,** 55 (1934); V. Self-sterile bisexual heterokaryons, *J. Genetics*, **28,** 425 (1934); VI. Bisexual and akaryotic ascospores from *N. crassa, Genetics*, **16,** 315 (1934); VII. Developmental competition between different genotypes within the ascus, *Z. Indukt. Abstamm.-u. Vererbungsh.*, **68,** 331 (1935).

22. MACKINNON, J. E., Nuevo sentido de variación en *Mycotorula albicans, Arch. soc. biol. Montevideo*, **7,** 162 (1936).

23. NADSON, G., and G. PHILIPPOV, Influence des rayons x sur la sexualité et la formation des mutantes chez les champignons inférieurs (Mucorinées), *Compt. rend. soc. biol.*, **93,** 473 (1925); De la formation de nouvelles races stables chez les champignons inférieurs sous l'influence des rayons x, *Compt. rend., Acad. Sci. (Paris)*, **186,** 1566 (1928).

24. NEGRONI, P., Variación hacia el tipo R. de *Mycotorula albicans, Rev. soc. argentina biol.*, **11,** 449 (1935); Ensayos para obtener la reversión de la

forma R a la S de *Mycotorula albicans, Rev. inst. bacteriol., dep. nacl. hig. (Buenos Aires)*, **7**, 393 (1936).

25. PUNKARI, L., and A. T. HENRICI, A study of variations in a chromogenic asporogenous yeast, *J. Bact.*, **26**, 125 (1933); Further studies in spontaneous variation of *Torula pulcherrima, J. Bact.*, **29**, 259 (1935).

26. SHEAR, C. L., and B. O. DODGE, Life histories and heterothallism of the red bread mold fungi of the *Monilia sitophila* group, *J. Agr. Research*, **34**, 1019 (1927).

27. SPRING, D., Heterothallism among the dermatophytes, *Arch. Dermatol. Syphilol. (Chicago)*, **24**, 22 (1931).

28. STAKMAN, E. C., and J. J. CHRISTENSEN, Heterothallism in *Ustilago zeae, Phytopathology*, **17**, 827 (1927).

29. WEIDMANN, F. D., Morphologic variations in a ringworm species of the toes, *Arch. Dermatol. and Syphilol. (Chicago)*, **13**, 374 (1926).

30. WILTSHIRE, S. P., A Stemphyllium saltant of an Alternaria, *Ann. Botany*, **43**, 653 (1929).

31. WINGE, Ö., and Ö. LAUSTSEN, On two types of spore germination and on genetic segregations in Saccharomyces demonstrated through single spore cultures. *Compt. rend. trav. lab. Carlsberg, Sér. physiol.*, **22**, 99 (1937); Artificial species-hybridization in yeast, *Compt. rend. trav. lab. Carlsberg, Sér. physiol.*, **22**, 235 (1938); **22**, 257 (1939).

CHAPTER III

METHODS FOR STUDYING MOLDS, YEASTS, AND ACTINOMYCETES

Culture Media. Molds may be cultivated on either solid or liquid media in tubes or dishes, as bacteria are. But molds generally grow more slowly than bacteria and, where both are present in the material to be examined, the latter are apt to overgrow Petri plate cultures before the former can develop. For isolation it is therefore desirable to use a medium favorable to the growth of molds and unfavorable for bacteria. Such a medium may be obtained by adding to ordinary nutrient agar a rather large amount of sugar, and by making the medium rather strongly acid, since most molds will tolerate higher degrees of acidity than bacteria will. A medium containing 5 per cent glucose and 0.5 per cent tartaric acid in addition to the usual meat extract and peptone is very satisfactory for some fungi but is not suitable for most pathogens of man.

If agar is autoclaved in such an acid medium, however, it will be markedly hydrolyzed and will fail to jell on cooling. This difficulty is obviated by sterilizing the glucose and acid separately in concentrated solution. A solution containing 50 per cent glucose and 5 per cent tartaric acid may be safely autoclaved. Such a sterile solution may be kept on hand and, when need for a medium for isolating molds arises, it can be quickly met by melting a deep tube (about 10 ml.) of ordinary agar (beef extract 0.3 per cent, peptone 1 per cent, pH 7.4) and adding to it 1 ml. of the glucose-tartaric acid solution. This gives a final concentration of nearly 5 per cent glucose and 0.5 per cent tartaric acid and a reaction of about pH 3.8. Less of the glucose-tartaric solution may be used for less acid media. If an agar medium with reduced buffer content and lower pH is used (e.g., A.P.H.A.) less of the glucose-tartaric solution will be used. On these media most molds and yeasts will grow luxuriantly, most bacteria not at all.

The growth on the above media is for some purposes, as in counting molds in soil, for instance, almost too luxuriant, since some of the rapid growers tend to spread over the plate and crowd out others. Media less rich in nutrients may be preferred for counting molds by the dilution plate method in soil or other habitats with a large fungus flora. Such a medium has been devised by Waksman [43] especially for soil work, but will prove of value for isolations from other material. It consists of

Glucose	10.0 grams
Peptone	5.0 grams
Monopotassium phosphate	1.0 gram
Magnesium sulphate (crystals)	0.5 gram
Agar	15.0 grams
Water	1 liter

Just before use, i.e., after sterilizing and while melted, sulphuric acid is added until the reaction is pH 3.8 to 4.0. About 0.5 to 0.6 ml. of normal acid is sufficient for 100 ml. This medium has less sugar than the preceding. The use of a mineral acid eliminates the danger of the acid being destroyed by the growth of the mold, as might occur with tartaric acid, thus eventually allowing the bacteria to develop.

Hydrogen-ion Concentration. Although these acid media serve well for the isolation of most of the common molds and yeasts, they will not permit a growth of all fungi. Many of the pathogenic species in particular may fail to grow. The pH limits of growth have been determined for only a few species of molds and yeasts. Talice [41] published data for a number of fungi pathogenic for animals and for some common saprophytes, when grown on three different agar nutrient media. Very little difference was found with the different media. A few examples will show the ranges. The organism of North American blastomycosis grew between pH 5 and pH 8, the optimum at pH 7; *Sprotrichum Beurmanni* from pH 3.0 to pH 9.6, the optimum at pH 5.0; *Microsporum Audouini* from pH 5 to pH 7, the optimum at pH 6. Saprophytic species showed a wider range. *Rhizopus nigricans*, for example, grew from pH 2.2 to pH 9.6; *Penicillium citrinum* showed a similar range, as did also *Oospora verticilloides*. In many cases fungi which tolerated a wide range of hydrogen-ion concentrations failed to show a distinct optimum, the top of the curve forming a broad plateau rather than a peak. The parasitic species, *Candida albicans*, resembled the saprophytic species, growing at all levels from pH 2.2 to pH 9.6, the optimum being pH 7.

Some molds may grow in media much more acid than pH 2.2. Starkey and Waksman [37] have grown certain molds in poorly buffered media of a normality of as much as 2 and 2.5! These observations have been confirmed. Mr. Owen Sletten (unpublished data) has isolated several molds growing in $2N$ sulphuric acid reagent, presumably deriving their energy from traces of organic materials.

These fungi were found to develop in normal and in some cases 2 N and 2.5 N sulphuric acid to which 1 gram of peptone and 1 gram of glucose per liter were added.

Kadisch [15] studied the influence of the hydrogen-ion concentration upon the growth of various dermatophytes, in the range from pH 6.7 to pH 7.9, and found that all of them grew better in slightly alkaline media. The optimum for most species was pH 7.4. Von Mallinckrodt-Haupt [25] observed that two species of dermatophytes when grown on media nearly neutral in reaction made the media progressively more alkaline (up to pH 8), whereas a Penicillium and a pink yeast produced acid. The alkali-preference of the ringworm fungi was offered by Levin and Silvers [18] as an explanation for the localization of these fungi in the interdigital spaces and the axillae, where the pH of the skin secretion is higher than on other parts of the body surface.

Nearly all actinomycetes prefer an alkaline medium. Soil actinomycetes grew in the range pH 5 to 9, with the optimum at pH 7 to 8. Jensen, however, found strains in acid peat soils which grew only in the range pH 2.5 to 5.8 with the optimum at pH 3 to 4. See page 362.

Types of Media. Culture media used in the study of molds may be divided into three groups:

1. Non-reproducible media, such as pieces or infusions of fruits, vegetables, skin, or hair, which may be valuable for the cultivation of certain species, but which are not reproducible because the substrates naturally vary in composition.

2. Reproducible media of unknown composition. In this group would fall the well-known Sabouraud's medium and its various substitutes. These are media containing complex substances such as peptone whose precise chemical constitution is unknown, but which are manufactured by standardized procedures so that the product from one manufacturer is reasonably constant over a period of time, and the same material is available to all laboratories.

3. Synthetic media, i.e., media prepared from pure chemicals of known constitution, which can be reproduced precisely in laboratories throughout the world independently of any manufacturer.

Non-reproducible Media. Media of this class are seldom used except in infusions or for particular purposes, as the cultivation of species of fungi which will not grow upon the other types of media, or which will produce characteristic fruiting bodies only upon a certain substrate.

Potato plugs may be prepared as for the growth of bacteria, but they are not very useful. Carrot plugs, prepared in the same way, are especially useful in studying spore formation in yeasts. Moistened slices of bread are sometimes used, especially in the study of Mucorales. Langeron and Milochevitch [17] proposed the use of moistened grains of barley, wheat, and rye for the cultivation of dermatophytes. Conant [2] found polished rice to be a more favorable medium, especially for the development of macroconidia in the genus Microsporum. One part of rice is added to three parts of water in flasks and sterilized in flowing steam on two successive days.

The restriction of the dermatophytoses to the skin, nails, and hair has led to a widespread belief that the skin and its appendages contain specific nutrients favorable to the dermatophytes. Hair, feathers, leather, and horn have been used for the cultivation of these fungi. Williams [47] has especially studied the growth of dermatophytes upon hair, using only hair and distilled water as a medium. The various dermatophytes grew, but more slowly and scantily than on Sabouraud's medium. Emmons [10] grow dermatophytes upon thin shavings of horn in order to study the development of spores. Davidson, Gregory, and Birt [7] similarly observed the development of spores of dermatophytes from the continued growth of fungi on the infected hairs after removal from the patient. Memmesheimer [28] has described a medium prepared from skin and hair for the cultivation of dermatophytes. The whole skin of guinea pigs is used. To pelts 75 to 80 grams in weight is added 20 ml. of 30 per cent potassium hydroxide and 75 ml. of tap water. This is boiled for 30 to 45 minutes, almost completely dissolving the skin. The solution is neutralized with hydrochloric acid and filtered, tap water is added to make 1 liter, and 40 grams of maltose and 18 grams of agar are added. This medium is said to give a more rapid growth of dermatophytes than the usual Sabouraud agar, and also to yield a higher percentage of positive cultures from cases of dermatophytosis.

The addition of serum or ascitic fluid to a medium stimulates and improves the growth of some strains of *Actinomyces bovis*. Other strains grow as well without this addition and it is not necessary for the isolation of most fungi. New or recently isolated strains of Blastomyces and Histoplasma when grown on blood agar at 37° C. grow as budding cells similar to those seen in tissue, but these fungi are probably more easily isolated on Sabouraud's agar medium.

It is usually preferable to prepare media from natural materials by making an aqueous solution of the nutritive constituents by infusion or decoction. Such liquid media may then be solidified by the addition of agar. A medium widely used by plant pathologists is potato-glucose agar:

Peeled sliced potatoes	300 grams
Glucose	10 grams
Agar	15 grams
Water	1 liter

The medium is boiled for 20 minutes and strained through cotton. The reaction, slightly acid, is not adjusted.

Corn meal agar is also widely used. It is especially valuable in observing the development of chlamydospores and for demonstration of mycelium in *Candida albicans*. Light-colored corn meal is preferable. If one uses dehydrated media he should make certain that no glucose has been used in the formula.

Corn (maize) meal	40 grams
Water	1 liter

This is heated to 60° C. for 1 hour and stirred frequently. It is filtered through paper and made up to 1 liter; then 20 grams of agar is added. The reaction is not adjusted. If it is sterilized by the fractional method, as is sometimes recommended, trouble may be expected from resistant spores of bacteria in this non-acid medium.

Brewery bacteriologists use beer wort and wort agar for the cultivation of their yeasts, and winery bacteriologists use grape juice or must. Industrial yeasts are said to maintain their special fermentation characteristics better on these natural substrates than on more artificial media. Malt-extract agar may be substituted for beer wort. These media naturally have reactions about pH 4.5 and, if autoclaved, the agar may be softened. Diluted honey has been used for growing both yeast and molds, but it is variable in composition and, save for the special study of honey and nectar yeasts, not very useful.

Manure infusion agar has been widely used for the cultivation of various coprophilic fungi. The following method is presented by Gwynne-Vaughan and Barnes.[14] About 1000 grams of horse, cow, or rabbit dung is soaked in cold water for 3 days; the liquid is poured off and diluted until it has the color of straw; 2.5 grams of agar is added for every 100 ml. of the diluted fluid.

Sterilized soil has been used successfully by Greene and Fred [13] for maintaining cultures of certain molds with a minimum of physiological or morphological degeneration.

Reproducible Media. The standard medium used by medical mycologists for the cultivation of pathogenic fungi is Sabouraud's agar. As originally described, this consisted of 4 per cent of the crude maltose of Chanut and 1 per cent of the granulated peptone of Chassaing. These were obtainable for many years from the Maison Cogit, 36 Boulevard St. Michel in Paris. Although the ingredients were of unknown composition, they were constant and gave reproducible results. The difficulty in obtaining these ingredients in other parts of the world has led to the development of substitute media which are often also called Sabouraud's agar. Attempts to reproduce the cultural characters of dermatophytes as described by Sabouraud on these substitute media indicated that the peptone rather than the sugar was the essential ingredient. For ordinary work a medium containing 2 per cent glucose and 1 per cent Neopeptone (Difco) is a satisfactory substitute for Sabouraud's agar. It may be adjusted to pH 5.6 and is commonly called Sabouraud agar or Sabouraud glucose agar. Pure glucose is more satisfactory than maltose for most fungi; it is more constant in composition, cheaper, and not so likely to change in sterilization. Usually a somewhat better growth is obtained if tap water is used instead of distilled water. There are very few molds, yeasts, or actinomycetes which will not grow abundantly on this medium. It is widely used for saprophytic and industrial fungi as well as for medical work.

The original formula for Sabouraud's agar presented in the preceding paragraph is that of Sabouraud's "proof" agar, originally intended primarily for the isolation and identification of dermatophytes. Species of these fungi have been based largely upon the color and texture of the colonies, which characters may vary markedly with slight variations in the medium. In addition to his proof agar, Sabouraud used a conservation agar for the continued cultivation of strains in a collection. He believed that medium was less likely to give rise to pleomorphism in dermatophytes than the proof agar. The conservation medium contained no sugar, only 3 per cent of peptone. Some fungi are more difficult to transfer from this medium because they produce fewer aerial hyphae and conidia. The dermatophytes can often be kept safely on the glucose agar if they are placed in the refrigerator (2° to 5° C.) immediately after reaching full development (10 to 15 days) and stored there until the next transfer.

The impression that the pathogenic fungi are fastidious in their nutritional requirements and will grow only on Sabouraud's medium is erroneous. Most of them grow well on a variety of media and, on the other hand, Sabouraud's medium is unsuitable for some pathogens such as *Actinomyces bovis*. In addition to being a good, easily prepared medium, it is very useful in the identification of dermatophytes because it permits comparison with the excellent photographs Sabouraud used to illustrate his taxonomic studies. The ingredients used by Sabouraud are no longer generally available and so many substitute formulas have been proposed that the name Sabouraud's medium as commonly used has no precise meaning. The substitution of 1 per cent Neopeptone (Difco) and 2 per cent C.P. glucose with 2 per cent agar and adjustment of pH 5.6 gives a medium which produces very nearly the same type of colony as the original formula and makes use of materials readily available and reasonably constant in composition. This medium is referred to in this book as Sabouraud or American Sabouraud agar. For most purposes the pH of the medium need not be adjusted.

It would of course be highly desirable to obtain a medium of known chemical composition which could be produced in constant form independently of commercial preparations. Unfortunately no medium yet devised will yield a characteristic growth of all of the fungi, especially not of the dermatophytes. Williams [46] found that asparagine was not a satisfactory substitute for peptone.

Synthetic Media. Synthetic media are most widely used in biochemical studies, since a known substrate is essential in order to study the products of metabolism. With a basic medium of precisely known concentration, one may vary the constituents one by one and so determine the influence of each upon growth, enzyme action, and the like. This aspect of the study of fungi has been extensively reviewed by Steinberg.[38] The first noteworthy studies of this sort were made by Raulin who developed a formula for the growth of *Aspergillus niger* containing eleven ingredients, all of known chemical composition. Such a medium seems unnecessarily complicated, but has served as the starting point for numerous studies, especially of the effects of small quantities of the metals. Raulin's medium is strongly acid (pH 2.9), and for many species the formula will need modification to provide a more favorable reaction.

Synthetic media are further used, where possible, as a standard substrate upon which to observe colony form and especially pigment production. Such a medium which has been widely used is Czapek's medium as modified by Dox and by Thom:

Sucrose	30.0	grams
Sodium nitrate	2.0	grams
Dipotassium phosphate	1.0	gram
Magnesium sulphate (crystals)	0.5	gram
Potassium chloride	0.5	gram
Ferrous sulphate	0.01	gram
Water	1	liter

This medium has been used by Thom for descriptions of species of Penicillium and Aspergillus, and by Waksman for descriptions of soil actinomycetes. In both cases color of the growth is of great importance in identification. Many fungi cannot, however, readily use sucrose, others cannot utilize nitrates. This medium cannot therefore be used for all fungi. An alternative medium is that of Barnes:

Tripotassium phosphate	10 grams
Ammonium nitrate	10 grams
Potassium nitrate	10 grams
Glucose	10 grams
Water	1 liter

All these synthetic media may, of course, be solidified by the addition of agar unless they are so acid as to hydrolyze agar.

Many if not most fungi require minute amounts of other elements, e.g., zinc, but unless purely synthetic media prepared from specially purified chemicals in special glassware are used, sufficient traces of these elements will usually be provided by the ingredients used, the water, or the glassware. Also some fungi require small amounts of growth-promoting substances and in purely synthetic media these may need to be provided for.

Dye Media. Various workers have experimented with the addition of dyes to culture media used for the identification of fungi, either to stain the growing mycelium differentially or to serve as pH indicators. Williams [48] grew a variety of fungi, mostly pathogenic species, on a 4 per cent peptone, 1 per cent glucose agar to which was added nigrosin, litmus, eosin Y, eosin B, fluorescein, methylene blue and eosin, Wright's stain, neutral red, and Janus green. Von Mallinckrodt-Haupt [24] grew various dermatophytes on media containing thymol blue, bromophenol blue, bromocresol purple, bromothymol blue, phenol red, and cresol red. Although the various cultures showed differing degrees of dye absorption by the growing fungi, or color changes in the media, no useful differential media have developed from the studies. Negroni and Loizaga [32] grew *Candida albicans* in a beer wort to which were added basic fuchsin, methylene blue, gentian violet, malachite green, and methyl green in minute quantities (1:50,000–1:10,000). These basic dyes, especially methyl green, induced the production of rough variants.

Quantity Production of Mold Mycelium. In many types of research, as for obtaining antigens, enzymes, antibiotics, or other intracellular products or for large amounts of growth for chemical analyses or animal feeding experiments, it is desirable to obtain a large amount of mycelium. Often oxygen is the limiting factor for growth and the greatest yield is obtained if the molds are grown in a thin layer (about 1 cm. deep) of liquid medium. Flasks take too much incubator space. We have in our laboratories used 1-liter, flat-sided, narrow-mouthed prescription bottles which contain about 100 ml. each of medium. After inoculation, these are placed on their sides and incubated so that the liquid is spread in a broad thin layer. Narrow-mouthed bottles are essential to prevent air contamination. When sufficient growth has occurred, the mycelium may be removed by pulling the mat through the mouth of the tube with a hooked wire, and the excess medium may be removed by straining through gauze or sieve. In our laboratories large amounts of growth for extracting antigens and also for feeding to rats on diets have thus been obtained. In industry special apparatus is used for mass production.

Media for Biochemical Studies. In general, one studies the enzyme actions of molds in the same manner as with bacteria, and such media as gelatin, litmus milk, coagulated egg, or blood serum are useful. Sugar fermentations are not important in the identification of molds or actinomycetes, but they are of great importance in identifying yeasts. Methods for studying sugar fermentations by yeasts will be discussed later. It is frequently desirable to determine the ability of molds and actinomycetes to hydrolyze starch and cellulose. The former may be determined by growing the organism in Petri dishes on agar in which starch has been incorporated. After growth has taken place the agar is flooded with diluted Lugol solution, which will stain the starch blue but will leave a clear zone about the mold if it has a diastatic action. The action on cellulose may be observed by growing the organism in a medium containing various nutrient salts, an inorganic source of nitrogen, but no source of carbon save strips of filter paper. If the mold can digest cellulose, the paper will be softened and eventually dissolved.

Isolation of Pathogenic Fungi. In making cultures from dermatophytosis of the scalp the infected short hair stubs. can be collected by means of forceps and placed directly on the surface of Sabouraud's agar slants or, better, placed first in empty sterile Petri dishes for sorting and selection of suitable portions. If long hairs are taken the infected basal portion should be cut off with sterile scissors or scalpel and only this part planted. Two to four plants can be made on one agar slant.

In making cultures from dermatophytosis of the skin the lesion should be first cleaned with a gauze sponge and 70 per cent alcohol. Care should be taken to avoid lesions recently treated with a fungicide and to collect material from the active border of the lesion. Scales or the roofs of vesicles can be removed with sterile scalpel or scissors. They can be placed directly upon the surface of agar slants but, especially in dermatophytosis of the foot, isolation of a pure culture is easier if the specimens are placed first in a sterile Petri dish, cut in small pieces with sterile scalpel, and flooded with 70 per cent alcohol. After exposure for 2 minutes, transferring the pieces to agar slants is begun and the procedure is timed so that the last specimens planted have been in the alcohol about 8 minutes. The 70 per cent alcohol, being more bactericidal than fungicidal, exerts a selective action and permits the isolation of a pure culture of the fungus without bacterial contamination.

In the isolation of dermatophytes when Staphylococcus and other bacteria may be present on the specimen, the latter should be laid carefully upon the unbroken agar surface at the point where it first touches. The fungus hyphae need no encouragement or aid to penetrate the agar. Rubbing the specimen across the surface of the agar and breaking the surface of the agar both increase the area over which contaminating bacteria will be deposited and if these bacteria are alive their growth will interfere with the development as well as the isolation of the fungus. If bacteria or saprophytic fungi grow in the primary culture with the pathogen, the latter can be isolated by transferring with a sharp stiff needle some of the conidia or aerial hyphae after they grow beyond the contaminants.

Most of the fungi pathogenic for man can be isolated in culture by the simple method of streaking or spreading pus, sputum, blood, macerated tissue, or other pathological material on the surface of Sabouraud agar slants. Usually no preliminary digestion on concentration is desirable or necessary. A few pathogens require special treatment and these exceptions will be briefly noted here. *Actinomyces bovis* will not grow on Sabouraud's agar; pus containing this fungus should be planted on veal infusion agar containing 1 per cent glucose, Brewer's thioglycollate glucose medium, or blood agar and incubated anaerobically. *Pityrosporum ovale* will grow on Sabouraud's agar or similar medium only if it is first covered with a thin layer of lanolin or other fat. A few of the pathogens will grow poorly on any media yet devised and are therefore very difficult to isolate in culture.

The separation of pathogenic molds from bacteria is often a difficult problem. In many cases bacteria are much more numerous than the fungi. Here success in isolation is in proportion to the number of cultures made. If a dozen or more slants are inoculated, one has a much better chance of obtaining a pure culture than if he merely streaks the pus or sputum over a single slant. The use of pour plates may increase the chances of isolating the fungus but is an unwise procedure with such pathogens as *Nocardia asteroides* and *Coccidioides immitis* in which there is grave danger of inhaling spores from an uncovered Petri dish culture.

Often fungi appear in a culture overcrowded with colonies of bacteria. In such cases the tuft of aerial mycelium may be free of bacteria, or may contain only a few, so that if one carefully touches the very surface of the mold colony he may obtain a relatively or absolutely pure culture. If the fungus produces few or no conidia it may be necessary to postpone subculturing until the fungus has grown well beyond the bacteria or up on the side of the culture tube, when a portion of the mycelium can be removed with a stiff, sharp needle.

Isolation of Saprophytic Actinomycetes. In studying actinomycetes it must be borne in mind that most of them cannot tolerate an acid medium. The acid-sugar media recommended for yeasts and molds cannot therefore be used. They will for the most part grow on the media used for bacteria, and their growth is generally stimulated by the addition of sugar.

In the isolation of these organisms the greatest difficulty is experienced in separating them from bacteria, since the latter for the most part grow more rapidly and, if they form spreading colonies, will overgrow the plates and suppress the actinomycetes. But most of the actinomycetes can grow with very small amounts of nutrient, and one may use a very weak medium on which many bacteria will not grow. Those that do will not spread much.

For general isolation of saprophytic species of actinomycetes, perhaps Czapek's solution agar has been most widely used. On it many bacteria will not grow and those that do are not spreaders. Some difficulty is experienced with spreading molds on this medium.

Conn's [3] glycerin asparaginate medium is excellent for isolating non-pathogenic actinomycetes.

Glycerol	10 ml.
Sodium asparaginate (or asparagine neutralized with NaOH)	1 gram
Dipotassium phosphate	1 gram
Agar	15 grams
Tap water	1 liter

Soil extract agar is a "natural" medium which may be used for the isolation of soil actinomycetes. It is made by heating 1000 grams of rich garden soil with 1 liter of water in the autoclave for half an hour. The liquid is decanted and filtered until fairly clear. To 100 ml. of this aqueous soil extract are added 900 ml. of water, 1 gram of glucose, 0.5 gram of dipotassium phosphate, and 15 grams of agar.

Isolation of Pathogenic Actinomycetes. Although such weak media serve for the isolation of saprophytic actinomycetes, they are not suitable for the pathogenic species. The strictly anaerobic *Actinomyces bovis* may be isolated in deep agar shake cultures, 1 per cent of glucose in veal infusion agar being used; or the method mentioned previously may be used. Various authorities have recommended the addition of blood serum or ascitic fluid, but this has not been found to be advantageous for all strains. Brewer's thioglycollate medium with glucose is also suitable for *A. bovis*. The aerobic species may be isolated readily on the same solid media as are used for *A. bovis*.

Single-cell Isolation. Although for most purposes isolation from a mixed culture by plating is readily accomplished, occasions may arise when other procedures are preferable. Where several molds are closely crowded together on a plate, it is sometimes quite feasible to pick off a spore head of a desired species with a sterilized wire under the higher-powered lenses of a binocular dissecting microscope. For certain types of work, as investigations of apparent mutation, cultures known to have developed from a single spore are necessary. Single spores may, of course, be picked up by the use of a micromanipulator (such as the Chambers instrument) more readily than bacteria, but much simpler procedures are available. Sass [36] has described such a method which he has used for growing single-spore strains of mushrooms. A spore suspension of proper density is sprayed over the surface of a sterile agar plate, which is then incubated for a time. The plate is then examined for well-isolated spores which have germinated, the low-power microscope lens being used. When such a spore is found, a small sterilized spatula with a minute hole in it is placed over the spore and pressed into the agar in such a way as to force a small cylinder of agar (bearing the spore on its upper surface) through the hole. The growing spore may then be easily removed with a sterile needle without danger of touching any other spore. It is simpler and safer to dispense with the perforated spatula, which may touch other spores when it is placed on the agar surface, and to remove the selected spore with a minute spade-shaped needle whose entire cutting edges can be kept in full microscopic view during the entire procedure.

Media for Yeast. In general, yeasts may be isolated and cultivated on the same media as are used for molds. Most species tolerate high acidities, and the glucose-tartaric acid medium is the most useful plating medium. Where synthetic media are desired, ammonium salts are preferable to nitrates as a source of nitrogen.

Observation of the spores is essential in identifying yeasts. Many species will not form spores readily on ordinary media. A number of methods have been devised to force yeasts to sporulate. Of these the plaster block method is most commonly used. Plaster of Paris mixed with water is put in small dishes and allowed to harden. When set, it is removed and placed in a larger dish or a large test tube, and sufficient water or dilute (0.1 per cent) peptone solution added to moisten the block thoroughly but not cover its surface. This is then sterilized in the autoclave. A young culture, say not over 24 hours old, is used for inoculation. A generous loopful of the growth is spread over the surface of the plaster. The temperature of sporulation is critical, and with unknown species it is advisable to prepare several blocks and incubate them at different temperatures, say 20°, 25°, and 30° C. After 24 hours spores should be searched for by microscopic examination. Other materials, as pieces of clay flower pots or blotting paper, may be used in place of the plaster, the idea being to maintain a limited amount of both nutrition and moisture, though there is some evidence that the calcium sulphate has some specific action in the process.

Many yeasts sporulate freely on corn meal agar and sporulation is said to occur quite regularly on Gorodkowa's medium, which has been widely used. The composition is

Glucose	2.5	grams
Sodium chloride	5	grams
Meat extract	10	grams
Agar	10	grams
Water	1	liter

Growth of yeasts on carrot plugs often leads to abundant spore formation. McKelvey[26] developed a medium which in our laboratories has yielded spores more consistently than have others. This consists of a weak carrot infusion (about 150 grams of chopped carrots to 1 liter of tap water) and 15 grams of agar melted together. Then 3.5 grams of anhydrous calcium sulphate is added and the mixture is thoroughly mixed, tubed, autoclaved, and slanted like any other agar medium. The medium of Mrak and associates[31] has also given excellent results in our laboratory.

Some recent work of Nickerson and Thimann[34] on spore formation in a yeast Zygosaccharomyces may well develop into a method which will allow ascospore formation to be much more easily brought about than heretofore. Those workers cultured a strain of *Aspergillus niger*, subcultures of which may be obtained from the American Type Culture Museum. The medium, after some days of incubation, was filtered and resterilized. When several species of Zygosaccharomyces were inoculated into this medium, conjugation and subsequent spore formation took place much more rapidly than in ordinary media and a much larger proportion of the cells conjugated. It was determined that two substances responsible for this stimulation of sporulation were also produced by Zygosaccharomyces itself, and it was believed that these substances are ordinarily set free into a medium only as the cells die and autolyze. Nickerson and Thimann furthermore found that the inclusion of riboflavin and sodium glutarate in ordinary media for yeasts gave as good results as the Aspergillus filtrate. They did not prove that the sporulation-inducing substances of the mold were the same as the chemicals used, but they did show that the results were the same. This work merits much extension.

A new method of Lindegren and Lindegren [21] for inducing spore formation in yeasts is given here. It has not been tried by the authors but in the hands of the Lindegrens it gave excellent results.

PRESPORULATION MEDIA

Beet leaves extract (1500 ml. H_2O, 450 grams beet leaves autoclaved)	100 ml.
Beet root extract (1500 ml. H_2O, 150 grams beet roots autoclaved)	200 ml.
Apricot juice (canned)	350 ml.
Grape juice	165 ml.
Dried yeast	20 grams
Glycerol	25 ml.
Agar	30 grams
Calcium carbonate	10 grams

Water is added to make 1 liter. The mixture is steamed until dissolved, tubed, and sterilized. Most strains will produce spores directly on the slants in a few weeks. If spores are needed sooner, the mixture is transferred to plaster of Paris. Instead of plaster of Paris blocks, the tubes of Graham and Hastings [12] are used. A mixture of equal parts of plaster of Paris ($CaSO_4$ anh.) and water are mixed and dispensed into test tubes and solidified in a slanting position, dried at 50° C. for 24 hours and autoclaved. About 1 ml. of sterilized water is poured over a 3-day growth of yeast on the presporulation medium and allowed to stand 10 minutes. A thick suspension is made by stirring. Some of the suspension is poured over the upper portion of the plaster of Paris slant with a sterile pipet. About 3 ml. of water made to pH 4.0 with acetic acid is pipetted into the lower half of the slant. The inoculated plaster of Paris slants are incubated for 1 to 2 days.

Fermentation by Yeasts. With yeasts and yeast-like fungi, if sugars are fermented the fermentation is usually alcoholic, and although acid is formed it is not of great significance in identification; an indicator is therefore optional, and greatest attention is given to gas production. In our experience, the observation of fermentation by yeasts requires higher concentrations of sugar and larger amounts of medium than are usually used in studying bacterial fermentation. With 1 per cent sugar in the customary small sugar tubes, results are likely to be variable. A medium containing 3 per cent of the sugar to be tested and 1 per cent of peptone, placed in 30-ml. amounts in 25 by 150 mm. tubes, with inverted 78 by 11 mm. tubes for gas traps, are suitable. Stelling-Dekker [39] used a 2 per cent solution of the test sugars in yeast infusion, placed in Einhorn fermentation tubes. To identify yeasts by Stelling-Dekker's key in many instances, it is necessary to determine whether the trisaccharide raffinose is fermented completely or only one third. For this purpose she uses a 4 per cent solution of raffinose in yeast infusion, and the fermentation is studied quantitatively in the van Iterson-Kluyver apparatus. Raffinose is a trisaccharide and each molecule is made up of one molecule of the disaccharide melibiose ($\frac{2}{3}$) and one molecule of the monosaccharide, fructose ($\frac{1}{3}$). If tubes of both raffinose and melibiose broth are used, it can be determined without the use of special chemical equipment whether all or only one third of the raffinose is fermented. If both raffinose and melibiose are fermented, obviously all the raffinose is fermentable; if raffinose and not melibiose, only one third, that is, the fructose portion of the molecule. Wickerham [45] has given details for making fermentation tests with melibiose.

Utilization of Specific Compounds. In addition to studying fermentation, the identification of yeasts, especially the asporogenous species, requires in many cases a determination of the carbohydrates or nitrogen sources which can be utilized by the organism. A medium is prepared which contains all the necessary ingredients for growth except a source of carbon, and to this medium the test sugars are added; or a medium is prepared which contains a known utilizable sugar (all yeasts can utilize glucose), but with no nitrogen source, to which various test nitrogen compounds may be added.

Lodder [23] has presented a simple procedure (originally devised by Beijerinck and called by him an auxanographic method) for determining the utilization of various substrates. For sugars, the basic medium is

Ammonium sulphate	5.0 grams
Monopotassium phosphate	1.0 gram
Magnesium sulphate	0.5 gram
Agar	20.0 grams
Water	1 liter

This medium, melted and cooled, is heavily seeded with the yeast to be tested and poured into Petri dishes. When solidified, the plate cultures are incubated for a few hours to dry the surface. Then small quantities of the dried sugar are deposited on the surface of the agar in labeled areas. Glucose is added to one spot in every case to serve as a control, since all yeasts can utilize this source of carbon. As many as six sugars may be tested on one plate, in addition to the glucose. The sugars dissolve and diffuse into the agar and, if utilizable, the yeasts will grow in that part of the plate culture.

Similarly, auxanographs of nitrogen utilization may be made. Here the basic medium is

Glucose	20.0 grams
Monopotassium phosphate	1.0 gram
Magnesium sulphate	0.5 gram
Agar	20.0 grams
Water	1 liter

Peptone, ammonium sulphate, asparagine, urea, and potassium nitrate are the test substances used. Some difficulty may be anticipated in these highly purified liquid media, for the reason that growth-promoting factors are necessary for some yeasts. Nickerson [33] used as criterion a medium including growth-promoting substances, glucose, and nitrates, and tested for nitrate reduction, rather than nitrate utilization. If further work shows that all organisms which are able to utilize nitrates as a sole nitrogen source also reduce nitrates to nitrites, this will be an improvement over previous methods. Nickerson used

Dipotassium phosphate	3	grams
Magnesium sulphate	0.25	gram
Calcium chloride	0.25	gram
Potassium nitrate	6	grams
Glucose	20	grams
Yeast extract	0.1	gram
Water	1	liter

After growth, the usual color tests for nitrites were made. It is quite possible that the ordinary peptone-glucose solutions such as Sabouraud's with added nitrates would serve as well as the above medium.

According to Zimmermann [49] and Mrak and McClung,[30] the auxanographic method cannot always be relied upon, and no doubt liquid media are to be preferred. The ability to utilize ethyl alcohol is also an important character in the identification of yeasts. This is determined by inoculating the organism into a liquid medium:

Ethyl alcohol	30.0 ml.
Ammonium sulphate	1.0 gram
Monopotassium phosphate	1.0 gram
Magnesium sulphate	0.5 gram
Water	1 liter

The alcohol will have to be added after sterilization. If growth occurs, as manifested by turbidity or sediment, the test is positive. Growth-promoting substances often have to be added to liquid media. In the auxanographic method, the large inoculum provides these substances.

Giant Colonies. The form and texture of colonies of yeasts are of diagnostic value, especially those of large isolated colonies (giant colonies) which have been allowed to grow for some time (4 to 6 weeks). See Fig. 114. Since lack of oxygen may modify growth, the containers cannot be sealed, and to prevent too much evaporation a large volume of agar is required. For this purpose round narrow-mouthed bottles 5 cm. in diameter and 12 cm. high are suitable. These are filled with 50 ml. each of the American Sabouraud agar described above and autoclaved. They are inoculated by touching a straight wire to the stock culture, then touching the tip of the wire to the center of the agar surface in the bottle. It is important to hold the bottle in an inverted position while inoculating to prevent air contamination. The agar surface should be allowed to dry a day or two before inoculating. The bottles are incubated at room temperature. For clear observation or for photographing, the bottles may be cut at the level of the agar surface by a short cut with a file and pressing the molten end of a glass rod against the file mark. The glass will usually crack neatly around the bottles at this level. The use of Petri dish cultures for photographic surfaces is more convenient and economical if contamination can be avoided and the plates do not dry too much in the long incubation period. Instead of giant colonies, Stelling-Dekker and Lodder used agar slant growth.

Temperature of Incubation. The optimum temperatures of molds, yeasts, and actinomycetes vary rather widely according to the species, and extensive studies are not available for most groups. Fortunately, with many species, the top of the temperature growth curve appears again to be a plateau rather than a peak, so that one has more latitude than with most bacteria. It is noteworthy that most of the pathogenic species do not grow best at body temperature but at a point considerably lower. Even the highly parasitic dermatophytes find their optimum temperature at 27° C. according to Kadisch.[16] In general, 30° C. falls near the optimum for most common pathogenic and saprophytic fungi, and the bacteriological laboratory which has frequent occasion to work with these microorganisms should be equipped with a special incubator kept at or near this temperature. Mrak and Bonar [29] showed that the temperature of incubation has a decided influence on the formation of yeast ascospores as well as on their size. Lower temperatures tend to reduce the size of the ascospores in relation to the ascus and therefore the individual spores are easier to delineate and study. In some groups, e.g., Rhizopus, the temperature range is of taxonomic significance.

Determination of Morphology. The identification of fungi depends more upon morphological characters than that of bacteria does. The appearance of the plant mass to the naked eye is frequently quite characteristic, and in many cases the organism can be recognized at a glance. It should be borne in mind, however, that both gross morphology and microscopic characters may sometimes vary not only with changes in the composition of the medium but also with the age of the culture.

For observing the morphology of molds a much better view can be obtained if the fungus is grown in a Petri dish rather than in a culture tube. Certain precautions must be observed, however. Great care must be exercised in handling plate cultures of pathogenic fungi, and certain agents of pulmonary and generalized mycoses such as *Coccidioides immitis* and *Nocardia asteroides* which produce large numbers of easily dissociated air-borne spores and hyphal fragments should never be planted in Petri dishes. In cases of non-pathogenic fungi it is likewise necessary to avoid dissemination of spores in the laboratory when the Petri dish cover is removed since such spores will be a troublesome source of contamination. Plate cultures can usually be uncovered safely when the colony is young and has just begun to form mature spores. Fortunately many of the morphological features of taxonomic interest are most easily seen in a young culture.

The first step in identifying a mold is to determine whether it belongs to the Phycomycetes or the Ascomycetes (or Fungi Imperfecti). In general, though there are exceptions, this may be readily done by a rather superficial examination. With those species which belong to the Fungi Imperfecti the plant mass is usually relatively compact, the aerial filaments of mycelium are relatively short, and the surface is thickly covered with spores which are frequently brightly colored. The surface may be compared to the nap of velvet. In the phycomycetous molds the mycelium is coarser and looser in texture, the aerial hyphae are longer,.and the sporangia are less numerous. The spore heads and frequently the aerial mycelium are usually dark colored, brown, gray or black. The whole plant mass has a texture comparable to cotton wool.

Molds take up considerable water from the medium and give off considerable into the air, which may condense in droplets on the surface of the plant. Large amounts of this transpiration (or guttation) water are characteristic of certain species. The droplets are frequently colored by pigments excreted by the mold. Beginners are frequently apt to mistake these droplets of moisture on the mycelium, especially if it is colored, for spores or other structures.

The general characters of the aerial mycelium and the spore heads may be determined by examining the growth with a magnifying glass or the low-power lens of the microscope from above, after removing the cover of the dish. For this purpose a binocular dissecting microscope is ideal.

After examining the upper surface of a Petri plate culture, one should reverse the plate and note the under surface of the colony. Frequently very characteristic colors are produced in the submersed mycelium or in the medium itself. These will vary markedly with the medium. Some of the pigments act as indicators, being perhaps yellow on one side of neutrality and red on the other. Occasionally one may find pigment only at the spot where two different molds come together. Particularly one should note if the submersed mycelium is light or dark in color. This is important as a primary separation of molds belonging to the Fungi Imperfecti.

In the examination and culture of sputum, species of Candida are frequently found. The most important of these, *Candida albicans*, can be readily identified in most cases by its appearance on corn meal agar in a plate culture. The agar is inoculated by placing the inoculum in several parallel streaks across the plate; a stiff needle is used so that some of the inoculum is below the agar surface. After 4 or 5 days of incubation at 20° to 25° C. the species produces characteristic clusters of blastospores and few to many large spherical chlamydospores. However, strains which have been kept in culture for long periods are not always typical in appearance, and fermentation reactions must be studied for identification.

For finer details of morphology it is necessary to prepare slides. Two stiff sharp Nichrome or steel needles are required. A bit of the aerial mycelium is removed with a single thrust of one needle held nearly parallel to the surface of the agar. The mycelium thus removed should be touched momentarily to a small drop of 95 per cent alcohol which has been previously placed on a slide, then removed quickly to a drop of 10 per cent sodium hydroxide also previously placed on the slide. It should then be carefully teased apart with two needles and covered with a cover slip. A thin film left on the slide by the rubbing of a finger across it just before the drops of alcohol and sodium hydroxide are deposited will usually prevent the spreading of the former and will facilitate the transfer of the material from one fluid to the other. The alcohol wets the mycelium which otherwise may be nearly opaque owing to the inclusion of air. The sodium hydroxide is a better mounting fluid than water because it swells the hyphal walls, making certain morphological details more apparent, and the preparation lasts longer. If the preparation is thin the sodium hydroxide crystallizes around the edge, thus sealing the cover and preventing dehydration for several hours. One may thus determine with certainty the presence or absence of septa in the mycelium, the structure of the sporophores and spores, the presence or absence of chlamydospores, and the like.

Instead of water some workers may prefer as a mounting fluid Amann's medium, which has the following composition.

Phenol, crystals	20 grams
Lactic acid, syrup	20 grams
Glycerol	40 grams
Water	20 ml.

These are dissolved together with gentle warming; then the following is added.

Cotton blue	0.05 gram

This is the formula given by Linder,[22] save that the amount of dye is greatly reduced. It serves as a combined fixing agent, stain, and mounting fluid. The mycelium and spores will be stained blue; thus much of the dye from the solution will be removed. Such a preparation, however, shows all the parts disarranged and is not permanent. Permanent preparations showing the complete structure of the thallus may be easily made with most molds by growing them directly on slides or cover glasses.

Slide Cultures. Slide cultures may be made either with solid or liquid media. It is best to have the medium not too rich in nutrients, since then the mycelium becomes rather densely packed and it is difficult to make out details of structure. The agar should be as clear as possible, because the presence of precipitates obscures the field. Since only small amounts are required, it is quite practical to filter the agar through paper. The slides or cover glasses used must be clean and free from grease, so that the medium will spread in a thin, uniform film. They may be kept in the usual acetic acid-alcohol mixture until used.

A convenient culture chamber may be prepared by placing in a Petri dish a piece of glass tubing bent to a V shape. A glass slide is laid across this and the dish, slide, and supporting tubing are sterilized in an autoclave. If, during sterilization, the slide has fallen off its support it can be replaced with sterile forceps. Melted agar is then placed on the slide at a sufficiently high temperature and in sufficient amount to cover with a thin flat layer of agar an area about half the length of the slide and three-fourths its width. When the agar has solidified, the fungus should be planted by streaking spores in two parallel rows extending the length of the agar. Water should then be placed in the bottom of the dish. Distilled water will provide a very humid atmosphere. By the addition of small amounts of salt to the water, various degrees of humidity can be maintained.

When the fungus has reached the proper stage of development it can be examined under the microscope. For the study of fine details it must, of course, be covered. If the fungus to be examined is a dry mold it must first be wetted. The slide is held by one end and absolute alcohol is dropped at the upper end of the culture. When it has drained off, the bottom and edges of the slide are wiped with blotting paper and the slide is placed on the table. Then 2 or 3 drops of 10 per cent sodium hydroxide or other mounting fluid is placed upon the culture and a large cover slip is carefully placed over it. The preparation is not permanent but is excellent for examination and photography of the unshrunken mycelium, conidiophores, and spores, and will keep for a few days. Because of the danger of scattering spores this method is not suitable for use in the examination of some fungi pathogenic for man.

Cover glasses require less space for incubation than slides, and a number of cover glasses can be incubated readily in a Petri dish. Stained cover glasses can be mounted in balsam to make permanent preparations very readily, but the small amount of nutrient is undesirable in some cases. A piece of blotting paper or several thicknesses of filter paper are placed in the bottom of a Petri dish and sterilized in an autoclave. Just before being used, the paper is wetted with sterile water. The cover glasses are cleaned, placed in alcohol, sterilized by flaming, and then placed on the surface of the paper. A tube of the agar is melted in a water bath, cooled to between 43° and 46° C., and inoculated rather heavily with spores of the mold to be studied. With a wire loop one or two loopfuls of the agar are deposited quickly on each cover glass and spread in a rather thin film. The Petri dish may then be incubated. If it is placed in a can, evaporation will be retarded. It is essential to maintain an atmosphere nearly saturated with moisture.

For preparations which are to be only temporary, agar is preferable to liquid media, since when hardened it will "stay put" on the cover slip. Agar cover slips placed on slides may be examined first, culture side up, with the low- and medium-power lenses, then turned over and mounted in a drop of Amann's fluid for more complete study. Semi-permanent preparations may be made by sealing the edges of the cover slip with asphaltum or other varnishes, first removing all excess of the mounting fluid. More permanent mounts may be made if glycerin jelly (1 part gelatin, 6 parts water by weight; 1 per cent phenol added) is used instead of Amann's fluid. This also requires sealing of the mount with asphaltum.

Beautiful permanent preparations mounted in balsam may be made from cover slip cultures, but for this liquid media are preferable to agar media because it is almost impossible to obtain a stain which does not color the agar rather deeply. A tube of the liquid medium is inoculated, and then with a sterile pipet small quantities (about 0.01 ml.) are deposited on the cover slips in the Petri dish. The dish must now be handled carefully so that the liquid does not run off on to the filter paper. Czapek's or corn meal solution is suggested for actinomycetes and for those molds which will grow on them.

When sufficient growth has taken place the cover slips are removed and *thoroughly* dried. If drying is not complete the film of mold (or of agar if it has been used) will wash off in the staining operations. It is well to dry the cover slips on some sort of warm plate and to let them continue to dry for about 5 minutes after they appear to be dry. Since the mold is not easily wetted by water, an alcoholic fixing solution is desirable. For ordinary purposes the formalin-alcohol-acetic acid mixture commonly used for plant material is satisfactory. It is made of

Alcohol (50 per cent)   100   ml.
Formalin (40 per cent)   6.5 ml.
Acetic acid (glacial)   2.5 ml.

Immersion for a few minutes in this solution will suffice. From this solution the cover clip is washed in several changes of water and then stained. For simple staining a 1 per cent aqueous solution of erythrosin or rose bengal is very satisfactory. These weakly acid dyes may be used with agar preparations, since they do not stain the agar so deeply as they do the mycelium. It may take up to 15 minutes to stain sufficiently. One may also obtain good preparations with agar slide cultures by the use of the acid thionine solution introduced by Frost for staining microcolonies of bacteria. The formula is

Thionine   1.0 gram
Phenol   2.5 grams
Acetic acid (glacial)   20.0 ml.
Water   400.0 ml.

About 1 minute is sufficient for staining. If the staining is prolonged, the agar will stain too deeply. With liquid media one may use other stains. Heidenhain's iron hematoxylin gives very clear preparations, but for routine use the simple aqueous erythrosin or rose bengal solution is very satisfactory for molds. For actinomycetes these stains are satisfactory but faint. Gram's stain gives a clearer picture if cultures are not too old.

One must not rely entirely upon slide cultures for the identification of molds. In some cases growth in the small volume of medium on a cover slip is not altogether typical. Spore heads may be small and imperfectly developed. Some Penicillia, for instance, will form only a single verticil of phialides in slide cultures, whereas they form polyverticillate spore heads in Petri dish cultures. *The slide culture supplements but is not a substitute for the examination of the plate culture.*

Another type of slide culture will prove of great value, particularly in determining details of the arrangement of the aerial mycelium, for example in untangling the branching of the sporangiophores of Mucors. Rather large cover glasses (24 by 40 mm.) are cleaned. With a small hot iron (for instance, the heated end of a small file) a drop of sealing wax or, better, de Khotinsky cement is deposited on each end. With the hot iron this is then spread out to form a layer about 5 mm. wide and 1 mm. or less thick across the ends of the cover glass. A clean slide is now heated in the Bunsen flame and the cover glass is placed upon it with the cement side down. The slide should be just hot enough to soften the cement so that it will adhere, not enough to liquefy it so that it will run. One now has a culture chamber arranged as shown in Fig. 29, with a space something less than 1 mm. deep between the cover glass and the slide. A tube of agar is melted, cooled, and inoculated with spores of the mold to be studied. With a sterile capillary pipet some of the agar is transferred

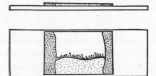

to the edge of the cover glass and allowed to run under until part of the space has been filled, as shown in the illustration. If the slides are prepared just before use, they will have been sufficiently sterilized by the heat used in their preparation. They may then be incubated in a glass staining jar containing moistened blotting paper in the bottom. The lid of the

FIG. 29. Method of growing molds between a slide and cover slip.

jar should be sealed with petroleum jelly or surgeon's plaster. After growth has occurred, the arrangement of both the aerial and submerged mycelium may be readily seen. Photomicrographs taken from such slide cultures are shown in Figs. 30 and 46. Paraffin can be used in the preparation and sealing of a culture cell of this type,

FIG. 30. *Aspergillus* sp., showing appearance of conidiophores as seen in a slide culture of the type shown in Fig. 29.

the sterile melted paraffin being handled in a sterile Pasteur pipet. It is less permanent but more convenient.

Microscopic Examination of Yeasts. The vegetative cells of yeasts and the determination of their mode of reproduction (such as type of budding and fission) are best determined in simple wet preparations made by mounting some of the growth from a young, actively growing culture in a drop of water. Smears are not good because of the marked shrinkage and distortion which occurs on drying. The cells may be mounted in a 5 per cent glycerin solution or in Amann's fluid.

The vacuoles and "dancing bodies" of yeasts may be stained vitally by suspending the cells in a dilute (1:8000) solution of neutral red. Fraser [11] has described the differential counting of living and dead yeast cells suspended in solutions of neutral red, Congo red, and methylene blue. Less shrinkage and distortion are observed if a suspension of the cells is made in the fixing fluid and run gradually through the alcohols; it should be centrifuged and resuspended at each change. Finally the sediment should be imbedded in paraffin and sections should be cut as thin as possible.

The spores of yeasts may be readily observed in unstained wet preparations after some experience. Beginners are likely to mistake fat droplets and water vacuoles for spores. Spores may be stained differentially in most cases by the use of the same procedures used for staining the spores of bacteria. The following will give beautiful preparations.

A dried smear is fixed in 5 per cent chromic acid for 10 minutes, stained in steaming carbol fuchsin for 10 minutes or for several hours in the cold stain, decolorized in 1 per cent sulphuric acid, and counterstained with Loeffler's methylene blue for 2 minutes or more. Spores will be bright red, vegetative cells blue. The cells within which the spores are found are frequently so poorly stained as to be difficult to see.

Morphology of Actinomycetes. For studying the morphology of actinomycetes one may use the same methods that serve for the larger molds, but may encounter difficulties due to their extreme minuteness. The very highest magnifications must be used to obtain a clear picture. The slide culture method may be used to good advantage. Here it is particularly important to use a medium poor in nutrients in order to prevent too dense massing of the mycelium. Czapek's medium is satisfactory for many species. For observing the spores and sporophores the method of Drechsler [9] has some advantages. It consists in moistening a cover glass with a thin film of albumen. This is then lightly dropped on to the surface of a sporulating colony and gently lifted off again. The spore-bearing filaments will adhere to the cover slip and will be pulled away from the colony, but will retain their normal arrangement. They can then be fixed, stained, and mounted.

The anaerobe *Actinomyces bovis* can be examined by withdrawing young colonies from a glucose veal infusion agar deep culture, crushing the agar containing the colony under a cover slip, and examining directly.

Microscopic Examination of Tissues and Exudates. The diagnosis of fungus diseases of man depends upon direct microscopic examination of tissues and exudates as well as upon cultural methods. In some cases the fungi grow so scantily that, if they are not abundant enough to be found on microscopic examination, it is not likely that they will overcome the competition of contaminants and grow in cultures. In sporotrichosis, however, the small size of Sporotrichum and the difficulties of differentially staining it make its isolation in culture the preferred method of laboratory diagnosis. In all cases, when possible, it is desirable to isolate pathogenic fungi in culture because the final identification of the fungus depends upon determination of its characters in artificial culture media. The specific methods of examination and the appearance of the fungus will be discussed in detail in the consideration of the various mycoses.

In searching for yeasts, molds, and actinomycetes in pus or other exudates or tissues from infections in man and animals, certain general facts must be kept in mind. Where it is possible to obtain pus from abscesses which have just been opened surgically before they have formed a fistula communicating with the exterior, it is usually relatively easy to find the organisms. After they have broken open, however, there is always an extensive secondary infection with bacteria, and it is often almost impossible to find the fungi. In cases where the parasites cannot be obtained in the pus' draining from the abscess, they may be found in sections of tissue removed from the wall of the abscess. A biopsy is thus frequently of great diagnostic value.

Fungi may be demonstrated in sections of tissue by the Gram-Weigert method or one of its various modifications. Unna [42] has described a modification of the Unna-Pappenheim stain which is said to give a very clear picture, especially in skin sections. The sections are removed from water and stained for 5 to 10 seconds in the following solution.

Pyronin	0.9 gram
Methyl green	0.1 gram
Alcohol (96 per cent)	9.0 ml.
Glycerol	10.0 grams
Aqueous phenol (½ per cent) to 100.0 ml.	

These sections are then rinsed in water and quickly dehydrated in absolute alcohol, cleared in xylol, and mounted in balsam. Fungus elements stain red, nuclei and leucocytes appear bluish green. Sections stained by Giemsa's method show the fungus elements very clearly in some cases. Hematoxylin and eosin will also usually show them, but their coloring is weak.

In general, fungus parasites are not so numerous in exudates as bacteria are. One must therefore not be satisfied with a hasty examination but must patiently go over many microscopic fields. Young growing elements of the fungi are all Gram-positive, but old mycelium becomes filled with fat and other materials, and the Gram-staining protoplasm may be but a small portion of the whole. In general, stained smears are not of much use in detecting pathogenic fungi. Some exceptions are: sporotrichosis, where the phagocyted fusiform bodies characteristic of this disease may be best demonstrated in smears of pus; infections with *Candida albicans* and *Cryptococcus neoformans*, where the yeast-like bodies may be readily demonstrated in smears of pus, sputum, or spinal fluid, stained by methylene blue or by Gram's method; and histoplasmosis, where the small Leishmania-like bodies phagocyted by large macrophages are best demonstrated in smears of bone marrow or splenic pulp, treated like a blood smear, carefully fixed, and stained with Wright's stain or Giemsa's stain.

In other fungus diseases the procedure of choice is to examine the pus or sputum or other material wet and usually unstained. If not too thick it can be covered with a cover slip and examined without any preparation. Many specimens need to be diluted or digested in one or another type of mounting fluid. The material most frequently used is a solution of sodium or potassium hydroxide. Such a solution serves to dissolve the leucocytes and other tissue elements, or at least to soften them and make them more translucent, without destroying the fungus elements which for the most part are rather resistant to strong alkali. The strength of the solution varies, according to different authorities, from 5 to 40 per cent. The stronger the solution is, the quicker its action and the greater the danger of producing artifacts and of destroying the fungus. In general a 10 per cent solution seems to be most useful. A loop of pus or sputum is stirred up in a drop of this solution on a slide, covered with a cover slip, and allowed to stand 15 to 30 minutes before examination. To prevent evaporation the edges of the cover slip may be sealed with petroleum jelly.

A number of other mounting fluids may be used. The Amann's fluid with cotton blue described on page 68 will serve to dilute the pus, stain both cells and fungus elements, and make them more translucent. Another solution consists of

Glycerol	20 parts
Ammonia (28 per cent NH₃)	10 parts
Alcohol	20 parts

In examining pus or sputum for fungi, beginners are apt to mistake fat droplets for yeast cells and elastic tissue fibers for mycelium. Fat droplets are highly refractile, and sometimes the edge may appear to be doubly contoured. Adjacent large and small droplets may look like a budding cell. Elastic tissue fibers vary in diameter and branch like mycelium. In both cases, however, there is no internal structure. Both fat droplets and elastic tissue fibers appear clear and homogeneous, whereas both yeast cells and mycelium will show internal vacuoles and granules. Myelin globules are present in large numbers in some specimens and may be mistaken for yeasts or hyphae.

Microscopic Examination of Hairs and Scales. In the diagnosis of dermatophytosis the microscopic examination of hairs and of scales of epidermis is of first importance. Here again the standard procedure is to mount the hairs or scales in a strong alkaline solution to soften the material so that it may be flattened under a cover slip, and to make it translucent so that the fungus elements may be seen. It is important to select hairs which appear to be infected, preferably the stumps of hairs which have broken off. The fungi will be found near the root of the hair. The use of ultraviolet light may be helpful in selecting infected hairs. With both hairs and scales of epidermis, it is best to collect material from just back of the advancing border of the lesion, where fungi may be expected to be most abundant.

The examination of hairs and scales mounted in strong sodium or potassium hydroxide presents all the disadvantages mentioned under the examination of exudates, and additional ones because the alkali may give rise to artifacts that can be mistaken for fungi— crystals of the alkali where evaporation has taken place under the cover slip, and the mosaic fungus. The latter consists of an irregular, branched filamentous structure, without internal granules or vacuoles, that appears in some scales of epidermis when treated with strong alkali. The exact nature of the artifact is unknown. First described by Weidman,[44] the mosaic fungus has been further studied by Davidson and Gregory [6] who suggested that it is made up of cholesterin crystals, by Dowding and Orr,[8] and by Swartz and

Conant.[40] Most authorities are now agreed that the mosaic fungus is an artifact.

Cornbleet [4] developed an alternative mounting fluid for hairs and scales. Water is added to crystals of sodium sulphide in minimum quantity to obtain complete solution. To this solution an equal volume of alcohol is added. A cloudy precipitate is formed which is redissolved by adding water drop by drop. This alcohol solution makes possible a quicker and more complete wetting of the hair; the sulphide serves to dissolve keratin. Swartz and Conant [40] soften scales of epidermis in 5 per cent potassium hydroxide, after which they are washed in several changes of water and then mounted in Amann's fluid with cotton blue (0.5 per cent cotton blue). This method may also be used with hairs. Thus prepared, the mosaic fungus does not appear in scales of epidermis. Clearer preparations with much less (0.05 per cent) cotton blue are obtained but a longer time is required for the stain to be absorbed by the fungi. Lewis and Hopper [20] have published numerous clear photographs of fungi in hairs and scales, and of the artifacts which may be confused with them.

Use of Ultraviolet Light. The discovery by Margarot and Devèze [27] that hairs infected with species of Microsporum exhibit a greenish fluorescence in ultraviolet light has led to a number of studies of this phenomenon both in clinical diagnosis and in the identification of cultures. If the patient is examined in a dark room under filtered ultraviolet light, single infected hairs can be readily seen although there may be no clinically apparent lesion. The method is particularly useful in detecting small satellite lesions in the scalp, infections of the eyebrows, and in checking the results of treatment. Davidson and Gregory [5] showed that the Microsporum species could be distinguished from species of Trichophyton in hairs, the former giving a greenish fluorescence due to a water-soluble substance, the latter a bluish fluorescence due to a substance which could not be extracted with water. Lewis [19] applied this method to the differentiation of dermatophytes in cultures and found that different species gave fluorescent light of distinguishing color; in particular, *Microsporum Canis* was said to be distinguished from *M. Audouini*. Redaelli and Cortese [35] studied a variety of sapprophytic and parasitic molds, yeasts, and actinomycetes, and found that, although many of them fluoresced with different colors, the fluorescence varied markedly with the medium and the age of the culture. The medium itself usually gave some fluorescence. Non-pigmented molds were most fluorescent, especially before spores were formed. Lewis and

Hopper [20] have discussed further the identification of mold cultures by ultraviolet light. Davidson and Gregory [5] described an inexpensive source of filtered ultraviolet light.

It appears that, although the use of fluorescence is a valuable clinical method, the conditions which determine the phenomenon and the specific color of the fluorescence are not yet well enough known for its satisfactory use in identifying cultures in the laboratory. The unreliability of the use of ultraviolet light for identification of cultures has very recently been emphasized by Benedek [1] who, however, stressed the great value of this tool in the clinic for distinguishing ringworms of the scalp due to Microsporum from those due to Trichophyton. Especially the value of ultraviolet light for detecting carriers was stressed.

LITERATURE

1. BENEDEK, T., Contribution to the epidemiology of tinea capitis. III. Some diagnostic problems in tinea capitis, *Mycologia*, **36**, 598 (1944).
2. CONANT, N. F., Studies in the genus Microsporum, *Arch. Dermatol. Syphilol.* (*Chicago*), **33**, 665 (1936).
3. CONN, H. J., The use of various culture media in characterizing actinomycetes, *N. Y. Agr. Exp. Sta.* (*Geneva*) *Tech. Bull. 83* (1921).
4. CORNBLEET, T., A reagent for demonstrating fungi in skin scrapings and hair, *J. Am. Med. Assoc.*, **95**, 1743 (1930).
5. DAVIDSON, A. M., and P. H. GREGORY, Convenient source of light for diagnosis of ringworm of the scalp, *Can. Med. Assoc. J.*, **27**, 176, 485 (1932).
6. DAVIDSON, A. M., and P. H. GREGORY, So-called mosaic fungus as an intercellular deposit of cholesterol crystals, *J. Am. Med. Assoc.*, **105**, 1262 (1935).
7. DAVIDSON, A. M., P. H. GREGORY, and A. R. BIRT, A clinical and mycological study of suppurative ringworm, *Can. Med. Assoc. J.*, **31**, 587 (1934).
8. DOWDING, E. S., and H. ORR, Transformation of *Trichophyton gypseum* into mosaic fungus, *Arch. Dermatol. Syphilol.* (*Chicago*), **33**, 865 (1936).
9. DRECHSLER, C., Morphology of the genus Actinomyces, *Botan. Gaz.*, **67**, 65, 147 (1919).
10. EMMONS, C. W., Dermatophytes. Natural grouping based on the form of the spores and accessory organs, *Arch. Dermatol. Syphilol.* (*Chicago*), **30**, 337 (1934).
11. FRASER, O. G., The action of methylene blue and certain other dyes on living and dead yeast, *J. Phys. Chem.*, **24**, 741 (1920).
12. GRAHAM, V. E., and E. G. HASTINGS, Studies on film-forming yeasts. I. Media and Methods, *Can. J. Research, C,* **19**, 251 (1941).
13. GREENE, H. C., and E. B. FRED, Maintenance of vigorous mold stock cultures, *Ind. Eng. Chem.*, **26**, 1297 (1934).
14. GWYNNE-VAUGHAN, H. C. I., and B. BARNES, *The Structure and Development of the Fungi*, Macmillan, New York, 1939.
15. KADISCH, E., Über die Bedeutung der Nährbodenalkalinität in der Mykologie, *Dermatol. Z.*, **55**, 385 (1929).

16. KADISCH, E., Der Einfluss der Zuchtungstemperatur auf das Wachstum der pathogenen Hautpilze auf den üblicken Nährböden und auf inneren Organen des Meerschweinchen, *Arch. Dermatol. Syphilis,* **160,** 142 (1930).

17. LANGERON, M., and S. MILOCHEVITCH, Morphologie des dermatophytes sur milieux naturels et milieux à base de polysaccharides, *Ann. parasitol. humaine et comparée,* **8,** 422, 465 (1930).

18. LEVIN, O. L., and S. H. SILVERS, The possible explanation for the localization of ringworm infection between the toes, *Arch. Dermatol. Syphilol. (Chicago),* **26,** 466 (1932).

19. LEWIS, G. M., Fluorescence of fungous colonies with filtered ultraviolet radiation (Woods filter), *Arch. Dermatol. Syphilol. (Chicago),* **31,** 329 (1935).

20. LEWIS, G. M., and M. E. HOPPER, *An Introduction to Medical Mycology,* Year Book Pub. Co., Chicago, 1939.

21. LINDEGREN, C. C., and G. LINDEGREN, Sporulation in *Saccharomyces cerevisiae, Botan. Gaz.,* **105,** 304 (1944).

22. LINDER, D. H., An ideal mounting medium for mycologists, *Science,* **70,** 430 (1929).

23. LODDER, J., Die Anaskosporogenen Hefen, 1ste Hälfte, *Verhandel. Akad. Wetenschappen, Amsterdam, Adfeel. Natuurkunde, 2nd Sect.,* **32,** 1 (1934).

24. MALLINCKRODT-HAUPT, A. VON, Vitalfärbung mit Indicatorfarben bei Hyphomyzeten, *Dermatol. Z.,* **46,** 263 (1926).

25. ———, P H Messungen bei Pilzkulturen, *Dermatol. Z.,* **55,** 374 (1929).

26. MCKELVEY, C. E., Notes on yeasts in carbonated beverages, *J. Bact.,* **11,** 98 (1926).

27. MARGAROT, J., and P. DEVÈZE, Aspect de quelques dermatoses en lumière ultraviolette—note preliminaire, *Bull. soc. sci. méd. biol. Montpellier Languedoc,* **6,** 375 (1925).

28. MEMMESHEIMER, A. M., Über eienem neuen Nährboden für Pilzkulturen, *Klin. Wochschr.,* **17,** 56 (1938).

29. MRAK, E. M., and L. BONAR, The effect of temperature on asci and ascospores in the genus Debaryomyces, *Mycologia,* **30,** 182 (1938).

30. MRAK, E. M., and L. S. MCCLUNG, Yeasts occurring on grapes and in grape products in California, *J. Bact.,* **40,** 395 (1940).

31. MRAK, E. M., H. J. PHAFF, and H. C. DOUGLAS, A sporulation stock medium for yeasts and other fungi, *Science,* **96,** 432 (1942).

32. NEGRONI, P., and D. LOIZAGA, Acción "in vitro" de los colorantes, sobre la morfología y biología de *Mycotorula albicans, Rev. argentina dermatosifilología,* **22,** 556 (1938).

33. NICKERSON, W. J., Studies in the genus Zygosaccharomyces. Transfer of pellicle-forming yeasts to Zygopichia, *Farlowia,* **1,** 469 (1944).

34. NICKERSON, W. J., and K. V. THIMANN, The chemical control of conjugation in Zygosaccharomyces. I and II, *Am. J. Botany,* **28,** 617 (1941); **30,** 94 (1943).

35. REDAELLI, R., and F. CORTESE, Sulla fluorescenza degli eumiceti alla luce di Wood, *Raggi ultravioletti,* **6,** 52 (1930); *Boll. soc. med.-chirurg. Pavia,* **44,** 49 (1930).

36. SASS, J. E., The cytological basis for homothallism and heterothallism in the Agaricaceae, *Am. J. Botany,* **16,** 663 (1929).

37. STARKEY, R. L., and S. A. WAKSMAN, Fungi tolerant to extreme acidity and high concentrations of copper sulfate, *J. Bact.*, **45**, 509 (1943).

38. STEINBERG, R. A., Growth of fungi in synthetic nutrient solutions, *Botan. Rev.*, **5**, 327 (1939).

39. STELLING-DEKKER, N. M., Die Sporogenen Hefen, *Verhandel. Akad. Wetenschappen, Amsterdam Adfeel. Natuurkunde, 2nd Sect.*, **28**, 1 (1931).

40. SWARTZ, J. H., and N. F. CONANT, Direct microscopic examination of the skin. A method for the determination of the presence of fungi, *Arch. Dermatol. Syphilol. (Chicago)*, **33**, 291 (1936).

41. TALICE, R. V., Le facteur pH en mycologie, son influence sur la culture de certaines espèces de champignons parasites de l'homme, *Ann. parasitol. humaine et comparée*, **8**, 183 (1930).

42. UNNA, P., JR., Über Färbung von Fadenpilzen in der Oberhaut, *Dermatol. Wochschr.*, **88**, 314 (1929).

43. WAKSMAN, S. A., A method for counting the number of fungi in the soil, *J. Bact.*, **7**, 339 (1922).

44. WEIDMAN, F. D., Laboratory aspects of epidermatophytosis, *Arch. Dermatol. Syphilol. (Chicago)*, **15**, 415 (1927).

45. WICKERHAM, L. J., A simple technique for the detection of melibiose fermenting yeasts, *J. Bact.*, **46**, 501 (1943).

46. WILLIAMS, J. W., Growth of certain pathogenic fungi on asparagine medium, *Proc. Soc. Exptl. Biol. Med.*, **31**, 1176 (1934).

47. ———, Scalp products and hair of men and women as culture media for certain pathogenic fungi, *Proc. Soc. Exptl. Biol. Med.*, **32**, 624 (1935).

48. ———, Effect of dyes on colonies of certain pathogenic fungi, *Proc. Soc. Exptl. Biol. Med.*, **31**, 1173 (1934).

49. ZIMMERMANN, J., Sprosspilze im Wein und deren Bestimmung, *Zentr. Bakt., Parasitenk.*, *II*, **98**, 36 (1938).

CHAPTER IV

MOLDS BELONGING TO THE PHYCOMYCETES

No Archimycetes are likely to be of interest to the bacteriologist. Probably the only genus of Oomycetes that he will ever come in contact with is Pythium, some species of which are pathogenic to plants but others of which are soil saprophytes. The mycelium is ordinarily coenocytic, but septa may occasionally be seen in older mycelium. The zoosporangia are usually numerous and rather small, and are mostly borne on the ends of the mycelial strands, although they may be found in the mycelium, resembling chlamydospores. On germination the contents of the zoosporangia are extruded into a thin-walled vesicle, after which they are differentiated into several motile zoospores (swarm spores) and these are set free. Sexual reproduction has not been seen in some soil species, but most species are heterogamous and homothallic.

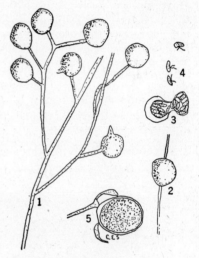

FIG. 31. Pythium (1, 2, and 5, unidentified species from soil; 3 and 4, from various authors): 1, mycelium and sporangia; 2, intercalary sporangium; 3, zoospore formation; 4, zoospores; 5, oogonium and antheridia.

The Zygomycetes are subdivided into two orders, the differentiation being based largely upon the structure of the non-sexual spores, the Entomophthorales multiplying by conidia, and the Mucorales reproducing mostly by sporangiospores. The so-called conidia of these phycomycetous fungi are not true exogenous conidia as are found in the Ascomycetes, for in some cases at least careful microscopic examination shows that they are really small sporangia containing only one or a few sporangiospores. They are sometimes referred to as sporangiola. It is also rather difficult to divide the two orders sharply on the basis described above, as some of the Mucorales are found to form definite sporangia with numerous sporangio-spores at the ends of the sporangiophores, and conidia (or sporangiola) on lateral branches. Other species which resemble the Mucorales in all other respects (and are therefore retained in that order) reproduce only by conidia.

FIG. 32. Stained section through the body wall of a house fly infected with *Empusa Muscae*, showing the development of conidiophores and conidia. Note the multinucleate character of the mycelium.

Entomophthorales. Members of this order will not be encountered in bacteriological work. As their name implies, they are mostly parasitic on insects. One of the best known, *Empusa Muscae*, causes a disease of the common house fly. The mycelium penetrates the body tissues and forms sporophores on the surface (Fig. 32). The flies are killed by the fungus, and are frequently found in the fall on walls or windows covered with a whitish powder-like coating. When mature, the conidia are projected forcibly for a distance of several millimeters, and form a white deposit about the dead fly, especially discernible upon window panes (Fig. 33).

Mucorales. There are three extensive monographs on the Mucorales and a very excellent treatise on the Phycomycetes as a whole.[1]

FIG. 33. A fly dead of *Empusa Muscae* infection. The white powder surrounding the fly is composed of conidia which have been discharged for some distance.

Lendner[5] divides the order into two suborders and eight families, Naumov[6] into three suborders and eight families, and Zycha[7] into three suborders and six families. The limits of genera as well as of families differ with the different authors. All agree on using the distinction between asexual reproduction by sporangiospores or by conidia (sporangiola) as an important point in subdividing the order. The following key derived from Zycha gives the characteristics of the families.

FAMILIES OF MUCORALES

A. Sporangia single, multispored sporangia always with columellae.
   1. All sporangia multispored. *MUCORACEAE*
   2. Sporangiospores with two kinds of spore-forming apparatus, terminal multi-celled sporangia, and numerous lateral verticillate sporangiola, each with few spores. *THAMNIDIACEAE*
B. Sporangiola or conidia united on special sporophores.
   3. Spherical, single, or many-spored sporangiola on specialized enlargements of the fruiting hyphae. *CHAENOPHORACEAE*
   4. Long chains of small sporangiola usually on specialized basal cells. Mostly parasitic on Mucorales. *CEPHALIDACEAE*
C. All sporangia without columellae, zygotes surrounded by thick covering of hyphae.
   5. Sporangia or zygotes single. *MORTIERELLACEAE*
   6. Sporangia or zygotes united in specialized fruiting bodies surrounded by hyphae. *ENDOGONACEAE*

Mucoraceae. The Mucoraceae are a group of molds, frequently referred to as the bread molds, found abundantly in soil, in manure, on fruits, and especially on starchy foodstuffs. They all have the same general structure and appearance and are easily differentiated from other groups of molds by the coarse, non-septate mycelium, by the abundant and loosely meshed aerial mycelium, and by the lack of distinctive colors, the spores being generally black or brown, the mycelium white or gray. In older literature the term mold is frequently restricted to fungi of this type, molds of the type of the Fungi Imperfecti being referred to as mildews.

The Mucoraceae and Thammidaceae are distinguished from the other families of the order by the presence of a columella in the sporangium. The columella may be looked upon as a septum separating the sporangium from the sporangiophore, which has become bulged into the sporangium. In addition to sporangiospores some species also reproduce by chlamydospores which appear as round black swellings, like beads, strung on the mycelium. These may be mistaken for zygospores. Several species also characteristically break up into a series of spherical oidia when immersed in liquid where aeration is not abundant. These oidia, yeast-like in appearance, may reproduce for a while by budding, forming new round cells of the same type. Sporangiola are not formed by the Mucoraceae.

Zygospores may be formed by the fusion of neighboring filaments from the same thallus in some cases (as in Zygorrhynchus) or only by fusion of filaments from two neighboring thalli in others (as most of the Mucors and Rhizopus). The first type is said to be homothallic, the second heterothallic. As pointed out in Chapter I, in the latter case there is a physiologically distinguishable sex, although the elements àre morphologically identical. Since the two sexes cannot be distinguished, they are designated as plus or minus strains rather than as male and female. Sometimes bodies resembling zygospores may be formed without fusion of the hypha with another. Such spores are called azygospores. They may be formed by an isolated thallus, or only by hyphae which approach filaments from another thallus of the opposite sign. It is noteworthy that plus and minus strains of different species may exhibit this evidence of sex when grown in contact, even though actual conjugation does not occur.

The zygospores are usually large cells, generally black, and with a rough, warty exterior. The filaments which form them become expanded near the spore, forming broad supporting bands called suspensors. These are sometimes of characteristic form. Unfortunately, zygospores are seldom formed in cultures on artificial media in the laboratory. They are found most frequently on strains freshly isolated from their natural habitat. Naturally, with heterothallic varieties no zygospores will be seen unless both plus and minus strains are included in the culture. According to Blakeslee, prune extract and moistened slices of bread are media most favorable to the production of zygospores.

The following key covers those genera of the Mucoraceae which contain species likely to be encountered by the bacteriologist.

A. The fungus spreads over its substrate by stolons or runners.
   1. Sporangiophores arise at the nodes of the stolons.   *RHIZOPUS*
   2. Sporangiophores arise at the internodes.   *ABSIDIA*
B. No stolons or runners are formed.
   1. Sporangiophores are simple or branched; sporangia borne apically on the sporangiophore and its branches.
      a. Zygospores formed from equal gametes, usually heterothallic.
         aa. Never parasitic on other Mucorales.   *MUCOR*
         bb. Facultative parasite on certain genera of Mucorales.
            PARASITELLA
      b. Zygospores formed from unequal gametes, homothallic.
         ZYGORRHYNCHUS
   2. Sporangia borne only on the lateral circinate branches of the sporangiophore.
      a. Sporangia globular, columella not constricted.   *CIRCINELLA*
      b. Sporangia pear-shaped, columella constricted.   *PIRELLA*

Mucor and Rhizopus. Of the various genera of the Mucoraceae, Mucor and Rhizopus contain most of the species of Phycomycetes encountered in bacteriological work. Mucor and Rhizopus may be readily differentiated from each other. Because of runners, or stolons, Rhizopus tends to cover the surface of the agar plates rapidly, to climb the sides of the Petri dishes and fill the latter with mycelium. The rhizoids, or holdfasts, attach themselves to the under sides of the lids. Although Mucors may fill up the Petri dish with mycelium, they do not thus attach themselves to the lid.

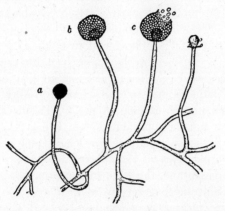

FIG. 34. *Mucor* sp.: (*a*) young sporulating head; (*b*) mature sporangium; (*c*) spores being liberated from sporangium; (*d*) columella after scattering of spores. From S. A. Waksman and R. L. Starkey, *The Soil and the Microbe*, 1931.

The rhizoids or holdfasts of Rhizopus may be seen readily by focusing through the lid of the Petri dish with the low-power lens. The sporangiophores of Rhizopus arise from the nodes of the runners, i.e., at the point where the holdfast or rhizoids are formed. In Mucor the sporangiophores are formed from all parts of the thallus. In Mucor the columella is always either round, cylindrical, or pear-shaped, never hemispherical, and is continuous with the sporangiophore. In Rhizopus it is hemispherical and rests in a cup-shaped expansion of the sporangiophore called the apophysis (Figs. 34 and 39). In Mucor the spores, though varying in form, are always smooth and regular; in Rhizopus they frequently appear to be angular because they collapse readily when mounted in water. Some species of Mucor show a positive phototropism. Sporangiospores of these species bend toward the source of light. This does not occur with Rhizopus.

There are many kinds of Mucor that are worthy of specific rank even to a conservative taxonomist, but owing to the large number of species (Lendner recognizes 51 species, Naumov 93 species and several varieties, and Zycha 42 species) keys for identification are not given here, but reference is made to the original monographs.

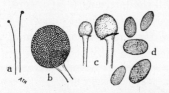

Lendner's key, in its essential points, is given in the first edition of this book and in Gilman and Abbott's [3] paper on soil fungi. In some ways the keys and description of species by Naumov and particularly by Zycha seem to be preferable. Keys based on this system will be found in Gilman,[2] but those in the original Zycha are more complete.

FIG. 35. *Mucor hiemalis: a,* sporangiophores; *b,* sporangium; *c,* columellae; *d,* spores.

The characters used for identification naturally vary with different authors. Lendner's system which has heretofore been generally followed uses as important characters for classification the occurrence of branching of the sporangiophores, their height and thickness, the diameter of the sporangium, the length and thickness of the columella, the dimensions of the spores, the degree of diffluence of the sporangial membrane, the form of the columella, and the shape of the spores. Since zygospores are so rarely formed in cultures, they cannot usually be used in diagnosis. Many of the characters given above are obviously subject to considerable variation even in a single individual and cannot be relied upon too much. The occurrence of branching of the sporangiophore is the most important single character. It cannot be easily determined in many cultures because of the close inter-twining of the hyphae. The developing sporangiophores are frequently unbranched; therefore, one cannot rely upon observations made at the edge of the growing colony where the

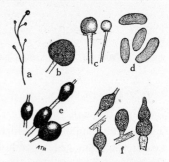

FIG. 36. *Mucor racemosus: a,* sporangiophore; *b,* sporangium; *c,* columellae; *d,* spores; *e,* chlamydospores on the aerial mycelium; *f,* chlamydospores on the submersed mycelium.

mycelium is not so dense. Branching is best observed in slide cultures of the type shown in Fig. 29. A binocular dissecting microscope is of great value. Three main types of branching are recognized: the Monomucors with unbranched sporangiophores, as in Fig. 35; the Racemomucors, with racemosely branched sporangiophores (i.e., a main stem with lateral branches) as in Fig. 36; and the Cymomucors, with sporangiophores typically branched as in *Mucor circinelloides* (Fig. 38) but frequently rather irregularly branched.

Zycha uses in his scheme of classification the presence or the absence of thallospores (Kugelgemmen) and Naumov uses the color of the colony mycelial growth and specialized organs. Neither of these two later workers puts so much stress on the branching of the sporophore. Otherwise, the characters used for identification of species of Mucor are much the same as those used by Lendner.

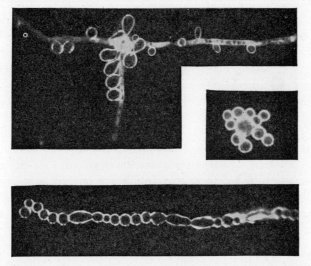

Fig. 37. *Mucor racemosus*. Production of oidia by submersed mycelium, and multiplication of these by budding. Photomicrograph by dark field illumination.

The same authorities are to be consulted for identification of species of Rhizopus. Zycha is much more conservative in his taxonomy in this genus. He recognizes only 8 species, whereas Lendner describes 22 and Naumov some 30 species.

M. Mucedo, being easily obtainable if fresh horse manure is incubated in a moist chamber, is perhaps the best-known species of Mucor. It has frequently been chosen as a type of the genus in physiological experiments. It is proteolytic and also capable of splitting fats. It is a cause of spoilage of various foodstuffs at times, is supposed to play a part in the ripening of snuff, may cause a decomposition of leather, and is found in retting flax. It may be recognized by the unbranched sporangiophore and cylindrical columella. No oidia or chlamydospores are formed. It is heterothallic. See Fig. 25.

M. hiemalis is very similar but the columella is typically spherical (Fig. 35). It is concerned with the retting of flax, secreting an enzyme which dissolves the middle lamella of the intercellular substance. It digests starch and gelatin and ferments dextrose but not sucrose. It also is heterothallic.

M. piriformis is recognized by its very large sporangia and pear-shaped columella. It is found on spoiled fruit and is claimed to be a cause of soft rot of pears.

M. racemosus is the most common of the Racemomucors, and though of little practical importance it is of some scientific interest.

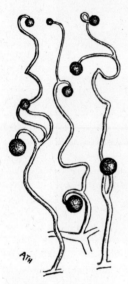

It is remarkable because it produces an alcoholic fermentation of sugars, and, when it is submerged in sugar solutions, the mycelium breaks up into a series of spherical oidia (Kugelzellen or Kugelgemmen in German literature) which may continue to grow as single cells by budding, like yeasts (Fig. 37). The association of the yeast-like form with alcoholic fermentation naturally attracted great interest. It is curious that these round oidia are formed only by Mucors which also produce alcohol. Their resemblance to yeasts is only superficial, as they are much larger and each cell contains many nuclei. *M. racemosus* is easily recognized by the characteristic branching of the sporangiophores. The sporangial wall is frequently covered with tiny crystals of calcium oxalate, and the columella is somewhat pear-shaped. Inoculation into glucose broth fermentation tubes will show the production of gas and yield the spherical budding cells in the sediment. Perhaps the most striking character is the abundant formation of the jet-black chlamydospores in the aerial mycelium. *M. racemosus* may be distinguished from the closely related *M. erectus* and *M. fragilis* by the form of the columella. The latter two species also form slight amounts of alcohol from sugar and give rise to budding oidia in the submerged portions.

Fig. 38. *Mucor circinelloides:* sporangiophores showing typical cymose branching.

M. circinelloides is frequently encountered in soil cultures. It exhibits true cymose branching (Fig. 38). Budding oidia are formed in mycelium submersed in liquid media. *M. plumbeus* is also a common soil form. It derives its name from the lead-gray color of the mycelium. It may be identified by the peculiar spiny columella and the prickles on the spores.

Although the preceding species form but small amounts of alcohol, another Mucor belonging to the Cymomucor group, *M. Rouxii* (sometimes called *M. Rouxianus*) has been used industrially for the production of alcohol. It secretes both diastase and zymase and can therefore produce alcohol directly without any malting process. It is used in the Orient for preparing alcoholic beverages from rice, which are often called wines. The fungus is sometimes marketed under the name Chinese yeast in little balls of rice meal, much as yeast cakes are marketed in the Occident. It has been used commercially for alcoholic production in Europe. More than 5 per cent of alcohol is produced in the fermentation. This species may be recognized by the characteristic Cymomucor branching of the sporangiophores, the spherical columellae, and large oval spores. In the submerged mycelium, large irregular, thick-walled cells may be formed. Like the Racemomucors mentioned above, black chlamydospores appear in the aerial mycelium and budding yeast-like cells in submerged portions. Abundant fat globules may develop in the mycelium, especially on starchy substrates; these take on a deep yellow color.

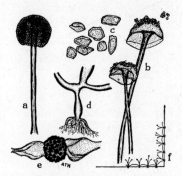

FIG. 39. *Rhizopus nigricans: a,* mature sporangium; *b,* ruptured sporangia, showing the flattened columellae (note the funnel-shaped expansion, apophysis, of the sporangiophore beneath the columella); *c,* spores; *d,* a rhizoid or holdfast; *e,* zygospore; *f,* diagram showing mode of growth by runners.

There are several other species related to *M. Rouxii* which have been isolated from other oriental yeasts, as *M. Prainii* from India and *M. javanicus* from Java.

Some authors have grouped together those Mucors which tend to break up into round oidia, or to produce numerous chlamydospores, in a separate genus, Chlamydomucor, but these structures are found in so many different kinds of molds that they should not be given much weight in classification.

Rhizopus nigricans is by far the most common of all the molds belonging to the Phycomycetes. It is continually encountered in all kinds of bacteriological work as an air contamination, and is particularly annoying because of its ability, by means of its stolons, rapidly to overgrow Petri plate cultures (it can cover the entire surface of the agar in 24 hours).

It is especially important as a cause of spoilage of fruits and stored potatoes, especially sweet potatoes. The small fruits, especially strawberries, are particularly susceptible. The disease in strawberries is known as leak, because of the softening and dripping of the fruit. It is a source of considerable loss in shipment and is prevented by refrigeration. In sweet potatoes, a characteristic soft rot is produced, the main factors determining which are injury to the potatoes and humidity of the storage bins. For a bibliography of the rots caused by *R. nigricans*, see Heald.[4]

Absidia. The genus Absidia is characterized by the formation of sporangiophores arising from the arched stolons themselves (rather

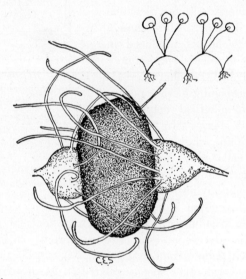

Fig. 40. *Absidia* sp. from soil: zygospore and suspensors with appendages; above, diagram of sporangia and rhizoids.

than at the holdfasts, as in Rhizopus). Further differential characters are the rounded or pear-shaped columella, which is quite different from the flattened hemispherical columella of Rhizopus, and the formation of peculiar curled filaments which surround the zygospores, arising from the suspensors. Some species are homothallic.

Zygorrhynchus. In Zygorrhynchus the zygospores are formed by the fusion of neighboring branches of the same hypha. This mold is therefore homothallic. But there is some apparent differentiation of the conjugating branches, one being larger than the other; only the larger branch develops into a suspensor. This condition then rather approaches the formation of oospores in Saprolegnia (compare Fig. 41 with Fig. 24). Zygorrhynchus is an exception to the isogamy general in the Mucorales.

Zygorrhynchus Moelleri is one of the most important of the Phycomycetes found in the soil. It is particularly abundant in loose sandy

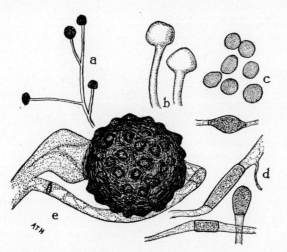

FIG. 41. *Zygorrhynchus Moelleri:* a, sporangiophore; b, columellae; c, sporangiospores; d, chlamydospores in submerged mycelium; e, zygospore.

soils, sometimes forming enough mycelium to bind the loose particles together. In subsoils it is frequently the only fungus present. Soils poor in organic matter seem then to be especially favorable for its growth. It is active in ammonification, but does not decompose cellulose.

Circinella. In Circinella the sporangia are formed only on lateral branches, not at the tips of the sporangiophores. These lateral branches frequently arise in whorls, six or eight branches arising from one point at regular intervals along the aerial filaments of mycelium. These lateral branches are also peculiarly curved upon themselves, a condition which is also found in *Mucor circinelloides* (Fig. 38). Species of Circinella are frequently found on the droppings of various animals.

Mucorales in Families Other than Mucoraceae. Thamnidium is the only member of the Thamnidiaceae frequently encountered. It has the characteristic of the family already described in the key. See Fig. 42. Cunninghamella (Chaenophoraceae) is a common air contaminant and is frequently isolated from soils. It has very tenuous

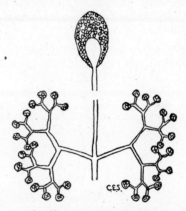

Fig. 42. Thamnidium: partly diagrammatic, showing terminal sporangium with columella and numerous lateral sporangiola without columellae.

rhizoids and forms clusters of unicellular conidia (sporangiola) on the swollen end of a hypha. See Fig. 43. Syncephalastrum (Cephalidaceae) is also occasionally encountered. In this several cells in chains are found attached to a sporophore with a swollen tip. Each

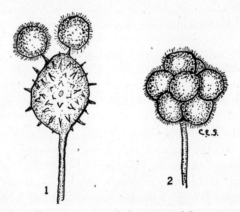

FIG. 43. Cunninghamella sp.: 1, most of the sporangiola removed from vesicular enlargement of sporophore; 2, small cluster of sporangiola.

chain is enclosed within a sporangial wall, but the appearance of the spore head does not always reveal the endogenous character of the spores. See Fig. 44.

Mucorales Parasitic on Mucorales. Many species of the Mucorales are frequently parasitized by other fungi and since both host and parasite are of the same order it may confuse the uninitiated into believing that two kinds of spores are produced from the same hypha. If the parasite belongs to the Cephalidaceae, and the host to Mucor or Rhizopus, the production of conidia from a sporophore, apparently arising from the same hypha which bears the sporangium, should make one suspect that the culture is parasitized. There are several genera of Cephalidaceae and descriptions and discussions of this parasitism will be found in the books of Zycha and of Gäumann. Still more confusing is *Parasitella simplex* which belongs to the Mucorales and is similar enough to Mucor to be put in that genus by some authorities. An interesting fact in connection with the heterothallism of Parasitella is that plus strains of the parasite are said to infect only minus strains of the host and vice versa. It would thus appear that the parasitism may have arisen from an abortive attempt at hybridization. On several occasions in our laboratories many freshly isolated cultures have been parasitized by other fungi when "isolated" but for years at a time we have not encountered this phenomenon.

Fig. 44. *Syncephalastrum* sp., isolated from soil. Chains of two or three spores surrounded by a membrane are formed over the inflated end of the sporophore. These spores are sometimes referred to as conidia, though they are really formed in small sporangia.

LITERATURE

1. Fitzpatrick, H. M., *The Lower Fungi. Phycomycetes*, McGraw-Hill, New York, 1930.
2. Gilman, J. C., *A Manual of Soil Fungi*, Collegiate Press, Ames, Iowa, 1945.
3. Gilman, J. C., and E. V. Abbott, A summary of the soil fungi, *Iowa State Coll. J. Sci.*, **1**, 225 (1927).
4. Heald, F. D., *Manual of Plant Diseases*, McGraw-Hill, New York, 2nd ed., 1933.
5. Lendner, A., Les Mucorinées, de la Suisse, *Beitr. Kryptogamenflora Schweiz.*, **3**, 1 (1908).
6. Naumov, N. A., *Clés des Mucorinées*, translated from the Russian by S. Buchet and I. Mouraviev, Lechevalier, Paris, 1939.
7. Zycha, H., Mucorineae, *Kryptogamenflora Mark Brandenburg*, **6A**, 1 (1935).

CHAPTER V

MOLDS BELONGING TO THE FUNGI IMPERFECTI AND THE ASCOMYCETES

Among the molds encountered by the bacteriologist, Ascomycetes are comparatively scarce. The Fungi Imperfecti, however, are abundant. Since many of the latter forms show a similarity to or identity with the conidial stages of known Ascomycetes, both classes may conveniently be considered together here.

Many species of Fungi Imperfecti, often only after extended study, have been found to be asexual stages of perfect fungi, and undoubtedly more species in the future will be found to have a perfect stage. But all species of Fungi Imperfecti are not necessarily merely conidial stages of perfect fungi; in the course of evolution they may have permanently lost their ability to form sexual spores at all. Some of the most widespread and vigorous molds have never been shown to possess a perfect stage although they have had almost continuous study for over half a century.

The point of view that Fungi Imperfecti are *merely* conidial stages of sexual fungi has led many mycologists almost to ignore them, or to treat them in their discussions with the perfect fungi which have a similar conidial apparatus and, often, as here treated, to give minor attention to the asexual stage. This in no way helps the worker who wishes to know the identity or to understand the morphology of the mold which he isolates from the lesion of a patient or one which he has found to have industrial or biochemical importance. His mold, as he must study it, does *not* form sexual spores. Even in those in which the perfect stage has been found, these sexual spores are in many cases produced only rarely and under exceptional conditions. Such a worker must depend upon classifications based on the asexual stage.

At best, any classification of the Fungi Imperfecti must be more or less artificial, not necessarily indicating phylogenetic relationships. However, it is evident that in many cases species closely related on the basis of their sexual spores had already been classified together on the basis of their conidial stages.[6, 13]

The problem is complicated by the fact that in many cases it is somewhat difficult to decide just what are the conidia. As pointed

94

out in the first chapter, many fungi, in addition to their spores multiply by the formation of oidia or yeast-like cells, by fragmentation of the mycelium, or by budding. These have been differentiated from conidia by the fact that the latter do not grow at once—they must first imbibe water and germinate. But at least some of the growth cells, although they may resemble conidia, are capable of growing at once if separated from the parent mycelium. One may find in some species all transitions between these growth cells and conidia. So it happens that the same organism may be classified in one genus by one authority, and in an entirely different genus by some other writer, owing to different interpretations of the same structure; for instance, the organism of thrush, now generally considered as a species of Candida, has been placed in half a dozen or more genera. Moreover, the same fungus may form more than one type of conidium, or may produce its conidia on more than one type of fruiting body. Thus one of the causative agents of chromoblastomycosis may produce conidia from flask-shaped conidiophores on some hyphae and show branching chains of conidia from unswollen conidiophores on others. Depending upon which spore-bearing apparatus predominated, or which one was seen by or most impressed the worker, the same fungus has been classified in the genus Phialophora or in the genus Hormodendrum (Cladosporium).

The classification of the Fungi Imperfecti followed by most mycologists is based upon the system proposed by Saccardo. Another, quite different, classification was introduced by Vuillemin and his system, or modifications of it, is much used in France, Italy, and Latin America. Since so much of the literature on medical mycology has come from those regions, this system cannot be ignored by the bacteriologist.

Vuillemin's Classification. Vuillemin divided the Fungi Imperfecti into three orders on the basis of the characters of the reproductive bodies. Later a fourth order, the Microsiphonales, was added to include the actinomycetes, but more recently this order has been reduced to a family. Vuillemin's [17] classification is based upon what were then new interpretations of reproductive bodies. See page 7.

CLASSIFICATION OF THE FUNGI IMPERFECTI (VUILLEMIN'S SYSTEM)

Order *Thallosporales,* reproducing by thallospores.
    Suborder *Blastosporineae,* reproducing by blastospores. This group includes the non-spore-forming yeasts and fungi with yeast-like forms, as Candida.

Suborder *Arthrosporineae,* reproducing by arthrospores. This group includes such forms as *Geotrichum candidum* and, according to the later rearrangement, the actinomycetes. It comprises two families.

Family *Mycodermaceae,* with "normal" septate mycelium.

Family *Nocardiaceae,* with "non-septate" mycelium, very fine, of bacterial dimensions (the actinomycetes).

Order *Hemisporales,* reproducing by hemispores. This order contains but one unimportant genus, Hemispora.

Order *Conidiosporales,* reproducing by conidia.

Suborder *Aleuriosporineae,* reproducing by imperfect conidia or aleuriospores. The ringworm fungi would belong here according to Ota and Langeron.

Suborder *Sporotrichineae,* reproducing by true conidia, which are not interpreted as being borne upon conidiophores, as in Sporotrichum.

Suborder *Sporophorineae,* reproducing by true conidia borne upon true conidiophores. This group would contain most of the common molds of the Fungi Imperfecti, save those of the next suborder.

Suborder *Phialidineae,* reproducing by true conidia borne upon phialides (or sterigmata), including Aspergillus and Penicillium.

Saccardo's Classification. Saccardo's arrangement makes a primary subdivision into three orders upon the following basis: Certain of the fungi parasitic on plants form conidiophores within a globular mass of protecting mycelium, called a pycnidium, from which conidia are discharged when mature through an opening on the surface of the plant tissue; these forms are placed together in an order known as the Sphaeropsidales. Other plant pathogens produce conidiophores closely packed together, from the surface of a flat, plate-like mass of pseudoparenchyma on the surface of the host plant, known as an acervulus; such species comprise the order Melanconiales. The third order, the Moniliales (frequently called Hyphomycetales), contains the remaining forms, whose conidiophores are produced neither in pycnidia nor upon acervuli, but are formed from superficial hyphae over the entire surface of the fungus colony. Those molds of interest to the bacteriologist will, of course, all be found in this last order.

The Moniliales are further subdivided into groups which have in some works been given the rank of families, in others of suborders. Two of these are based upon a characteristic grouping or bunching of the conidiophores. In the Stilbaceae the conidiophores are clustered to form characteristic stalked bodies of cylindrical form, the coremia. In the Tuberculariaceae the clusters of conidiophores form globose bodies without stalks, the sporodochia. Neither of these families contains species important to the bacteriologist, save that coremium-forming Penicillia have sometimes been included with the Stilbaceae and the important genus Fusarium is usually included with the Tuberculariaceae.

The remaining Moniliales are grouped into two families according to the color of the mycelium. If this is hyaline or brightly colored, the mold is included in the Moniliaceae (Mucidinaceae); if it is dark, smoky (black or shades of deep grey, brown, or olive), the mold belongs to the Dematiaceae. This is not a good character for such an important division. Many genera vary considerably in this character and frequently hyaline variants (saltants) are produced in some cultures of the Dematiaceae. These if isolated in nature would be included in a different family from their parent!

Perhaps it is fortunate that the Fungi Imperfecti have not been accorded the continual reclassification to which mycologists have (for very good reason) subjected the perfect fungi. Since a natural system at our present stage of knowledge can hardly be attained, any classification has been one for convenience only and such reclassifications as have been proposed are not very great improvements upon the original Saccardo system. The imperfect yeasts and yeast-like fungi are put into four additional families of the Moniliales. See page 285.

A very large number of genera and species of the Moniliales have been described. A very large proportion of these are rare, many of them of doubtful validity. To present a complete key would defeat the purpose of this book. But experience shows that the molds likely to be encountered by the bacteriologist will fall within a few genera; fully three-fourths of those encountered in routine work will be species of Aspergillus and Penicillium. We shall, therefore, describe very briefly only a few genera and indicate where further information may be obtained.

The key to the molds belonging to the Fungi Imperfecti published by Lindau in Rabenhorst's *Kryptogamenflora* has been followed by most mycologists. It has been published in translation in Waksman's *Principles of Soil Microbiology* [18] and in Buchanan's *Bacteriology*.[2] Very complete keys with descriptions of species found in soil will be found in Gilman's *Manual of Soil Fungi*.[8] Soil forms are naturally likely to appear as laboratory contaminants.

The fungi parasitic to man and animals will offer special difficulties. A very excellent *Manual of Clinical Mycology* by Conant [4] and associates gives descriptions and illustrations of the most common and important species. Many other forms will be found in Lewis and Hopper's *Introduction to Medical Mycology*.[10] The older books of Castellani and Sartory are no longer of much value. A very large, fairly recent book of Dodge [5] may also be consulted. However, the inclusion in it of a large number of species for which pathogenicity has not been proved convincingly, together with an excessive splitting of genera and species, and the inclusion of many fungi under more than one name with no indication that they refer to the same fungus, makes this book of limited value. Interested bacteriologists are referred to the international journal *Mycopathologia* for recent work on medical mycology. Under an international editorial board, published in Italy and printed in the Netherlands, it is a war casualty. It is to be hoped that this journal will be revived.

Aspergillus. The word aspergillus (or aspergillum) means a special type of brush for sprinkling holy water used in the ceremony

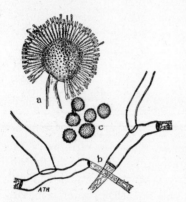

FIG. 45. *Aspergillus niger: a,* vesicle and sterigmata; *b,* foot cells; *c,* conidia.

the "Asperges" which Latin word is the first one of Psalm 51:7 that is sung during the ceremony. The resemblance of the common *Aspergillus niger* to this brush is striking. The literature on this important genus is enormous but two recent books have so thoroughly covered the field from so many points of view that further references here are neither necessary nor desirable. These books are Thom and Church's monograph *The Aspergilli* [15] and Thom and Raper's *A Manual of the Aspergilli.* [16]

The genus Aspergillus may be recognized by the very characteristic arrangement of the conidia and conidiophores. The unbranched conidiophore arises from an enlarged cell of the vegetative mycelium, the foot cell, and terminates in a swollen portion, the vesicle. From the latter, there arise a number of little stalks of characteristic bottle shape, the sterigmata or, as they are sometimes called, the phialides. From these primary sterigmata there may arise one, two, or, rarely, more secondary sterigmata. From the tips of the primary sterigmata in some species, or from the tips of secondary sterigmata in those species which have them, chains of conidia are borne. A conidium is formed by a partial abstriction of the sterigma, which has elongated lightly, followed by formation of a septum separating the conidium from the sterigma. Further cutting off of the tip of the sterigma thus results in more conidia. Since these spores remain attached together, they occur in chains and the whole arrangement presents the spores arranged on compact masses, "conidial heads," at the tip of the conidiophores. In some species the sterigmata and chains of conidia are borne over the whole vesicle and the spore head is thus spherical; in other species the sterigmata are found only on the upper part of the vesicle and the sterigmata and chains may spread out, in cross section like a fan, or all sterigmata may point upward, and the head appears like a long cylinder.

In some species of Aspergillus, ascospores are found, i.e., these molds are perfect fungi and should be included in the Ascomycetes. A strict interpretation of International Rules would seem to make it obligatory to transfer these species to the genus Eurotium as many authors have done. However, the fact that the whole group of Aspergilli appear to be so obviously homogenous, falling naturally into one genus, together with the fact that so many species do not form ascospores at all, makes it preferable for the sake of convenience, if for no other reason, to follow the lead of most of the workers who have actually worked extensively with these molds, and put all species in the genus Aspergillus. The ascospores are all more or less of the same basic pattern. The "thickening of the cell-wall of the ascospore develops in the form of two symmetrical valves suggesting the arrangement found in the shell of a bivalve mollusk (*Venus mercenaria*). The ripe

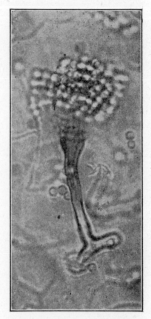

FIG. 46. A conidiophore of *Aspergillus nidulans*, showing the foot cell, stalk, vesicle, and chains of conidia. Photomicrograph from a slide culture.

ascospore is commonly shaped as a double convex lens with the valves more or less closely in contact at the edges. A series of variations upon this basic pattern occur and characterize particular species." (Thom and Raper.) The ascospores are borne eight per ascus in round to oval asci and the asci are scattered throughout the perithecium in an irregular arrangement.

The perithecia are often very abundant and they may determine the color of the colony. In most species of Aspergillus the perithecia are formed on ordinary media with sugar, either regularly and abundantly or not at all. They are found throughout the aerial mycelial growth. They are formed after homothallic conjugation. By crushing the perithecia under a cover slip, one can usually demonstrate the asci and ascospores readily. In some cases the asci may be few in number and in some species one may find bodies having the general appearance of perithecia but containing no asci. These are known as sclerotia and are usually looked upon as being incomplete perithecia.

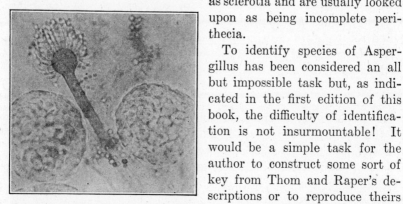

FIG. 47. *Aspergillus amstelodami:* small conidial head and two small perithecia. ×375. From Charles Thom and Kenneth B. Raper, *U. S. Dept. Agr. Misc. Pub. 426* (1941).

To identify species of Aspergillus has been considered an all but impossible task but, as indicated in the first edition of this book, the difficulty of identification is not insurmountable! It would be a simple task for the author to construct some sort of key from Thom and Raper's descriptions or to reproduce theirs but, beyond giving the names of the species, little would be gained. Rather the worker is referred directly to their manual.[16] There he will find that by means of a key based primarily upon the color of the conidial heads, the perithecia, or the colonies on Czapek's agar, he can readily place his isolate in one of fifteen "species groups." Or he can arrive at the same group by means of another key, based primarily upon morphology. Then the worker will have to refer to a section devoted to that species group where he will find the fullest kind of description of each separate species. In some cases it is apparent that the identification of species will be readily made from the keys to species groups and then the diagnosis can be verified from the description itself. In other cases it appears that this will be much more difficult. In all cases the extent of expected variation within a species is indicated, something sadly lacking in many taxonomic treatises. Throughout he will find excellent photo-

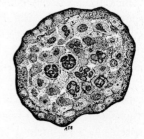

FIG. 48. Section through a perithecium of *Aspergillus* sp. showing development of asci and ascospores.

graphs in abundance, of colonies (many in color) and of morphological details. He will also find exact directions to duplicate the conditions under which the molds so described and photographed were made. Identification of a species group only is, for most purposes, in effect no identification at all; but it may satisfy the worker, which was often unfortunately, and to Henrici's misgiving, the effect

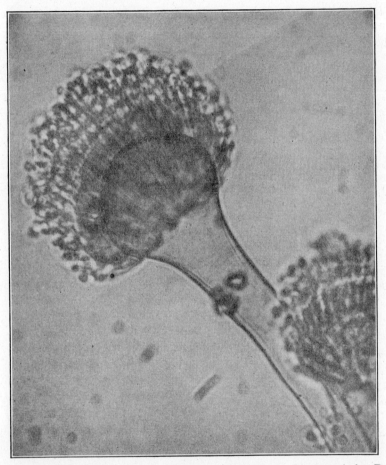

FIG. 49. *Aspergillus fumigatus* (×1400): conidial head. Photograph by Dr. Kenneth R. Raper.

of the key to species groups published in the first edition of this book. Hence no key is given here.

Aspergillus species are found on a wide variety of substrates. They are numerous in soil and particularly so on dried vegetable matter, as hay and grains. They can apparently tolerate very high osmotic concentrations and extract their necessary water from relatively dry substrates. In contrast to Penicillium they can, as a group, tolerate higher temperatures, many of them growing readily in the 37° C. incubator, a temperature too high for most molds.

Among the important species, many of which will be discussed in later chapters, are *A. fumigatus* and *A. nidulans,* pathogenic to man and other animals but also occurring widely distributed as sapro-

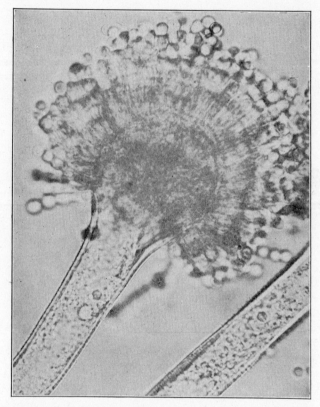

Fig. 50. *Aspergillus Oryzae* (×800): conidial head. Photograph by Dr. Kenneth R. Raper.

phytes; *A. Oryzae* which, owing to the abundance of various enzymes, has so many industrial applications; *A. niger,* and related species, used in citric and gluconic acid production and in assaying available phosphorus and potassium in soil; *A. clavatus* and other species from which antibiotics may be prepared; *A. terreus* which produces itaconic acid from sugar; and *A. niveus* which produces citrinin.

Penicillium. The genus Penicillium is characterized by the production of conidia from sterigmata much like those of Aspergillus, which are produced in clusters or whorls, known as verticils, from short branches (metulae) given off, usually also in verticils, from the tip of the conidiophore. The appearance of a low-power view of the spore head is somewhat like that of a brush; and the spore head is called a penicillus, which is Latin for a brush. Some species produce ascospores after homothallic conjugation. These have been extensively studied.[6]

Our knowledge of the Penicillia has been greatly extended in recent years by the extensive work of Biourge[1] and the still more exhaustive treatise of Thom.[13] The latter authority describes (including three closely related genera) over six hundred species! The differentiation of these is more difficult than that of Aspergilli. In such a condition it is obvious that the precise determination of particular strains must remain a task for specialists.

In the earlier literature (and all too frequently even today) papers were published on the ecology, physiology, morphology, etc., of various "species" of Penicillium without an accurate determination of identity. For instance, any and all green forms were often referred to as *Penicillium glaucum*. This term has been used so indiscriminately for a variety of species that the name is worthless and should be avoided. The problem of identifying species of Penicillium (and to a less extent other genera as well) is not one that is easily solved by the bacteriologist who works on the biochemistry of molds. If he cannot identify them accurately (and few mycologists even attempt to identify species of Penicillium) or if he cannot get them identified by specialists, he had better not give them Latin binomials at all, but deposit them in a culture museum if possible, or at least keep his cultures so that others may verify or extend his work. There are very few of us who have done biochemical work on molds who have failed to make such insufficient identification or to let cultures die out. There is thus no way to find the identity of the molds that were studied. One might as well make a physiological study of a "grasshopper," a "wild sunflower," or a "spore-forming bacillus."

The Penicillia are subdivided by Thom into four sections, and these are further subdivided into subsections. The basis for the primary subdivision is the nature of the branching of the spore heads, whether this is symmetrical about the axis of the conidiophore or asymmetrical. The symmetrical types are separated into three groups: the Monoverticillata, with a single whorl of sterigmata at the tip of the conidiophore; the Biverticillata-symmetrica, in which the verticils of sterigmata arise from short branches or metulae, which themselves form a verticil on the end of the conidiophore; and the Polyverticillata-symmetrica, in which three or more stages of branching occur. The asymmetrical forms make up the fourth group, the Asymmetrica. This classification can be more readily understood from a diagram than from descriptions (Fig. 51). These char-

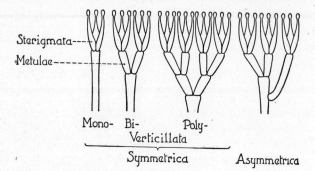

FIG. 51. Diagram illustrating the different types of spore heads of Penicillia.

acters are subject to some variation, even in a single culture, but a dominant tendency will be manifest.

Monoverticillata. Certain molds which formerly were classed as a separate genus, Citromyces, fall in this group. The name was

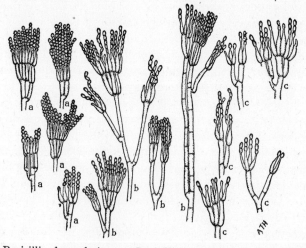

FIG. 52. Penicillia from fruits: *a, Penicillium expansum; b, P. italicum; c, P. digitatum.*

given (by Wehmer) to two species producing citric acid from sugar. These forms were first considered as occupying a position transitional between Aspergillus and Penicillium, since some strains showed a slight swelling of the tip of the conidiophore. But Thom places them with the Penicillia, because numerous other typically penicillate forms have been found subsequently, and because the foot-cell characteristic of the Aspergilli is lacking.

Species of the Citromyces group were investigated at one time as a possible means of producing citric acid commercially, but without much success.

Biverticillata-symmetrica. This section contains a fairly homogeneous group, of which *P. luteum* is the commonly known species. Ascospores are formed regularly by some strains of *P. luteum* in loose masses of pseudoparenchyma, not in well-defined perithecia. This section is also characterized by the production of pigment, in the form of granules on the mycelium, which varies from yellow through orange to red, the color changing with the species, substrate, and age of the culture. *P. pinophilum*, producing stains on wood, belongs in this section, as does also the organism used in gluconic acid production.

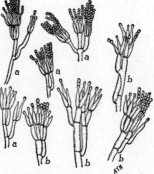

Polyverticillata-symmetrica. This is a small group of four species, none of which is of practical importance.

Fig. 53. Penicillia from cheese: *a, Penicillium roqueforti; b, P. camemberti.*

Asymmetrica. The great majority of the Penicillia fall in the asymmetric group, including most of those of any economic importance. This section is divided into several subsections.

Velutina. The colonies have a velvety appearance. *P. digitatum* and *P. expansum* are important species.

Brevi-compacta. Colonies are partly velvety, partly woolly in texture, the penicillus biverticillate and showing characteristically a short compact base with divergent sterigmata and conidial chains. *P. stoloniferum*, growing on mushrooms and other fungi, and spreading by means of aerial runners, belongs here.

Lanata-typica. This is characterized by an abundance of aerial mycelium which gives the colony a woolly texture. Conidia appear first in the center of the colony after the felt of aerial mycelium has been established. *P. camemberti* is an important species.

Lanata-divaricata. Here the branches of the penicillus are widely divergent and a looser type of spore head is produced than in the other groups. A series of species characteristically found in soil, of which *P. janthellinum* is typical, belongs here. The soil species show yellow to red colors in the mycelium; the spores are green.

Funiculosa. Trailing ropes or bundles of hyphae are found at the edge of the growing colony.

Fasciculata. Species forming coremia, or tending to form coremia, are grouped together in this section. *P. expansum* and *P. italicum* are important.

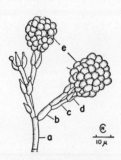

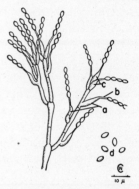

Fig. 54. Gliocladium: *a,* conidiophore; *b,* branch; *c,* metulae; *d,* sterigmata; *e,* clusters of conidia. From Conant *et al., Manual of Clinical Mycology,* 1944.

Fig. 55. Paecilomyces. Single sterigmata (*a*) bend (*b*) away from the main axis. Sterigmata (*c*) are elongated. Conidia (*d*) are oval. Many conidiophores resemble those of Penicillium. From Conant *et al., Manual of Clinical Mycology,* 1944.

Although species of Penicillium have been found from time to time in various pathological lesions of man, it is doubtful that any of them is truly pathogenic.

Gliocladium. Members of this genus form branched spore heads resembling those of Penicillium, but the conidia become surrounded by a mass of slime which bind together all the spores of one spore head into a rounded mass. But the conidia, in some species at least, are formed in chains, as in Penicillium.

Paecilomyces. Paecilomyces is differentiated from Penicillium by its longer tubular sterigmata, the tubular processes being bent away from the axis of the sterigma, and by greater irregularity of the branching, which is only in part verticillate. The perfect stage of this fungus has been found at least once.[12] Spicaria is a generic name sometimes used instead of Paecilomyces.

Scopulariopsis. This group contains members which were formerly included with Penicillium, but which differ even more markedly than the above. They may form Penicillium-like branching systems (but frequently the branching is irregular) or the conidiophore may remain unbranched. The terminal branches which form the spores may not be constricted at their apex to a narrow tubular process, as is characteristic of Penicillium. And finally the large, thick-walled, spiny conidia with their ring at the base (Fig. 56) are quite different from those of Penicillium. Species of this genus are the imperfect stages of one or more genera of perfect fungi.

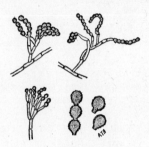

Scopulariopsis brevicaulis (formerly *Penicillium brevicaule*) is a common species of some importance. The spores are yellowish brown in color. It is important as a cause of spoilage of various substances. Growing more slowly than many other molds, it takes part in the final disintegration of the product. It is very active in proteolysis, producing ammonia abundantly in gelatin cultures. In the presence

FIG. 56. *Scopulariopsis brevicaulis:* conidiophores and conidia.

of sugars, it produces from arsenical compounds a substance, diethylarsine, which has a very characteristic garlic-like odor. This reaction has been used as a test for arsenic, the reaction being said to be more delicate than the usual chemical tests. Only arsenous acid or its salts of the alkaline metals may be detected readily, salts of the heavy metals not so surely, and arsenic sulphide not at all. But disagreeable odors may be produced on other substrates, described as ammoniacal, or like turnips or cabbage. According to Thom it is an important secondary invader and cause of spoilage of Camembert cheese and other dairy products. It may be found, along with other molds, in corks, and may give rise to very disagreeable odors in bottled products which have been stoppered with such contaminated corks, without any evidence of mold growth in the product itself. Various strains similar to *S. brevicaulis* have been isolated from cases of infection about the finger nails (onychomycosis); that they are really pathogenic is doubtful.

Sporotrichum. The genus Sporotrichum is characterized by the formation of its rather small, round, oval, or pear-shaped conidia sessile on the mycelium or on very small conidiophores, not in chains but in clusters. The conidia arise laterally and at the tips of the conidiophores or hyphal strands from all parts of the mycelium. A number of species is known, mostly saprophytes, but at least one is known to be a plant pathogen and one, *Sporotrichum Schenckii*, is the cause of an important mycosis, sporotrichosis. See page 193.

FIG. 57.   *Sporotrichum Schenckii* from stained slide culture.

Verticillium. In this genus the erect conidiophores are septate and branched. They are arranged in whorls and these branches rebranch also in whorls. From these numerous tips, whorls of round, elliptical, oval, or short spindle-shaped conidia are borne. Either conidia or mycelium or both may be hyaline or they may be slightly pigmented.

Trichoderma. Not infrequently one finds growing on plate cultures a mold which is of a very bright pure green color; the aerial mycelium is very abundant, and frequently little tufts of white (sterile) aerial mycelium project above the conidiophores. Microscopic ex-

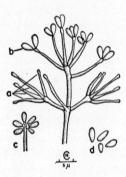

FIG. 58. *Verticillium* sp.: *a*, conidiophores in whorls; *b* and *c*, conidia attached to conidiophores; *d*, conidia. From Conant *et al.*, *Manual of Clinical Mycology*, 1944.

FIG. 59.   Trichoderma: *a*, mycelium; *b*, conidiophores; *c*, cluster of conidia; *d*, conidia. From Conant *et al.*, *Manual of Clinical Mycology*, 1944.

amination reveals numerous small clusters of conidia attached directly to the tips of the many-branched conidiophores (Fig. 59).

This is *Trichoderma viride*, one of the most numerous of the soil fungi, and a very common contaminant in bacteriological work. It is the most active of the soil fungi in ammonification; it liberated 57 per cent of the nitrogen in dried blood as ammonia within 12 days in one experiment. It is also very active in decomposing cellulose.

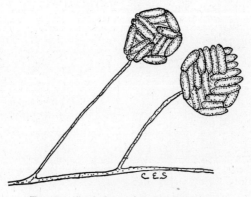

FIG. 60. *Cephalosporium Acremonium.*

On the other hand, it has no diastatic action at all. This common soil fungus is also a common contaminant and, owing to the abundance of the spores and its propensity to grow rapidly and spread over a plate, it may be very troublesome in the laboratory.

Cephalosporium. In this genus the conidiophores are short erect branches of aerial hyphae and are non-septate. The conidia are borne one by one at the tips of the conidiophores but successive conidia push them aside and they form into small balls. These balls of conidia are held together by a secretion of sticky material. Conidia are colorless or nearly so and in most species are elongated or elliptical. *Cephalosporium Acremonium* is the best known species. Certain species of Cephalosporium are pathogenic to man, being among the organisms capable of causing mycetomas. See page 210.

FIG. 61. Conidiophores and conidia of *Cephalothecium roseum.* Many of the conidia have become scattered.

Cephalothecium. *Cephalothecium roseum,* often called *Triothecium roseum,* is a fairly common bright pink mold. It may be readily identified by its clusters of two-celled conidia formed in clusters at the ends of short conidiophores. The cell closest to the conidiophore is the smallest. It occurs widely upon a great variety of substrates, fruit, wood, paper, soil, and is weakly pathogenic to some plants.

Fusarium.   Fusarium is a large, widespread, and very difficult genus. Forty-odd species and many more varieties have been found in soil and frequently they are encountered as air contaminants. Many other species are of considerable importance as the cause of diseases of plants. One species, *Fusarium oxysporum*, has been widely distributed in culture among bacteriologists, bearing the label *Trichophyton rosaceum*, and this culture, supposedly a dermatophyte,

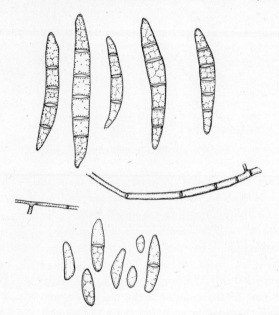

Fig. 62. *Fusarium Equiseti:* above, macroconidia; middle, mycelium; below, microconidia. ×1000. Camera lucida drawing by Dr. Roderick Sprague.

but actually a saprophyte,[7] has been used extensively to test substances designed to be used in the treatment or prevention of fungus infections of man. Conidiophores arise in verticillate arrangement from short hyphal branches. On these are borne long fusiform or sickle-shaped multinucleate conidia. The crosswalls of the conidia are frequently somewhat indistinct. In addition to these large multinucleate conidia, often designated macroconidia, several species produce also small, one- or few-celled, egg-, pear-, spindle- or kidney-shaped microconidia. See Fig. 62. The perfect stage is known in several species. The genus Fusarium has been monographed by Wollenweber and Reinking.[19]

Cladosporium (Hormodendrum).   One not infrequently finds as a contaminant on Petri plate cultures a rather small dark olive-green colony with a velvety surface. The reverse of the colony is almost black. The same mold is found from platings of soil, especially soil with an abundance of decomposing plant residues. These are found most frequently to be organisms designated as *Cladosporium herbarum* or *Hormodendrum cladosporoides*. Cladosporium and Hormodendrum have been separated on the basis of production of two-celled as opposed to one-celled conidia. However, the bicellular conidia usually do not develop until late, unicellular spores forming first, and cultures which are regularly one-celled may occasionally show a few two-celled spores. It is usually agreed that there is but one genus and species may or may not develop two-celled spores. Since Cladosporium has priority, this name should be used and Hormodendrum reduced to synonymy.[14] One species of Cladosporium is the imperfect form of an Ascomycete, *Mycosphaerella Tulasnei,* which is parasitic on various plants.

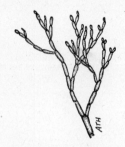

FIG. 63. Spore head of Cladosporium.

In Cladosporium the conidia are formed differently than in molds like Aspergillus and Penicillium. In these molds the conidia are formed by a constriction of the tip of the sterigma, which then forms a second spore that pushes the first one ahead of it, and so on; thus the terminal spore of a chain is the oldest and frequently the largest. In Cladosporium, however, after the first spores have formed on the conidiophore they bud to form secondary spores and no further conidia are formed directly by the conidiophore. Then only the terminal spores bud and in the chains thus formed the youngest, and frequently the smallest, spores are found at the ends of the chains. Moreover a spore may develop more than one new spore by forming more than one bud and thus we find that the chains of conidia are branched (Fig. 63).

These molds are found, as was stated, in soil, and they are also found in large number on decaying leaves, straw, and other vegetation on the surface of the soil. They are said to be of some importance in the spoilage of malt and of stored tobacco. From time to time members of this group are reported as causes of superficial skin lesions in man without clear evidence of their pathogenicity. For relationship of Cladosporium to chromoblastomycosis, see page 199.

"Black Yeasts," "Torula nigra," "Monilia nigra." There has been described from time to time a series of yeasts or yeast-like organisms which produce a characteristic black color. They have been named variously *Saccharomyces niger, Torula nigra, Schizosaccharomyces niger,* and *Monilia nigra.* They have been isolated from a variety of substrates, mostly dairy products. Organisms of this type have been found to produce outbreaks of black spots in Emmenthaler cheese. An apparently identical organism as a cause of spoilage of raw sugar has been reported. Similar forms have been isolated from soil, from air, from commercial yeast cakes, from insects, and from certain pathological lesions of man where, however, they may not be in all cases the causative agent of the disease.

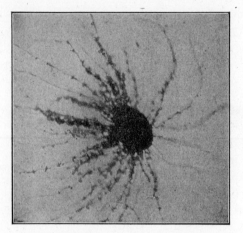

Fig. 64. *"Monilia nigra."*

There has been some question regarding the identity of the various forms described and their proper classification. Henrici examined a dozen or more strains of so-called black yeasts from various sources, and though each strain might be fitted to the description of one organism or another in certain stages of development, they all showed marked transformations of the same general character on continued cultivation, so that he was not convinced that there is more than one species.

These morphologic transformations have been very completely described and illustrated by Maurizio and Staub.[11] When first isolated the organisms grow as soft, pasty, yeast-like cultures, at first a pale yellow color but rapidly becoming a dark greenish black. Examined at this stage, they show only oval budding yeast cells. If pour-plate cultures are made, the deep colonies, at first lenticular, will eventually sprout out numerous radiating filaments of mycelium that develop lateral clusters and chains of budding cells exactly as in cultures of

Candida species. In later subcultures mycelium also develops under aerobic conditions, the growth becoming tougher in consistency, and eventually producing an olive-green aerial mycelium which gives rise to branched chains of conidia.

The aerial conidial apparatus closely resembles that of Cladosporium, the color also being the same. Hansen was of the opinion that these black yeasts are but yeast-like growth forms of dematiaceous molds of the type of Cladosporium, and this view was also supported by Lindner. Henrici also concurred in this opinion. Several of the strains which were examined by Henrici produced, at times from the pasty yeast-like growth, at times from the aerial mycelium, characteristic two-celled conidia exactly like those of Cladosporium. This is probably the explanation for the use of the generic name Schizosaccharomyces by Marpmann.

The above paragraphs are essentially as Henrici wrote them in 1930. Since then Henrici and one of us have isolated several more strains of these organisms. For the most part, the "degeneration"

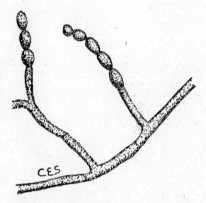

FIG. 65. "*Torula nigra.*" When first isolated from soil, it grew as a budding yeast without mycelium.

(see Chapter II) was as described. In some cases, for long periods of time, they "degenerated" into the form known as *Torula nigra*, that is, they formed chains of round black spores directly from the mycelium or from short lateral branches. Unlike in Cladosporium, the chains did not branch. Later, some of these strains appeared with branched chains of conidia as in Cladosporium but we have some strains that still show the Torula type of growth. This whole group seems poorly understood but it seems clear that the "black yeasts" are but a unicellular growth phase of certain of the Dematiaceae including Cladosporium and possibly other genera as well. See Chapter II.

Alternaria. Members of this genus are also frequently encountered by the bacteriologist. They form dark olive-green or brown colonies similar to those of Cladosporium, save that the aerial mycelium is much looser, forming a more woolly type of growth.

Molds of this group may be recognized by the peculiar spores of rather large size, multichambered, and composed of a number of cells. These conidia occur in chains, sometimes with short stretches of mycelium between the spores. There are a number of species, many of which are plant pathogens. Stemphyllium is a closely related genus. For a discussion of both genera, consult the articles by Groves and Skolko.[9]

Species of Alternaria have been found growing in pus of superficial wounds, and it has been suggested that they have some patho-

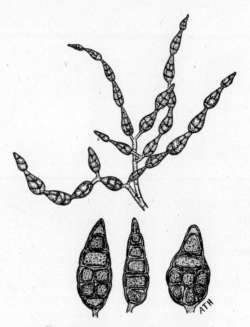

FIG. 66. Conidia of Alternaria.

genic action. But this is probably not true, because the organisms may be growing merely as saprophytes upon the pus, or more likely upon the cellulose of the dressings. Their relation to asthma is mentioned on page 136.

Helminthosporium. Next to Cladosporium and Alternaria, probably the most common dematiaceous mold encountered by the bacteriologist is Helminthosporium. The conidiophores usually arise in groups and are unbranched and septate in most cases. The conidia are large, elongate, and cylindrical or ovate. The ends of the conidia may be rounded or pointed. Many, usually more than four, crosswalls are found in each conidium, which is very dark in color. Curvularia is a related genus. See Fig. 67.

Neurospora. Under the name of *Monilia sitophila*, this genus has been known for a long time in its imperfect stage. Several years ago it was found that ascospores were formed readily and more recent studies on cytology and genetics by Shear, Dodge, and Lindgren (see Chapter II) have made this one of the most completely known of fungi. Because the commonest species of the genus, *Neuro-*

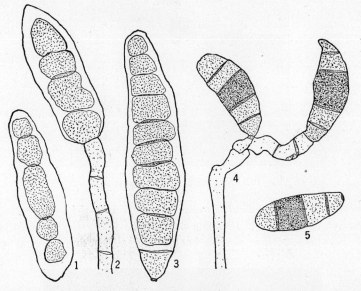

FIG. 67. 1, 2, and 3, *Helminthosporium sativum;* 5 and 6, *Curvularia geniculata.* ×800. Prepared from outline camera lucida drawings of Dr. Roderick Sprague.

spora sitophila, is heterothallic, the ascospores are large and easily isolated mechanically, and growth and sporulation are easily induced, this species and mutants of it are excellent "tools" for geneticists. (See Fig. 68.)

Since *N. sitophila* is heterothallic, only the conidial stage will ordinarily be encountered in routine bacteriological work. Conidia are borne from short hyphal branches and the chains are much branched. See Fig. 69. They develop in the same manner as those of Cladosporium. The conidia are cylindrical to ovate and are numerous and bright orange-red in color. This together with the fact that the mycelial growth is so copious and floccose, often ascending for several centimeters in the culture tubes, gives the mold a characteristic appearance in culture.

N. sitophila is found in soil and on vegetation. It has been especially found in burned-over forest areas. It is most important as a cause of trouble in bakeries because it results in infected bread.

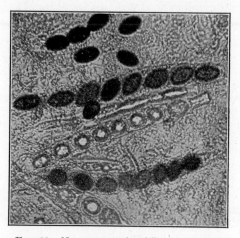

FIG. 68. *Neurospora sitophila* ascospores.

The organisms are difficult to eliminate and are said to be extraordinarily resistant to heat when they are not wetted. This species may become a serious pest in bacteriological laboratories, and spe-

FIG. 69. *Neurospora sitophila* showing arrangement of conidia. Photograph by dark field illumination.

cial care should be taken not to let the spores be scattered. See Chapter VIII for industrial use of this mold.

Monascus. *Monascus purpureus* is a mold not often isolated by the bacteriologist, but it is one of some importance and interest. Its character of producing a brilliant red soluble pigment is utilized by the Chinese to color various food products. Certain Chinese so-called wines, Chinese red-rice, and soybean cheeses are such products imported into the United States. This organism has been found in silage where it sometimes caused the formation of large "balls" up to one-third meter in diameter.[3]

The conidia are large and are found singly on the conidiophores, or in short chains. The asci (the fungus is homothallic) are produced in perithecia which are rather small, at least in the strains studied

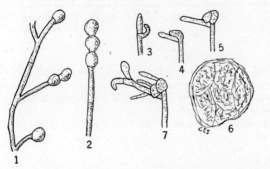

FIG. 70. *Monascus purpureus:* 1 and 2, mycelium and conidia; 3, 4, and 5, oogonium and antheridium; 7, ascogenous and ordinary hyphae; 6, perithecium.

in this laboratory, and the oogonia and antheridia may be easily seen in unstained Petri plate cultures or in stained slide preparations. Although this organism had not been cultured in our laboratories here in Minnesota for over fifteen years, we isolated this species as an air contaminant on one occasion, and years previous to that Henrici had isolated another strain. It is undoubtedly not very common, however. Gilman does not list it as ever being found in soil.

LITERATURE

1. BIOURGE, P., Les moissures du groupe Penicillium Link. Étude mono-graphique, *La cellule*, **33**, 1 (1923).
2. BUCHANAN, E., and R. BUCHANAN, *Bacteriology*, Macmillan, New York, 4th ed., 1938.
3. BUCHANAN, R., Monascus purpureus in silage, *Mycologia*, **2**, 99 (1910).
4. CONANT, N. F., D. S. MARTIN, D. T. SMITH, R. D. BAKER, and J. L. CALLA-WAY, *Manual of Clinical Mycology*, Saunders, Philadelphia, 1944.
5. DODGE, C. W., *Medical Mycology*, Mosby, St. Louis, 1935.
6. EMMONS, C. W., The ascocarps in species of Penicillium, *Mycologia*, **27**, 128 (1935).
7. ———, Misuse of the name "Trichophyton rosaceum" for a saprophytic Fusarium, *J. Bact.*, **47**, 197 (1944).

8. GILMAN, J. C., *A Manual of Soil Fungi*, Collegiate Press, Ames, Iowa, 1945.

9. GROVES, J. W., and A. J. SKOLKO, Notes on seed borne fungi. I. Stemphylium. II. Alternaria, *Can. J. Research, C*, **22**, 190, 217 (1944).

10. LEWIS, G. E., and M. E. HOPPER, *An Introduction to Medical Mycology*, Year Book Pub. Co., Chicago, 1939.

11. MAURIZIO, A., and W. STAUB, Monilia nigra Burri u. Staub. Weitere Untersuchungen über Schwarzfleckigkeit bei Emmenthalerkäse, *Zentr. Bakt., Parasitenk., II*, **75**, 375 (1928).

12. OLLIVIER, M., and G. SMITH, Byssochlamys fulva, sp. nov., *J. Botany, Brit. and For.*, **71**, 196 (1933).

13. THOM, C., *The Penicillia*, Williams and Wilkins, Baltimore, 1930.

14. ———, Naming molds, *J. Wash. Acad. Sci.*, **30**, 49 (1940).

15. THOM, C., and M. CHURCH, *The Aspergilli*, Williams and Wilkins, Baltimore, 1926.

16. THOM, C., and K. B. RAPER, *A Manual of the Aspergilli*, Williams and Wilkins, Baltimore, 1945.

17. VUILLEMIN, P., Classification normale, classement auxiliaire, et groupement pratique des champignons, *Compt. rend., Acad. Sci.* (*Paris*), **180**, 102 (1925).

18. WAKSMAN, S. A., *Principles of Soil Microbiology*, Williams and Wilkins, Baltimore, 2nd ed., 1932.

19. WOLLENWEBER, H. W., and O. A. REINKING, *Die Fusarien*, Parey, Berlin, 1935.

CHAPTER VI

FUNGUS DISEASES OF MAN AND ANIMALS—GENERAL CONSIDERATIONS

Many different fungi have been described as causing various diseases in man and animals. Some of these fungi are known only as pathogens, and the diseases they cause, although sporadic and sometimes rare in occurrence, are fairly well known. Other fungi are known both as pathogens associated with lesions in man and as saprophytes in man's environment, and the circumstances under which they sometimes become parasitic are not fully understood. General discussions of the pathogenic fungi are to be found in many review articles and textbooks.[10, 13, 19, 33, 42, 45, 51]

Etiology. In many cases the etiological relationship between mold and disease can be proved by repeated demonstration of the fungus in lesions, its isolation therefrom, production of an infection in experimentally infected animals, and recovery of the fungus from the latter. There are numerous papers in the literature of medical mycology, however, in which this rigid proof of an etiological relationship is lacking. The careless acceptance of an unproved mycotic etiology frequently has led to error. Pinta, a tropical spirochetosis, long thought to be a mycosis from which many different fungi were isolated, is an example of such a mistake. Many of the fungus diseases are superficial lesions of the skin or mucous membranes. Mold spores are ubiquitous and it is not at all surprising that they may be cultivated frequently from exposed skin lesions, pus, and sputum. Viable airborne spores of harmless saprophytes are often present in pathological material, and they germinate and grow when the material is planted upon culture media. The isolation of such a fungus in culture may then be interpreted erroneously as evidence that it was growing in and causing the lesion. One must develop a healthy degree of scepticism with regard to the pathogenicity of fungi isolated in culture from pathological material.

In a general consideration of mycoses it is interesting to note that fungi have been more successful as pathogens of plants than of animals. The majority of plant diseases, whether of weeds, trees, or commercially important crop plants, are caused by fungi, and the rusts, smuts, mildews, and leaf spots can be mentioned as familiar examples. Comparatively few plant diseases are caused by bacteria. Among the diseases of man and animals, on the other hand, bacterial diseases predominate, and the list of important fungus diseases is short. Furthermore, at least in the case of most of the generalized and frequently fatal mycoses, the fungus appears to be an accidental invader and does not spread from man to man. Fungi therefore appear to be poorly adapted to a parasitic existence in man except in a few instances.

Importance of Mycoses. Although fatal fungus diseases in man are less common than bacterial infections they are nevertheless numerically important. In Vital Statistics of the United States for 1942 mycoses are reported as causing 359 of 1,385,187 deaths in man. This is less than 0.03 per cent of the total, yet it is more than half the number of deaths caused by either typhoid, tetanus, or poliomyelitis and polioencephalitis; more than the number of deaths due to Rocky Mountain spotted fever and the other typhus-like diseases together; and nearly twice as many as the sum of all those caused by paratyphoid fever, undulant fever, smallpox, rabies, leprosy, plague, cholera, yellow fever, and relapsing fever. It should be pointed out, of course, that the low mortality rates of some of the well-known diseases just mentioned are due to the enforcement of effective control measures, whereas in the case of the generalized mycoses control measures are not practiced nor, indeed, are they known. Non-fatal mycoses such as the dermatophytoses (ringworm, athlete's foot) are perhaps as common as any bacterial disease.

Besides their numerical importance, as compared with some of the better known bacterial diseases, the fungus infections provide useful material for the study of certain biological principles. For example, the phenomena of variability and mutation are more apparent in the fungi and can be studied with greater confidence because the larger size and the abundance of measurable morphological characteristics of fungi make it easier to distinguish between a true mutant and a contaminant.

Types of Mycoses. Fungus infections are referred to as mycoses, frequently with a prefix or qualifying word to indicate the part affected, as otomycosis (ear), onychomycosis (nail), pulmonary mycosis. More frequently the type of mycosis is designated according to the etiological agent, as actinomycosis, blastomycosis, coccidioidomycosis. In any case it is usually necessary to indicate the specific fungus responsible since different fungi may invade the ear or the lungs, and different species of actinomycetes (*Actinomyces bovis,*

Nocardia spp.), for example, are etiologically related to different types of actinomycosis. The fungi which cause ringworm have certain peculiarities which set them apart from most of the other pathogenic fungi, and because they are interrelated and the diseases they cause are limited to the skin it is convenient and appropriate to refer to them as the dermatophytes, and to the disease which they cause as dermatophytosis. The term dermatomycosis is sometimes used in the same sense, but the suffix mycosis is generally understood to imply a deeper involvement than is found in dermatophytosis. Another type of mycosis which is set apart by certain characteristics is the mycetoma. The various mycetomas differ in etiology, but all are characterized by deep invasion of the subcutaneous tissues with the formation of sinuses. In the pus which drains from these sinuses the fungus is found usually in the form of rather firm, well-organized granules which differ in size, shape, consistency, and color according to the species of fungus involved.

Human mycoses can be placed in two groups, those in which there is only a very superficial penetration, represented by the dermatophytoses, and those involving the subcutaneous tissues and frequently causing generalized infections, represented by a considerable number of mycoses of varied types and etiologies. In any attempt to generalize upon the fungus diseases this diversity must be remembered. The dermatophytoses are caused by a group of closely interrelated fungi, the dermatophytes, which are physiologically adapted to growth upon keratinized structures. They are able to grow saprophytically upon a wide variety of animal and vegetable debris, but their preference for keratinized material, their ability to grow in the epidermis, frequently for long periods without actually causing lesions of clinical importance, and their transmission from one person to another indicate a high degree of adaptability to the parasitic habit.

Host Specificity. Some of the dermatophytes show a considerable degree of host-specificity. *Microsporum Audouini*, for example, is the species usually responsible for epidemics of ringworm of the scalp. It attacks only children, causing in most cases a dry scaling lesion with little host reaction. Because of its good adaptation to the host it is difficult to eradicate and a single epilating dose of x-ray should be given before fungicidal treatment is begun. Although the disease is chronic, with little or no tendency to self-limitation in the child, spontaneous cure usually occurs at puberty. It is thought that the change in endocrine balance occurring at this time makes the host no longer susceptible to parasitism by this fungus. Infection of the adult by *M. Audouini* is very rare.

M. Canis, on the contrary, is a pathogen of cats and dogs and invades the human host by accident from an animal source. It does not cause epidemics in man although transmission may occur in instances where there is intimate exposure, as within the family. Both children and adults may be infected. Unlike *M. Audouini, M. Canis* typically excites considerable reaction on the part of the host, the lesions frequently being edematous and exhibiting pustules. Although this difference in the clinical type of lesion may be considered typical, exceptions are too frequent to make it a dependable method of determining which of the two species is involved in a given case. As a result of the host reaction in most cases there is a tendency toward spontaneous shedding of hairs infected by *M. Canis* and, as Lewis and Hopper [83] have shown, thorough scrubbing with soap and water may suffice to cure the infection without the use of fungicidal ointments.

Similar relationships can be pointed out in the case of several other dermatophytes. *Trichophyton violaceum* and *T. tonsurans* are pathogens of man; they cause chronic dermatophytosis in which the infected hair stubs are so firmly anchored that their removal requires special attention, and subsequent fungicidal treatment may be required for a considerable time. By contrast, *T. faviforme,* which is a pathogen of cattle, and the *granulosum* and *asteroides* varieties of *T. mentagrophytes,* which are pathogens of the horse and other animals as well as man, when they attack man, cause boggy lesions of the type designated kerion. From this type of lesion the infected hairs are spontaneously shed. In rare cases true granulomata are produced. There is occasionally such a severe pustular folliculitis that when the patient is seen in the clinic infected hairs may be difficult to find and several attempts may have to be made before the fungus is isolated in culture. In general, the granular varieties of *T. mentagrophytes* are more apt to be of animal origin and to evoke a more marked tissue reaction in the human host than are the cottony varieties of that species. There are exceptions, however, to the usual correlations between the type of fungus and the type of lesion, as Dowding and Orr [17] have pointed out.

The species causing dermatophytosis of the foot in man show a high degree of adaptation to this host, in many cases. They may grow for months or years in the epidermis or nails without causing subjective symptoms, becoming clinically important only at rare intervals. A clinical flare-up may be due to altered host resistance;

a changed environment in the interdigital spaces of the foot due to increased activity on the part of the host, change of season or climate, or to some other unrecognized factor. In any case the fungus is a frequent inhabitant of the epidermis and nails of the feet, and the reactivation of a quiescent lesion is probably a more important factor in the frequent occurrence of dermatophytosis of the foot than is reinfection from an exogenous source.

Systemic Mycoses. In spite of the contrasts just cited between the lesions caused by dermatophytes of human origin on the one hand, and of lower animal origin on the other, they become insignificant when one contrasts the dermatophytoses with the generalized mycoses. The dermatophytes, despite their adaptation to specific hosts, form a rather closely interrelated group of fungi. They have certain morphological characteristics and physiological adaptations in common, and they appear to be primarily parasites of man and animals. Dermatophytes have been isolated from stable litter and manure, and they undoubtedly grow saprophytically on desquamated epithelium, hairs and similar debris, but their presence in such environments and such substrata is secondary to their parasitism of man and animals.

The systemic mycoses, on the other hand, are with few exceptions caused by fungi which are rarely found in man and animals, but apparently have a natural habitat elsewhere and attack man and animals only under exceptional circumstances. In American blastomycosis, sporotrichosis, chromoblastomycosis, the type of actinomycosis caused by the acidfast *Nocardia asteroides,* mycetomas of various types, aspergillosis, and other rarer mycoses, the evidence indicates that the fungus has a natural habitat in soil, vegetation, or possibly in some cases in another animal host. The fungi causing these mycoses apparently need to be introduced into the human host by inhalation or subcutaneously by accident on splinters or thorns and under special circumstances in which sensitization may be an important element. These mycoses are not contagious, transmission directly from person to person occurring very rarely if at all.

The factors influencing the incidence of these deeper mycoses vary to some extent with the individual mycosis and can best be discussed later in connection with the particular infection. It may be said in general, however, that age may be a factor in some mycoses, occupational exposure appears to be important in others, residence is important in the case of those with an endemic distribution, and repeated exposure with ensuing sensitization may be important in several.

Occupational exposure may be important more because of the opportunity for repeated exposure than because it provides a single exposure. For example, *Aspergillus fumigatus* is a common soil fungus and everyone may have inhaled its conidia at times, yet pulmonary aspergillosis in man is rare. It is said to occur most often in France in people engaged in two occupations in which they come into frequent and intimate contact with molded grain, namely, those who feed pigeons in one case, and those who use meal in cleaning hair in the other.

Clinical Course. The theoretical implications involved in the initiation of these mycotic infections were discussed by Henrici [27] in a comparison of bacterial infections and certain of the deeper mycoses. He pointed out a fundamental difference between the course of most bacterial diseases and that of most of the deep mycoses. A typical bacterial disease has a sudden onset with rapid resolution. A typical mycosis, on the other hand, has an insidious onset. The development of the disease is slow and frequently the infection spreads at first only by extension to contiguous tissues. Even in generalized mycoses with fatal termination this early stage of the disease may be most important in respect to time if hematogenous dissemination intervenes late in the disease. The primary lesion may be in the skin or in the lungs, in either case spreading slowly by peripheral extension. When hematogenous or lymphatic dissemination finally occurs the progress becomes rapid and death of the host may ensue.

It should be pointed out that there are exceptions to this sequence. Some bacterial diseases follow a slow chronic course and, conversely, in some mycoses there is a rapid extension of the infection. The most common form of coccidioidomycosis is an acute respiratory disease which ordinarily follows a course not unlike that of a common cold or, in more severe cases, influenza. The disseminated form, which is comparatively rare, may follow a rather rapid course to a fatal termination in a few weeks or it may extend over a period of years with very slow progression. Most of the mycetomas, with the exception of the common form of actinomycosis, remain localized so that widespread dissemination never occurs. Mycetoma of the foot, for example, may have a duration of 15 or 20 years, yet never extend much above the ankle. Chromoblastomycosis has a similar slow extension without dissemination, but satellite lesions arise by autoinoculation and influence the rate and extent of the involvement.

Sensitization. The importance of trauma in the initiation of some of the mycoses, their slow initial progress, and their final rapid acceleration suggest that the fungi causing them grow at first only on dead or injured tissue or its products, that they have slight inherent invasive power, and that they are able to spread only after some change has occurred in the fungi themselves or in their environment. If some change in the fungi has occurred the fungus, when isolated from the disease at a late stage, might be expected to show an increased primary virulence when introduced into a new host. Such a change has not been demonstrated. It seems more probable that the host tissues become altered.

Increased susceptibility of the host might be explained by the endotoxin theory of Pfeiffer or the allergic theory of von Pirquet. According to the former, as the cells of the parasite die or are killed by the host they liberate toxins which so alter the neighboring host tissue that the surviving cells of the pathogen are able to grow and extend the lesion. According to the second theory it is assumed that the pathogen exerts little toxic action directly upon the host, but that its long-continued presence in the primary lesion sensitizes the neighboring cells so that they become susceptible. Actually both of these mechanisms may be operative. In most of the pathogens technical difficulties prevent the demonstration of endotoxins and their presence therefore is speculative. There is some circumstantial evidence for the presence of toxins, however, in the case of certain mycoses. In blastomycosis Martin and his associates have shown that the administration of iodides in systemic blastomycosis may cause a rapid extension of the disease unless the patient is first desensitized, presumably because of substances liberated by killed cells of the fungus. In the histopathology of coccidioidomycosis the immature cells of the fungus may cause comparatively little response, but upon reaching maturity, when the sporangium ruptures and permits the dissemination of the endospores, it incidentally releases a substance, unable to pass the previously intact wall of the fungus cell, which excites an immediate tissue response. At the same time, it is conceivable that this substance may promote the invasion of the neighboring tissues by the newly liberated endospores.

As with the bacteria, the pathogenic fungi have various portals of entry to the body which are to some extent specific. Thus there are the dermatophytes mentioned above which grow on the skin and hair; others like the thrush organism are primarily parasites of mucuous membranes, causing lesions of the mouth and vagina. In some cases the primary lesions are in the lungs, the fungi being inhaled. There are fungi which are primarily saprophytes but are capable of growing superficially in the external ear causing otomycosis. Other fungi appear to require introduction to the subcutaneous tissues through wounds.

Some species of pathogenic fungi have a very low invasive power. In fact, in some of the so-called fungus infections there is no infection in the strict sense, for the parasites do not invade the tissues except to grow in the most superficial epidermal layers. This is true of tinea versicolor; and in many cases of otomycosis the fungus hardly invades the epithelium of the ear but grows as a saprophyte upon the ear wax. In dermatophytosis and in most cases of thrush the fungi invade principally the epithelium and rarely penetrate beyond it.

Pathological Anatomy of Mycoses. In the generalized mycoses already mentioned extensive and deep-seated lesions may occur and the disease may spread to other parts of the body either by way of the lymph vessels or the blood stream. The tissue changes brought about in these cases are in part of the nature of abscesses, and in part of the nature of granulomata. Immediately surrounding the parasite there is usually death of the tissues, with softening and the accumulation of leucocytes and the formation of pus. Many of these abscesses become surrounded by granulation tissue consisting of a dense layer of new fibrous tissue infiltrated with mononuclear leucocytes and sometimes containing giant cells. The degree to which one or the other of these processes predominates varies with the virulence of the strain and the mode of infection. Thus the primary lesions of blastomycosis in the skin are mainly granulomatous, the secondary lesions following a blood-stream distribution are usually pure abscesses. In animals experimentally inoculated with rather large doses, pure abscesses similar to those produced by the pyogenic cocci usually develop. However, in some human infections the lesions may so closely resemble various granulomatous processes, such as those of tuberculosis and syphilis or even cancer, as to make the diagnosis difficult. In experimental infections in laboratory animals the type of lesion may vary widely with the dosage and mode of inoculation. Thus if large doses of *Aspergillus fumigatus* spores are injected intravenously into pigeons, areas of necrosis with hemorrhage and very little cellular infiltration will develop about the germinating spores. With very small doses one gets typical tubercles in internal viscera after a much longer time (see Fig. 110). If one blows a mass of spores into the trachea, there develops an acute pneumonia fatal within 24 hours, whereas, if the pigeons are fed on infected grain so that only an occasional spore is inhaled from time to time, there are found cavities in the lungs and a massive growth of mycelium in the air sacs.

Toxins of Fungi. It is not clearly understood how the pathogenic fungi injure the tissues. Although fibrosis and giant cell reactions about some lesions bear a resemblance to a foreign body reaction, the extensive necrosis and suppuration which occur in the center of most lesions cannot be readily explained in this way. Moreover, the experimental lesions produced with freshly isolated and highly virulent strains of some species, as *Aspergillus fumigatus* and *Candida albicans*, are so acute as to suggest that these diseases may be caused by the same mechanisms as those found in bacterial infections. A pigeon inoculated intravenously with a suspension of spores of *A. fumigatus* may die within 24 hours, showing at autopsy multiple punctate hemorrhages and areas of degeneration or necrosis in parenchymatous tissues, in short, just such a picture as may be produced by a highly virulent Streptococcus. Such findings naturally suggest that a potent toxin is formed.

Considerable investigation has been carried on with regard to the toxins of other pathogenic fungi, but it is largely contradictory and inconclusive. No exotoxins have been definitely established. The occurrence of endotoxins is of considerable theoretical interest. Our conception of endotoxins is based largely upon the demonstration of endoenzymes by Buchner's classical experiment. It is not possible to express the cell sap of bacteria by pressure, as Buchner did with yeasts, because of their minute size. All other attempts to remove toxins from within the cells of bacteria by chemical extraction, autolysis, grinding (after drying or freezing) may be criticized as introducing factors that might readily alter the toxins. However, the cell sap of molds may be expressed readily in a Buchner press. It is remarkable that very few attempts to obtain a toxin from pathogenic fungi by this method are recorded in the literature.

Gortner and Blakeslee,[23] during the course of some experiments dealing with antibody production, accidentally discovered that the cell sap of *Rhizopus nigricans* is highly toxic to rabbits. The toxic substance was obtained both by expressing the juice of the mold and by extraction of dried mycelium with hot water. It gave the reactions of proteins, was non-dialyzable, and was precipitated by alcohol. Intravenous injections in rabbits produced almost immediate death, with both symptoms and autopsy findings "practically indistinguishable from anaphylactic intoxication." Subcutaneous injections gave rise to abscesses which broke down to form ulcers. The material was quite harmless by mouth. It is quite possible that these results were due to their using rabbits which had somehow become sensitized to the proteins of this mold. Henrici obtained a toxin from *R. nigricans* which, when injected into rabbits, killed some, but caused anaphylactic reactions only in surviving rabbits given a second injection.

A number of investigators have been concerned with the toxins of *A. fumigatus* because of the high and constant virulence of this fungus for laboratory animals. Renon [43] was unable to find any toxic substance either in the medium or by extracting the mycelium with various solvents. Similar results were obtained by Kotliar,[32] Macé,[34] and by Martins,[35] although the latter author did observe death with one rabbit inoculated with spores heated to 100° C.

On the other hand, Ceni and Besta [12] found in extracts of *A. fumigatus* a heat-stable toxic substance affecting mainly the nervous system, and this was confirmed by Bodin and Gautier.[7] Bodin and Lenormand [8] studied the matter further and concluded that there were two toxins, one a substance soluble in fat solvents which produced convulsions and a rapid death in rabbits, the other a volatile substance obtained by distillation which produced paralysis and death in guinea pigs.

Henrici [28] obtained a toxin from the cell sap of a strain of *A. fumigatus* isolated from aspergillosis in a chick. The toxin was extracted from a glucose-peptone broth culture by squeezing from the mycelial mat as much of the medium as possible, mincing the mycelium with scissors, passing it repeatedly through a food chopper, and expressing the cell sap in a hydraulic press. The toxin resembled the so-called toxalbumins, the exotoxins of bacteria, and the snake venoms in sensitivity to heat, hemolytic action, production of local necrosis and edema, delayed action, and antigenicity. Unlike the toxalbumins, however, its toxicity was augmented rather than destroyed by sodium ricinoleate and it appears to be non-protein in nature. In these characteristics and in the type of lesions it produces in animals it resembles the toxin of the poisonous mushroom *Amanita phalloides*.

The cell sap was lethal by subcutaneous, intraabdominal, and intravenous injection (but not by mouth) for rabbits, guinea pigs, mice, and chicks. Injected subcutaneously in rabbits it produced in about 5 hours large boggy lesions in which there was a large amount of gelatinous fluid similar to that in lesions caused by the toxin of *Clostridium oedematiens*. After a few days the swelling subsided, the center became necrotic and sloughed away leaving an ulcer which required about 10 days to heal. Guinea pigs reacted by developing less gelatinous edema but more necrosis and ulceration. Intravenous inoculation was fatal to rabbits, the survival time decreasing from 10 days to 48 hours with doses varying from 1 cc. to 5 cc. The time of survival varied according to the potency of the particular lot of toxin and the individual susceptibility of the rabbit as well as to the volume of dose.

The post mortem findings were hemorrhages in the lungs, serous or serofibrinous effusion into the peritoneal and pleural cavities, sometimes accumulation of fluid around the kidneys, and a pale or mottled liver. There was extensive damage to the secretory tubules of the kidneys. Some rabbits showed necrotic and fatty changes in the liver. Guinea pigs were more uniformly susceptible to the toxin than rabbits, but lesions were similar. In mice and chicks necrosis of renal tubules was the only pathological change found.

The toxin is antigenic. Henrici immunized rabbits and demonstrated passive transfer of immunity to guinea pigs and mice. Immune serum neutralized the hemolytic action of the toxin *in vitro*.

Toxins of Mushrooms. A word or two may be properly interpolated here concerning the toxins of the poisonous mushrooms. These vary with different species. It may be worthwhile to emphasize a fact too often ignored by the amateur mycophagist who seeks to supplement his diet by gathering wild mushrooms. There are many poisonous species of mushrooms and these may closely resemble edible forms. Several genera contain both edible and poisonous species. There is no simple rule or characteristic such as excellent flavor, failure to tarnish a silver coin, or an easily peeled cap which distinguishes an edible from an inedible species. The only safe basis for selecting edible species is a thorough acquaintance with the species collected.

A survey of the mushroom poisons has been presented by Ford.[22] In the case of the fly Amanita (*Amanita muscaria*) one of the poisons is an alkaloid, muscarin. The poisons of the most deadly of the mushrooms, *A. phalloides* (Fig. 71), have been studied by several investigators. The work of Ford has established that there are two poisonous substances present. One is a hemolytic agent called phallin, the other a general toxin known as amanito-toxin. The former is easily inactivated by heat, the latter is not. Laboratory animals may be immunized with extracts of the fungi, their serums developing both antihemolytic and antitoxic properties. The hemolytic substance has been isolated and is said to be a pentose-containing glucoside. It is, however, contrary to the opinion of most immunologists that a non-protein substance may give rise to antibodies.

The amanito-toxin alone did not give rise to protective antibodies in Ford's experiments. It was found to be neither a protein, an alkaloid, a glucoside, nor a conjugate sulphate.

Contrary to the experience of Ford, de la Rivière [16] found that the toxin affects mainly the nervous system, spasmodic convulsions being

FIG. 71. *Amanita phalloides*, the "Death Cup." The cup-shaped envelope (volva) about the base of the stem and the ring or collar about the stem near the cap are distinguishing signs. (White varieties, of which the above are an example, are sometimes known as *A. verna*.)

the most prominent symptoms. Both authors agree, however, that the toxin is not bound by nerve tissue. A wide variety of animals, from monkeys to fish, are susceptible. Sheep are apparently immune to poisoning by mouth, but succumb to injections. De la Rivière succeeded in obtaining an antitoxin (with the whole extract) by immunizing horses. This not only protected laboratory animals but was shown to have some therapeutic value in cases of human poisoning.

Green and Stoesser [24] have studied the effect of sodium ricinoleate upon the toxins of *A. phalloides*. Whereas this soap destroys the toxins of diphtheria and tetanus bacilli and scarlet fever streptococci, it augments the toxicity of Amanita and botulinus.

Ford proposed a classification of mycetismus (mushroom poisoning) which recognized five types and listed some of the species of mushrooms associated with each type. In reporting four cases of mushroom poisoning caused by *A. phalloides*, Vander Veer and Farley, for practical purposes, simplified Ford's classification and recognized a rapid type of poisoning caused by *A. muscaria* and a delayed type caused by *A. phalloides*.[49] In the rapid type symptoms appear within a few minutes or at most within 3 hours and include "salivation and lacrimation; pupils contracted and not reacting to light or accommodation; nausea and vomiting; abdominal pains with profuse watery evacuations; pulse at times slow and often irregular; dizziness and confusion with convulsions and coma in severe cases; fatal cases, death within a few hours." [49] The prognosis is good even in severe cases if atropine is administered.

In the delayed type symptoms appear 6 to 15 hours after ingestion and include sudden onset "with severe abdominal pains; nausea, vomiting, and usually diarrhea; vomitus and stools often showing blood and mucus; extreme thirst; anuria at times; usually jaundice in from two to three days; cyanosis and coldness of extremities; increasing prostration with coma and death usually from the fifth to eighth day." [49] The mortality rate is 50 to 70 per cent, often 100 per cent in a given group. If the mushroom meal has contained other poisonous species in addition to *A. phalloides* the prognosis may be better because the early action of other toxins aids in early evacuation. Emetics, gastric lavage, and thorough purging are important even though several hours have elapsed since ingestion. Rest in bed is essential until there is definite recovery. Apparent improvement may be followed by fatal relapse if patients are allowed to resume activity too soon. A high carbohydrate liquid diet is recommended, with forced fluids, intravenous dextrose solution, and physiological salt solution subcutaneously. An antitoxin serum has been used in France and Germany.

Immunity Reactions of the Fungi. The available information about immunity reactions in the fungi is somewhat contradictory. It would appear that in general fungi give rise to antibodies only in small amounts and that the antibodies so formed are not highly specific, reacting in some cases with widely divergent types. The difficulty may be due in part to the relatively thick wall of the fungus cell which allows only a slow diffusion of the intracellular proteins into the tissues. This is indicated by the results of Balls[1] who obtained precipitating serums of relatively high titer and specificity with yeasts by inoculating, not the cells, but proteins liberated from them by autolysis.

Agglutinins. Most attempts to carry out agglutination reactions with fungi have been unsuccessful. This is due in part to the difficulty of obtaining stable suspensions. Generally spores have been used although some workers have used suspensions of ground-up mycelium.

Moore and Davis reported that agglutinins were produced in sporotrichosis and considered the agglutination reaction useful in diagnosis and in demonstrating the close relationship between different strains of *Sporotrichum Schenckii*.

Cummins and Sanders [14] could demonstrate no agglutinins for *Coccidioides immitis* in experimentally infected animals. Similarly Nicaud [39] found no agglutinins for spores of *Aspergillus fumigatus* in the sera of human cases of aspergillosis, and Matsumoto [36] did not obtain any agglutination of spores of *A. amstelodami* in the sera of intensively immunized rabbits.

On the other hand, Widal [50] and others found that the sera of sporotrichosis cases would agglutinate the spores of *S. Schenckii* in rather high dilutions, 1:300 to 1:400 on the average, and this observation has been confirmed by numerous later authors. However, the same Sporotrichum spores are also agglutinated in rather high dilutions by the sera of thrush cases and cases of actinomycosis, according to Widal and his coworkers. This observation, however, was not confirmed by Fineman [21] in the cases of thrush studied with American strains of Sporotrichum. Widal and his coworkers found that the sera of thrush cases would agglutinate Sporotrichum spores at a higher titer than they would suspensions of the thrush parasite. Fineman could obtain agglutinins only in a very low titer for *Candida albicans* in immunized rabbits. According to Epstein [20] this organism agglutinates spontaneously too readily to be used for agglutination reactions. Blakeslee and Gortner [2, 3] obtained rather strong agglutinating sera for the spores of Mucor, with some cross reactions. It should be pointed out that the spores of Sporotrichum and of the Mucors have thinner walls than do many mold spores, and they form suspensions fairly readily.

Benham demonstrated the usefulness of the agglutination and reciprocal absorption of agglutinins tests in determining relationships between species of Candida. Most investigators have found it possible to produce serums of good antigen titer with these yeast-like fungi. Martin, discussing the application of immunological principles to the diagnosis and treatment of mycoses, reported that agglutination reactions were generally unsatisfactory for most of the mycoses. Drake [18] demonstrated "natural agglutinins" against five different yeast-like fungi and concluded that they are normal human serum constituents.

Precipitins. Very little study of precipitins has been carried on. Cummins and Sanders [14] recorded negative results with sera of patients and inoculated guinea pigs in coccidioidal granuloma. Michel obtained no reactions with *Candida albicans* in cases of sprue. Matsumoto obtained precipitates when the sera of rabbits immunized with species of Aspergillus were tested against broth filtrates, but not with extracts of mycelium. The reactions were not definitely specific. Henrici was unable to demonstrate precipitins with sera of rabbits intensively immunized with cell sap of *Aspergillus fumigatus* and *Cephalosporium Acremonium*.

Stone and Garrod [46] reported that the precipitin and complement fixation reactions of strains of *C. albicans* they cultivated from thrush were similar. Kesten and Mott [31] prepared polysaccharides from several yeasts and yeast-like fungi and with them obtained serums which they used to produce precipitin reactions.

Complement Fixation. Widal [50] and his coworkers found complement fixation positive in sporotrichosis, as with agglutination, and found the same cross reactions with thrush and actinomycosis. Epstein [20] found the complement fixation reaction positive only once in twenty cases of thrush. Cummins and Sanders [14] obtained no complement fixation in coccidioidal granuloma. Matsumoto [36] obtained more marked results with complement fixation than with precipitation in his studies of the Aspergilli, but found no correlation between the grouping of species by complement fixation and their morphological characters.

Smith, although much of the details of his work are not yet published, reported that the complement fixation reaction gives useful information about the progress and probable prognosis in disseminated coccidioidomycosis. Martin states that in blastomycosis the titer of complement-fixing antibodies is low even in the presence of extensive skin lesions if the infection is not systemic. With increasing involvement of the internal organs there is usually a corresponding rise in antibody titer. Conversely, a fall in titer indicates in most cases an improvement in the prognosis. Some individuals do not produce antibodies and the complement fixation reaction alone, therefore, is not a reliable diagnostic test.

Negroni [38] isolated a carbohydrate which he believed came from the capsular material of *Candida albicans* and was responsible for the agglutinating and complement-fixing properties of the fungus. Martin, using a saline suspension of the yeast-like form of *Blastomyces dermatitidis* and otherwise following the usual procedures of the Wassermann tests, demonstrated complement-fixing antibodies in the serum of three of four patients with generalized blastomycosis. There did not appear to be any cross reaction with other pathogenic fungi. He found no relationship between the clinical condition of the patient and the presence of complement-fixing antibodies in the blood.

Allergic Reactions. More significant results seem to have been obtained from a study of allergic reactions than from other phases of immunity with the fungi. In 1908 Bloch [4] established that after an experimental skin infection with *Microsporum quinckeanum* had been established in guinea pigs, the animals were immune to reinoculation over the entire skin surface. This immunity is in general not species-specific, the animal remaining also refractory to other distantly related species of dermatophytes. If one does succeed in establishing a second infection, the inflammatory reaction is more acute and the lesion heals more quickly than in a control animal. A similar immunity was demonstrated in human cases where deep-seated lesions occurred.

Inoculations of filtrates of old broth cultures of the fungus gave rise to a characteristic papule in human cases if deep-seated lesions were present, but not when the lesions were superficial. This allergic reaction also proved non-specific, infections with different species of dermatophytes giving reactions with the same antigen.

Further observations were reported later by Bloch and Massini,[6] among them the following interesting experiment. Skin from a patient allergic to ringworm fungi was transplanted to a non-sensitive individual. After the graft was established, it was found that this area of skin was still hypersensitive, although the "native" skin of the recipient did not become sensitized. It was also claimed that deep-seated infections healed more rapidly after establishing an artificial infection with *M. quinckeanum,* an observation which was confirmed by Plaut.

The use of trichophytin (extracts of species of Trichophyton) diagnostically and therapeutically has been widely studied by dermatologists. It seems to have been established that these extracts regularly give reactions in patients in whom deep-seated lesions occur, less regularly in others; that the reaction may persist for some time after the lesions have healed; and that some individuals, even those in whom a previous history of ringworm cannot be established, may react; so that, as with tuberculin, a negative reaction is of more diagnostic value than a positive one. Trichophytin is claimed by some to have some therapeutic value in certain deep-seated infections, but the effect is not a specific one. There occurs a focal reaction in the lesion as well as the local one at the site of inoculation, and such therapeutic effect as is noted is to be attributed to this increased inflammatory reaction, which is no greater than that obtained when irritants are applied locally. The trichophytins have been prepared in various ways. According to Bloch, the best procedure is to evaporate the broth filtrate to one-twelfth its original volume, to which is added the cell sap expressed from the mycelium. The active substance has been chemically investigated by Bloch, Labouchere, and Schaaf,[5] who claim that it is a starch-like, nitrogen-containing, levorotatory polysaccharide.

Trichophytid. In connection with the allergic reactions of ringworms, mention should be made of the condition known as *trichophytid*, first described by Jadassohn. This is a generalized skin eruption occurring during the course of a ringworm infection, similar to the generalized eruptions occurring in scrofula or other forms of tuberculosis, and designated tuberculide by Darier. It is as yet uncertain whether this affection is due to a toxic reaction of some sort (perhaps caused by an allergic state of the patient) or to a dissemination of the fungus by the blood stream. The former hypothesis seems more reasonable, but positive blood cultures have been reported. Experimental trichophytid in the guinea pig has been described.[26]

Cutaneous Reactions in Other Mycoses. The cutaneous reactions in coccidioidomycosis have been studied more thoroughly than in other mycoses. Dr. C. E. Smith has prepared most of the coccidioidin used in skin testing and has had a very extensive experience in its use. He prepares the material by growing strains of *Coccidioides immitis* on a synthetic broth medium like the medium used in the preparation of old tuberculin except that there is a reduction in the amount of glycerin. The composition of the medium and the method of preparation and use are outlined in the section on coccidioidomycosis.

Coccidioidin appears to be highly specific, but some lots give nonspecific reactions and have to be discarded. A small number of persons who have had no recognized exposure to Coccidioides react to coccidioidin, and these reactions have so far not been satisfactorily explained.

Other mycotic antigens are less specific or have had less extensive use than coccidioidin. Histoplasmin has been prepared by a number of investigators. Palmer,[40] using histoplasmin prepared from the synthetic broth mentioned above, reported that in student nurses tested there was a very high correlation between positive histoplasmin skin reactions and pulmonary calcification, and suggested that Histoplasma might be responsible for non-tuberculous calcification. It is known, however, that this histoplasmin gives cross reactions with other mycoses.[52]

A skin-testing antigen prepared from *Aspergillus fumigatus* at the National Institute of Health and used in testing experimentally infected guinea pigs had a primary irritating effect and gave nonspecific reactions.

The use of a skin-testing antigen in the diagnosis of a mycosis has definite limitations which are not always recognized. A positive reaction may be due to a non-specific factor common to several pathogenic fungi; or, if it is a true specific reaction, the person may have been sensitized by a previous exposure to the fungus quite unrelated to the condition in which a diagnosis is sought. Skin sensitivity, once it is acquired, persists for many years and perhaps for life.

Asthma. Considerable attention has been directed toward mold spores as possible etiologic agents in asthma. It now seems well established that asthma is due to an allergic state toward inhaled substances which may be present in the air as dust. That mold spores may be the exciting agents was suggested by van Leeuven.[48] Cadham[11] demonstrated that the spores of the wheat rust fungus, *Puccinia graminis*, excited asthmatic attacks in certain cases he studied. Hansen[25] observed a number of cases apparently due to mold spores. These cases are first detected by cutaneous reactions, but Hansen applied rather strict criteria for establishing the diagnosis, involving demonstration of the mold in the habitual surroundings of the patient, complete relief after removal from these surroundings, an immediate relapse after experimental exposure to the mold in question, and finally a positive Prausnitz-Kustner reaction (passive transfer of the skin sensitivity to a normal person). He found various species of Aspergillus most frequently gave reactions. Hopkins, Benham, and Kesten[29, 30] reported a case due to a species of Alternaria, and suggested that an eczema from which the same patient suffered might be due to a similar cause.

Allergists have made extensive surveys of the mold spore content of the air in different geographical areas and at different times of year. It is routine practice to skin-test allergic patients with stock fungus extracts or with extracts of fungi isolated from the particular patient's environment. The role of fungi in allergy has been reviewed by many allergists, including Sulzberger,[47] Peck,[41] and Brown.[9]

Treatment of Fungus Infections. The treatment of mycoses is frequently unsatisfactory, the infections persisting for long periods of time in spite of treatment. In actinomycosis, blastomycosis, and histoplasmosis the prognosis is grave and the mortality high. In superficial infections, as the dermatophytoses and thrush, local applications of strong antiseptics may sometimes lead to a rapid cure.[37] Many of these, however, are also stubborn and persistent.

In sporotrichosis the internal administration of iodides causes the rapid disappearance of the lesions. Similar, though less marked, beneficial results are obtained in localized actinomycosis and blastomycosis, so that it has come to be generally considered that the iodides are a specific for fungus infections comparable with the arsenicals in protozoan infections. However, Davis [15] showed for Sporotrichum (as did Reynolds and Henrici [44] for an actinomycete) that the iodides have no effect upon the fungi themselves either *in vivo* or *in vitro;* growth occurred in media containing as much as 10 per cent of potassium iodide. Such therapeutic results as are obtained therefore must be due to an action on the tissues rather than on the parasite. The iodides probably stimulate the formation of fibrous tissue which tends to wall off the organisms. On the other hand Martin and Smith point out that in systemic blastomycosis administration of iodides may cause a rapid extension of the lesions unless the patient is first desensitized. They suggest that the reason for this is that the iodides cause the death of many fungi, and that a toxin is thereupon liberated from the dead fungus cells.

Many attempts have been made to find other specific drugs for the treatment of fungus infections, but without much success. Probably because they have been extensively used as fungicides in the treatment of fungus diseases of plants, copper salts and colloidal copper have been used. Neither copper nor sulphur is as useful against the fungus pathogens of man as against those of plants. Tartar emetic and preparations of arsenic and mercury are also used. Although apparent cures and improvements under such treatments have been reported, the results in general are not sufficiently striking to indicate that any specific chemotherapeutic agent has been found.

Thymol, instilled into the lesion locally and taken by mouth, has been used with success in some cases of actinomycosis and cocci-dioidomycosis. Sulfadiazine is effective in actinomycosis. Penicillin is also reported useful in this disease, but has not yet been tried in enough cases to permit a critical evaluation.

No effective specific treatment is yet known for most of the systemic mycoses. Rest and supportive therapy are recommended to aid the patient in arresting the infection. Many of the mycoses, even of the more severe types, tend to remain localized, spreading by extension only, for long periods. Where medication proves useless in such cases complete surgical excision or even amputation may be the best treatment.

LITERATURE

1. BALLS, A. K., The precipitin test in the identification of yeasts, *J. Immunol.*, **10**, 797 (1925).

2. BLAKESLEE, A. F., and R. A. GORTNER, On the occurrence of a toxin in juice expressed from the bread mould *Rhizopus nigricans, Biochem. Bull.*, **2**, 542 (1913).

3. ———, Reaction of rabbits to intravenous injections of mould spores, *Biochem. Bull.*, **4**, 45 (1915).

4. BLOCH, B., Zur Lehre von den Dermatomykosen, *Arch. Dermatol. Syphilol. (Berlin)*, **93**, 157 (1908).

5. BLOCH, B., B. A. LABOUCHERE, and F. SCHAAF, Versuche einer chemischen Charakterisierung und Reindarstellung des Trichophytins. *Arch. Dermatol. Syphilol. (Berlin)*, **148**, 413 (1925).

6. BLOCH, B., and R. MASSINI, Studien über Immunität und Überempfindlichkeit bei Hyphomycetenerkrankungen, *Ztschr. f. Hyg. u. Infektionskr.*, **63**, 68 (1909).

7. BODIN, E., and L. GAUTIER, Note sur une toxine produite par l'*Aspergillus fumigatus, Ann. inst. Pasteur*, **20**, 209 (1906).

8. BODIN, E., and C. LENORMAND, Recherches sur les poisons produits par l'*Aspergillus fumigatus, Ann. inst. Pasteur*, **26**, 371 (1912).

9. BROWN, G. T., Hypersensitiveness to fungi, *J. Allergy*, **7**, 455 (1936).

10. BRUMPT, E., *Précis de parasitologie*, Masson et Cie., Paris, 1936.

11. CADHAM, F. T., Asthma due to grain rusts, *J. Amer. Med. Assoc.*, **83**, 27 (1924).

12. CENI, C., and C. BESTA, Ueber die Toxine von *Aspergillus fumigatus* und *A. flavescens* und deren Beziehungen zur Pellagra, *Centr. Pathol. Anat.*, **13**, 930 (1902).

13. CONANT, N. F., D. S. MARTIN, D. T. SMITH, R. D. BAKER, and J. L. CALLAWAY, *Manual of Clinical Mycology*, Saunders, Philadelphia, 1944.

14. CUMMINS, W. T., and J. SANDERS, The pathology, bacteriology and serology of coccidioidal granuloma, *J. Med. Research*, **35**, 243 (1916).

15. DAVIS, D. J., The effect of potassium iodide on experimental sporotrichosis, *J. Infectious Diseases*, **25**, 124 (1919).

16. DE LA RIVIÈRE, R. D., Étude d'une toxine vegetale: la toxine phallinique, *Ann. inst. Pasteur,* **43,** 961 (1929).

17. DOWDING, E. S., and H. ORR, Three clinical types of ringworm due to *Trichophyton gypseum, Brit. J. Dermatol. Syphilis,* **49,** 298 (1937).

18. DRAKE, C. H., Natural antibodies against yeast-like fungi as measured by slide-agglutination, *J. Immunol.,* **50,** 185 (1945).

19. EMMONS, C. W., Medical mycology, *Botan. Rev.,* **6,** 474 (1940).

20. EPSTEIN, B., Studien zur Soorkrankheit, *Jahrb. Kinderheilk.,* **104,** 129 (1924).

21. FINEMAN, B. C., A study of the thrush parasite, *J. Infectious Diseases,* **28,** 185 (1921).

22. FORD, W. W., The distribution of haemolysins, agglutinins, and poisons in fungi, especially the Amanitas, the Entolomas, the Lactarius and Inocybes, *J. Pharmacol.,* **2,** 285 (1911).

23. GORTNER, R. A., and A. F. BLAKESLEE, Observations on the toxin of *Rhizopus nigricans, Am. J. Physiol.,* **34,** 353 (1914).

24. GREEN, R. G., and A. V. STOESSER, Biological study of mushroom extract and effect of sodium ricinoleate on its toxicity, *Proc. Soc. Exptl. Biol. Med.,* **24,** 913 (1927).

25. HANSEN, K., Über Schimmelpilz-Asthma, *Verhandl. Deut. Ges. inn. Med.,* **40,** 204–206 (1928).

26. HENRICI, A. T., Experimental trichophytid in guinea pigs, *Proc. Soc. Exptl. Biol. Med.,* **41,** 349 (1939).

27. ———, Characteristics of fungous diseases, *J. Bact.,* **39,** 113 (1940).

28. ———, An endotoxin from *Aspergillus fumigatus, J. Immunol.,* **36,** 319 (1939).

29. HOPKINS, J. G., R. W. BENHAM, and B. M. KESTEN, Asthma due to a fungus—Alternaria, *J. Am. Med. Assoc.,* **94,** 6 (1930).

30. HOPKINS, J. G., B. M. KESTEN, and R. W. BENHAM, Sensitization to saprophytic fungi in a case of eczema, *Proc. Soc. Exptl. Biol. Med.,* **27,** 342 (1930).

31. KESTEN, H. D., and E. MOTT, Soluble specific substances from yeastlike fungi, *J. Infectious Diseases,* **50,** 459 (1932).

32. KOTLIAR, E., Contribution a l'étude de la pseudotuberculose Aspergillaire, *Ann. inst. Pasteur,* **8,** 479 (1894).

33. LEWIS, G. M., and M. E. HOPPER, *An Introduction to Medical Mycology,* Year Book Pub. Co., Chicago, 1943.

34. MACÉ, T. C., Étude sur les mycoses experimentales, *Arch. parasitol.,* **7,** 313 (1903).

35. MARTINS, C., Études experimentales sur l'*Aspergillus fumigatus, Compt. rend. soc. biol.,* **100,** 525 (1928).

36. MATSUMOTO, T., The investigation of Aspergilli by serological methods, *Trans. Brit. Mycol. Soc.,* **14,** 69 (1929).

37. MYERS, H. B., and C. H. THIENES, The fungicidal activity of certain volatile oils and stearoptens, *J. Am. Med. Assoc.,* **84,** 1985 (1925).

38. NEGRONI, P., Propiedades antigénicas *in vitro* de la substancia capsular de *Mycotorula albicans, Rev. inst. bacteriol. dept. nacl. hig. (Buenos Aires),* **7,** 568 (1936).

39. NICAUD, P., Étude des reactions humorales dans l'Aspergillose, *Paris médical,* No. 22, p. 531, 1929.

40. PALMER, C. E., Nontuberculous pulmonary calcification and sensitivity to histoplasmin, *Public Health Repts.*, **60**, 513 (1945).

41. PECK, S. M., Fungus allergy, *J. Allergy*, **11**, 309 (1940).

42. PLAUT, H. C., and O. GRÜTZ, Die Hyphenpilze oder Eumyceten, Kolle, Kraus u. Uhlenhuth's *Handbuch de Path. Mikroorganismen*, Fischer, Jena, **5**, 133 (1927).

43. RENON, L., *Étude sur l'Aspergillose chez les animaux et chez l'homme*, Masson et Cie., Paris, 1897.

44. REYNOLDS, G. S., and A. T. HENRICI, Potassium iodide does not influence the course of an experimental actinomycosis, *Proc. Soc. Exptl. Biol. Méd.*, **19**, 255 (1922).

45. SARTORY, A., *Champignons parasites de l'homme et des animaux*, Le François, Paris, 1921.

46. STONE, K., and L. P. GARROD, The Classification of Monilias by serologic methods, *J. Path. Bact.*, **34**, 429 (1931).

47. SULZBERGER, M. B., Allergy in dermatology, *J. Allergy*, **7**, 385 (1936).

48. VAN LEEUVEN, W. S., *Allergic Diseases*, Lippincott, Philadelphia, 1925.

49. VANDER VEER, J. B., and D. L. FARLEY, *Mushroom poisoning (mycetismus), Report of four cases*, Arch. Internal Med., **55**, 773–791 (1935).

50. WIDAL, F., P. ABRAMI, E. JOLTRAIN, E. BRISSAUD, and A. WEILL, Serodiagnostique mycosique, *Ann. inst. Pasteur*, **24**, 1–33 (1910).

51. DODGE, C. W., *Medical Mycology*, Mosby, St. Louis, 1935.

52. EMMONS, C. W., B. J. OLSON, and W. W. ELDRIDGE, Studies of the role of fungi in pulmonary disease, I. Cross reactions of histoplasmin, *Public Health Repts.*, **60**, 1383 (1945).

CHAPTER VII

INFECTIONS CAUSED BY MOLDS

COCCIDIOIDOMYCOSIS

(Valley Fever, Coccidioidal Granuloma)

Coccidioidomycosis is an acute, usually mild and self-limited respiratory mycosis, which in exceptional cases becomes chronic and generalized; it then produces granulomatous lesions in almost any organ and has a high fatality rate.

History. The first recognized case of coccidioidomycosis was reported by Posadas and Wernicke from the Chaco region of Argentina. The second and third were seen in 1894 in California by Rixford and Gilchrist.[13] * The pathogen was believed to be a protozoan, and Rixford and Gilchrist, seeing a resemblance to Coccidium, followed a suggestion of Stiles and named it *Coccidioides immitis.* Four years later Ophuls and Moffitt,[12] studying the third North American case, isolated the organism in culture and showed that it was a fungus. Although the fungus was named under the erroneous impression that it was a protozoan the generic name was created for it and actually no protozoa have ever been placed in the genus. The name is therefore valid and the disease is properly designated coccidioidomycosis, the name given it by Dickson.[5, 6] One frequently hears the disease miscalled coccidiosis which is an unrelated protozoan disease common in some animals.

The condition was known for 40 years after its discovery as a chronic, generalized, usually fatal granulomatous disease called coccidioidal granuloma. After 1936 the investigations of Gifford [11] and of Dickson revealed that an acute, benign, respiratory disease called Valley fever or desert rheumatism was a mild form of coccidioidomycosis. The subsequent studies of Dickson, Smith, [14, 15, 16] Aronson [1] and others have shown that most of the residents of an endemic area react to the intradermal injection of an antigen, coccidioidin, prepared from the fungus. This is interpreted to mean that the

---

* In Chapter VII literature citations will be found at the end of each section. Citations for this section are on page 152.

individual reacting has had a sensitizing contact with the fungus since few non-residents react to the test. This specific skin sensitivity is usually acquired early in childhood by the residents of an endemic area, usually without having had a recognized infection. A small percentage (higher in those exposed for the first time as adults) of reacting persons may have had a respiratory infection of some clinical importance. Very few infected individuals (probably a small fraction of 1 per cent of those who become skin sensitized) develop the grave generalized form of the disease. During the period 1893 to 1931 only 254 cases of the generalized form were known from California where it is a reportable disease. There is probably no notable increase in the incidence of coccidioidal granuloma, except as recent mass movements of susceptible adults in the armed forces have enormously increased the number of exposures. However, since 1936 there has been a great increase in the recognition of the acute respiratory type of the disease. Dickson suggested the latter be designated primary coccidioidomycosis and that coccidioidal granuloma be called progressive or secondary coccidioidomycosis.

Clinical. The present concepts of coccidioidomycosis have been well summarized by Smith.[16] Although primary skin lesions have been reported in a few cases the important portal of entry is the respiratory tract. Cases in which the time of exposure is known or can be estimated accurately show that symptoms may appear 8 to 21 days after inhalation of the chlamydospores of the fungus and skin sensitivity to coccidioidin is acquired 10 to 45 days after the exposure.

Initial or *primary coccidioidomycosis,* which follows inhalation of the spores of the fungus, is self-limited and focalized in the lungs. It is usually asymptomatic and is then recognized only by the acquisition of skin sensitivity to coccidioidin. However, it may be an acute respiratory condition following an influenzal or pneumonic pattern. There may be pleural, joint, and muscle pains, headache, cough which is usually non-productive, malaise, fever, chills, nightsweats, and anorexia. In some cases there may be formation of pulmonary cavities which close spontaneously and promptly, or persist for a considerable time. It is estimated that 2 to 5 per cent of individuals with initial coccidioidomycosis develop erythema nodosum or erythema multiforme. When this allergic manifestation is present the disease is commonly called San Joaquin fever, Valley fever, desert rheumatism, or desert fever, designations given to the condition as it was seen within the endemic area of the San Joaquin Valley of California long before its etiology was known. Human pathological material of primary coccidioidomycosis has not been available for histological study. It is evident that even when cavitation occurs and Coccidioides is present in the sputum the infection is usually effectively controlled and remains well localized.[4, 5, 6, 10, 18]

In a very few primary infections, perhaps one in 500 or 1000, dissemination of the fungus occurs. This happens if at all usually within a few weeks or months after the primary infection. In some cases this secondary form (originally designated coccidioidal granuloma) may be the first recognized manifestation of the disease. This was invariably true in the early history of the mycosis, but its relationship to initial coccidioidomycosis is now better understood. This form of the disease is properly designated *progressive* or *disseminated coccidioidomycosis*. In its clinical manifestations disseminated coccidioidomycosis closely mimics tuberculosis and a differential diagnosis can be made only by demonstration of the fungus, although in certain cases the coccidioidin and tuberculin reactions are helpful. There may be multiple subcutaneous and joint abscesses. Skin lesions may present a verrucous appearance or there may be extensive ulceration. Although in some cases a skin lesion may be the first recognized evidence of infection there may have been, and probably was in most cases, an earlier unrecognized pulmonary infection. When dissemination occurs there may be miliary spread to the meninges, bones and joints, lymph nodes, peritoneal cavity, and to any organ, with the notable exception of the digestive tract which is usually spared. The lesions, except for the presence of the fungus, resemble those of tuberculosis to a remarkable degree.

Diagnosis. The diagnosis rests finally upon the demonstration of the fungus in pus, sputum, or tissues. Coccidioidin skin and serological tests are, however, helpful, and investigations based on the use of these methods have contributed greatly to knowledge of the disease. Coccidioidin is prepared by growing the fungus for 2 months in a broth medium similar to that used in making old tuberculin. The formula, as recommended by Dr. C. E. Smith, is as follows.

Ammonium chloride (NH_4CL)	7.00 grams
1-Asparagine	7.00 grams
Dipotassium phosphate C.P. (K_2HPO_4)	1.31 grams
Sodium citrate C.P. ($Na_3C_6H_5O_7 \cdot 5\frac{1}{2}H_2O$)	0.90 gram
Magnesium sulphate U.S.P. ($MgSO_4 \cdot 7H_2O$)	1.50 grams
Ferric citrate U.S.P. VIII (scales)	0.30 gram
Glucose of the grade known as cerolose U.S.P. X	10.00 grams
Glycerol C.P. (U.S.P.)	25.00 ml.
Water to make	1000.00 ml.

"Dissolve asparagine in about 300 cc of hot distilled water, 50 degrees C. Dissolve each of the organic salts in 25 cc of water, ferric citrate being dissolved in hot water. Add each salt in order, starting with K_2HPO_4 to the hot asparagine solution and mix well each time the salt is added. Then add dextrose and glycerine [glycerol] and finally make up to volume. Fill 1500 cc to each 3 liter Fernbach culture flask. Then sterilize at 115 degrees for 25 minutes. Incubate."

After the culture has grown for 2 months at room temperature or 30° C. the broth is filtered, made up to the original volume, tested for sterility, a preservative is added, and the product is tested for potency and specificity by skin-testing persons whose degree of sensitivity is known. Many lots of coccidioidin fail to meet the latter tests and must be discarded. A suitable lot is stable over a period of several years. The skin test is performed by injecting 0.1 ml. of a dilution of 1:1000 of the filtrate intracutaneously. The test is read after 48 hours as a tuberculin test would be read. Individuals failing to react to the first dose can be retested by a dilution of 1:10. Those who have had primary coccidioidomycosis even in an inapparent form and recovered from it retain the skin sensitivity for many years, perhaps for life in many cases. Some individuals appear to lose their skin sensitivity gradually. A coccidioidin skin test may not be informative in the diagnosis of a present condition in an individual who has previously been within the endemic area of coccidioidomycosis for even a few hours since it may merely reflect an early infection from which the patient has recovered. Aronson, Saylor, and Parr [1] in a study of calcified pulmonary nodules in tuberculin negative persons living within endemic areas concluded that some of these nodules may be due to a previous coccidioidomycosis. They found a high percentage of reactions to coccidioidin in persons living within the endemic areas of this disease and few or no reactions in other groups. It was shown that there was no cross reaction with tuberculin.

Coccidioidin can be used as an antigen in precipitin and complement fixation tests which give some indication of the extent and probable course of the disease. According to Smith, a high antibody titer follows spread of the infection and, conversely, a fall in titer indicates a good prognosis. Skin sensitivity is retained after recovery, but in cases of fatal infection it is greatly decreased during the terminal stages.

Demonstration of the fungus by direct examination or by culture may be difficult in initial coccidioidomycosis where sputum is often scanty or is not produced. In the disseminated form the fungus can be found more readily. Pus or sputum may be placed on a slide under a cover slip and examined directly. Often the fungus can be demonstrated more easily if the material is placed on the slide and mixed with a drop of 10 per cent sodium hydroxide. This digests the tissue elements while the fungus is relatively resistant. The appearance of the fungus will be described in a later paragraph. Sputum contains so many diverse elements that there may be some difficulty in finding the fungus. In such cases isolation in cultures

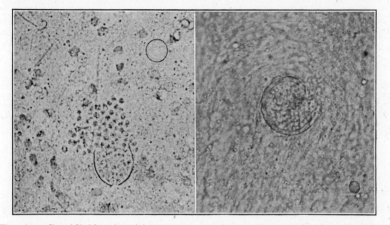

Fig. 72. *Coccidioides immitis* in sputum after sodium hydroxide digestion: left, an immature spherule and a mature sporangium from which spores have escaped; right, a nearly mature sporangium.

may be more productive. This is usually relatively easy because of the rapid growth of the fungus. Sputum should be streaked out on the surface of agar slants. The digestion and concentration methods used in isolating the tubercle bacillus kill Coccidioides, but sputum may be treated with 0.05 per cent cupric sulphate which destroys most of the bacteria. American Sabouraud agar or a selective culture medium devised at Stanford University may be used. The latter consists of 1 per cent ammonium chloride, 1 per cent sodium acetate, 0.8 per cent tribasic potassium phosphate, and 2 per cent agar. The medium is autoclaved for 10 minutes at 15 pounds pressure and 0.04 per cent cupric sulphate is added just before pouring. If plates are used in the isolation of Coccidioides the fungus should be transferred to agar slants soon after it appears and the original plate cultures must be autoclaved promptly. The fungus begins to produce spores usually within 8 to 10 days and there is grave danger of laboratory infection if old plate cultures are opened. It is probable that most laboratory personnel where cultures of *Coccidioides immitis* are handled sooner or later become infected. Fortunately most of these infections are mild or inapparent, but unnecessary risks should be avoided.

If, in making a laboratory diagnosis by culture, there is doubt about the identity of a fungus isolated, 1 ml. of a heavy suspension of the spores can be injected intraperitoneally into a white mouse. Lesions in which the characteristic parasitic growth phase of the fungus can be demonstrated appear in animals killed after 5 or 6 days, and most inoculated mice die in 7 to 14 days. Intratesticular inoculation of guinea pigs has been recommended as a diagnostic procedure but the mouse is a cheaper as well as a more susceptible test animal.

Treatment. No specific treatment has been found uniformly successful in coccidioidomycosis. According to Smith treatment should consist of rest and supportive therapy directed toward assisting the patient in the arrest of the infection.

Morphology in Tissue. *Coccidioides immitis* exhibits in a striking manner the dimorphism found in most pathogenic fungi. In animal tissue the spores of the fungus are small spherical cells 1 to 4 microns in diameter. They are to be found frequently within phagocytes (Fig. 73). These cells never bud but increase in size to upwards of 80 microns in diameter, the usual range of mature cells being 20 to 60 microns in diameter. The structure during this period of development varies to some extent with the tissue invaded and the strain of fungus. The stainable protoplasm may fill the cell or, especially in experimental infections in mice and guinea pigs, be confined to a comparatively narrow peripheral layer. In the latter case the large central vacuole is eventually filled with an indefinite number of endospores (sporangiospores). The process of spore formation was first clearly described in detail by Wolbach and by Ophuls. Their observations have been confirmed by many later students. The protoplasm becomes cut up by radial and periclinal cleavage planes, the process originating at the periphery and progressing toward the center. The first cleavage planes cut out large multinucleate masses which are usually subdivided by other cleavage planes to form very numerous small spores. However, in some cases the process may be interrupted at an intermediate point and only a few large spores may form. After spore formation is completed the wall of the parent cell ruptures and the spores pass into the adjacent host tissue where they repeat the cycle. No other cell form is known in the parasitic growth phase. The endospores are infective, as can be demonstrated experi-

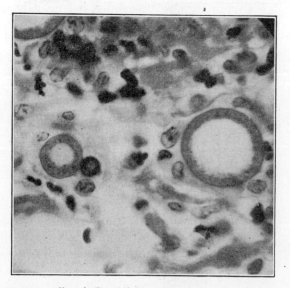

FIG. 73. Immature cells of *Coccidioides imm'tis* in experimentally infected guinea pig. From C. W. Emmons, *Mycologia,* **34,** 454 (1942).

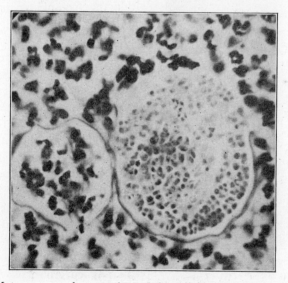

FIG. 74. Mature ruptured sporangium of *Coccidioides immitis* and empty sporangium invaded by leucocytes. From C. W. Emmons, *Mycologia,* **34,** 456 (1942).

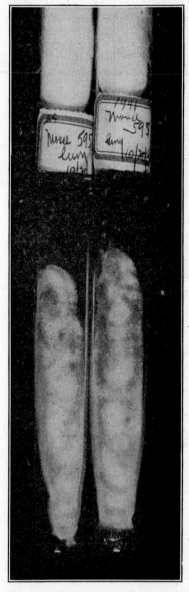

FIG. 75. Cultures of *Coccidioides immitis*. From C. W. Emmons, *Mycologia*, **34**, 460 (1942).

mentally, but actually are not effective in the direct transmission of coccidioidomycosis in man. Segregation of patients is not necessary.

The nuclear condition was first described by Emmons [7] who showed that the very numerous nuclei, which frequently lie in a peripheral zone of protoplasm, are typical of those found in other fungi. There is a distinct nuclear membrane enclosing small amounts of basophilic material and a deeply staining nucleolus. The ultimate spores were described as usually uninucleate. Baker, et al.,[3] reported that they may be multinucleate. The number of nuclei per spore probably depends upon whether or not progressive cleavage proceeds within the sporangium to the normal final stage of subdivision of the protoplasm.

Morphology in Culture. When pus containing Coccidioides is planted upon agar the fungus grows in a very different fashion. The recently liberated spores, large vegetative cells, and sporangiospores still within the unruptured sporangium germinate at once by the development of hyphae. If, however, the material is incubated under anaerobic conditions on special media there may be a limited development of the parasitic growth phase. When grown on American Sabouraud agar at 30° C. spores begin to form in most strains in about 8 days. Some of the aerial hyphae bear specialized side branches which are about twice the diameter of the hyphae from which they arise. The protoplasm in these conidiophores condenses or accumulates at intervals and septa are formed. A typical conidiophore then resembles a chain of spores separated from each other by spaces devoid of protoplasm. Frequently the original septum can be observed midway of the space separating two spores, indicating a condensation of the protoplasm to form the spore. These spores are usually called chlamydospores and they resemble chlamydospores except in their relationship to specialized hyphal branches. As the culture ages similar spores form in many of the aerial hyphae without any apparent specialization and the designation of chlamydospore seems to be justified. These chlamydospores are highly infectious and their accidental inhalation by laboratory personnel who handle cultures has resulted in many infections. Spores of this type are formed in large numbers when the fungus grows saprophytically on either natural or artificial substrates and it is supposed that they are present in wind-blown dust and initiate infection when contaminated air is inhaled. They have not actually been found in

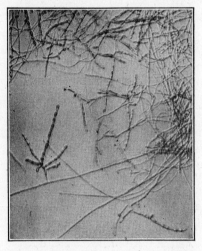

Fig. 76. Chlamydospores in a young culture of *Coccidioides immitis*. From C. W. Emmons, *Mycologia*, **34**, 460 (1942).

air, and although they have been isolated in culture from soil the actual growth of the fungus in soil has not been demonstrated except in the laboratory.

When chlamydospores from a culture are injected intraperitoneally into a laboratory animal each spore is capable of rounding up and growing directly into a sporangium as previously described. The spores may remain in short chains during at least the early stages of development in experimentally infected animals, thus giving rise to a chain of sporangia. Unless one realizes the origin of these chains they may cause confusion, especially when only two sporangia are connected by a short empty cell, thus bearing a superficial resemblance to conjugating cells. Closely appressed sporangiospores of the parasitic growth phase may also remain adjacent after dissemination from the ruptured sporangium and give a false appearance of budding.

Taxonomy. In the method of endosporulation exhibited in the parasitic growth phase of *Coccidiodes immitis* the resemblance to the Zygomycetes is so great that it seems reasonable to identify the mature Coccidioides cell as a sporangium and its endospores as sporangiospores. Baker and his coworkers [3] reported that small sporangia are produced in culture by some strains, but this phenomenon is not often observed. The hyphae which normally develop in culture are richly septate, a condition which is rare among the Zygomycetes, but in rate of growth and in the general aspect of cultures there is a resemblance. It is true that the sporangium formed in tissue is not associated with a mycelium and that there is no columella, but the sporangia of many of the Zygomycetes (e.g., Mortierella and Syncephalis) present so many anomalies that Coccidioides may well find a place within the group.

Geographical Distribution. Contrary to the earlier belief that the disease was limited to the Chaco region of Argentina and to the San Joaquin Valley of California, it is now recognized that it occurs throughout the arid Southwest in southern California, Arizona, and New Mexico, and western Texas. The migration of infected persons from these areas has not established recognized new endemic foci. The cases which have been observed in other parts of the United States, Italy, and elsewhere, are probably in persons who were infected in the Southwest and developed the disease after an incubation period, or who were infected from dusty fruit, packing material, or similar sources originating in an endemic focus.

Natural Habitat. Coccidioidomycosis is not transmitted from one person directly to another. It is evident therefore that the fungus grows in some habitat outside the human host. The primary lesions, with few exceptions, are in the lungs and they follow inhalation of spores of the fungus. Epidemiological evidence and study of case histories indicate that the spores of the fungus are wind-blown. Infections follow exposure to dust storms and appear in agricultural workers and others exposed to wind-blown soil. Most primary infections occur in the summer and fall and few are seen during the rainy season. It has been assumed, therefore, that the fungus grows in soil during or following the rainy season and that spores mature and are disseminated during the dry season. The fungus has, in fact, been isolated directly from soil, first near Delano, California, at a ranch house occupied by men who had coccidioidomycosis; second in Panoche Valley, California, near a burrow from which a group of university students (who subsequently developed coccidioidomycosis) dug a rattlesnake; and third, from five soil samples taken from various soil types collected on the desert near San Carlos, Arizona, distant from human habitations but near numerous rodent burrows. Hundreds of other attempts to isolate Coccidioides from the upper layers of soil within endemic areas have failed.

Recent studies in southern Arizona have suggested the possibility of a rodent reservoir of the disease.[2, 8, 9]   Among small rodents trapped in this area the white-footed mouse, grasshopper mouse, and wood rat were never or very rarely infected; but 15 per cent of three species of pocket mice and 17 per cent of one species of kangaroo rat trapped had pulmonary coccidioidomycosis.   Surprisingly, a second fungus, *Haplosporangium parvum*, which resembles Coccidioides in its parasitic phase but is different in culture, was found with even greater frequency (66 per cent of pocket mice) causing a similar pulmonary disease in rodents.   No human infections with the latter fungus have yet been recognized, but many individuals who react to the intradermal injection of coccidioidin also react to an antigen (haplosporangin) prepared from this fungus.

Coccidioidomycosis in these rodents seemed to be a slowly progressive chronic disease which did not exterminate the species and, in fact, appeared to interfere little with normal development and reproduction.   Further investigations will be required to determine whether these rodents are infected because of their intimate exposure to infested soil or whether the fungus is primarily a pathogen of rodents and is present in soil that has been contaminated by infected rodents. Certain circumstances seem to suggest the latter as probable.   The disease in rodents is known in species of Perognathus and Dipodomys which are desert species with ranges coinciding generally with a part of the known geographical range of coccidioidomycosis.   Species of Peromyscus, however, although more common than Perognathus, and living in adjacent burrows, were rarely found infected under field conditions.   Their exposure to the fungus would seem to be equal to that of Perognathus, and they are very susceptible to experimental infections, but they apparently do not serve as hosts under the field conditions investigated.   There are no doubt other rodent hosts of the fungus.   There appears to be the sort of adjustment between pathogen and the Perognathus host which is compatible with the theory of a rodent reservoir.   The difficulty of isolating Coccidioides from desert soil in which it seems to have a spotty distribution not correlated with any recognized differences in vegetation or soil types makes the hypothesis of a rodent reservoir attractive.

Coccidioidomycosis occurs also in other animals within the endemic area.   Stiles and Davis [17] have described the focalized infection in the mediastinal and bronchial lymph nodes in cattle and sheep, and Farness [10] has observed the disseminated form of the mycosis in dogs.

LITERATURE

1. Aronson, J. D., R. M. Saylor, and E. I. Parr, Relationship of coccidioidomycosis to calcified pulmonary nodules, *Arch. Path.*, **34**, 31 (1942).
2. Ashburn, L. L., and C. W. Emmons, Experimental Haplosporangium infection, *Arch. Path.*, **39**, 3 (1945).
3. Baker, E. E., E. M. Mrak, and C. E. Smith, The morphology, taxonomy, and distribution of *Coccidioides immitis* Rixford and Gilchrist, 1896, *Farlowia*, **1**, 199 (1943).
4. Cox, A. J., and C. E. Smith, Arrested pulmonary coccidioidal granuloma, *Arch. Path.*, **27**, 717 (1939).
5. Dickson, E. C., "Valley fever" of the San Joaquin Valley and fungus Coccidioides, *Calif. and Western Med.*, **47**, 151 (1937).
6. ———, Primary coccidioidomycosis, *Am. Rev. Tuberc.*, **38**, 722 (1938).
7. Emmons, C. W., Coccidioidomycosis, *Mycologia*, **34**, 452 (1942).
8. ———, Coccidioidomycosis in wild rodents. A method of determining the extent of endemic areas, *Pub. Health Repts.*, **58**, 1 (1943).
9. Emmons, C. W., and L. L. Ashburn, The isolation of *Haplosporangium parvum* n. sp. and *Coccidioides immitis* from wild rodents, *Pub. Health Repts.*, **57**, 1715 (1942).
10. Farness, O. J., Coccidioidomycosis, *J. Am. Med. Assoc.*, **116**, 1749 (1941).
11. Gifford, M. A., Coccidioidomycosis, Kern County, *Ann. Rept. Kern County Dept. Pub. Health*, 1938–1939, pp. 73–79.
12. Ophuls, W., and H. C. Moffitt, A new pathogenic mould (formerly described as a protozoön: *Coccidioides immitis pyogenes*), *Phila. Med. J.*, **5**, 1471 (1900).
13. Rixford, E., and T. C. Gilchrist, Two cases of protozoan (Coccidioidal infection of the skin and other organs, *Johns Hopkins Hosp. Repts.*, **1**, 209 (1896).
14. Smith, C. E., Epidemiology of acute coccidioidomycosis with erythema nodosum, *Am. J. Pub. Health*, **30**, 600 (1940).
15. ———, Parallelism of coccidioidal and tuberculous infections, *Radiology*, **38**, 643 (1942).
16. ———, Coccidioidomycosis, *Med. Clinics N. America*, pp. 790–807, 1943.
17. Stiles, G. W., and C. L. Davis, Coccidioidal granuloma (coccidioidomycosis), *J. Am. Med. Assoc.*, **119**, 765 (1942).
18. Winn, W. A., Pulmonary cavitation associated with coccidioidal infection, *Arch. Internal Med.*, **68**, 1179 (1941).

THE DERMATOPHYTOSES

(Dermatomycosis, Epidermatophytosis, Ringworm, Tinea, "Athlete's Foot")

The term dermatophytosis is generally used to indicate a series of diseases caused by a group of fungi which practically never invade any other tissue. These fungi for the most part produce only a superficial infection, not tending to involve the deeper tissues or to spread to internal organs, but they are nevertheless important because of their frequent occurrence and, to a certain extent, contagiousness. They are closely related species with numerous intermediary forms which make up a fairly homogeneous group. They are frequently referred to as the dermatophytes.

A clear knowledge of this group of fungi can be obtained only by first-hand acquaintance with them. The subject is quite complicated for several reasons. Attempts have been made to classify the causative fungi according to the nature of the disease which they produce; but the same disease may be produced by several different species and, conversely, a single species is capable of producing very different clinical types of disease. On the other hand, attempts at a purely mycological classification based upon morphological characters has been somewhat unsatisfactory because of the pronounced pleomorphism of the fungi and the incorrect interpretations and evaluation of morphological features.[5, 7] * The parasites exhibit a certain amount of geographical specialization, some species isolated from cases in one part of the world being different from those obtained in other parts. Some of the parasites occur only on man, some on certain lower animals. The latter may be transmitted from animals to man.

A very large number of species have been described. Many of the species names are synonyms and the number of true species can perhaps be reduced to one tenth the reported number by a critical comparison of strains and a proper evaluation of variability. For these reasons an extensive knowledge of the group can be attained only after long and intensive study. The subject is one for the specialist. We can do no more here than point out some of the more important general characteristics of the diseases and their etiologic agents, and describe a few of the more common species.

Although a very large number of investigators have contributed a voluminous literature to the subject, the work of one man, Sabouraud,[17] overshadows all the rest and dominates the field. To his long-continued, patient, and intensive studies we are indebted for a revival of interest in the subject during the first years of this century. He systematically studied different types of dermatophytosis; correlated the clinical features, the microscopic appearance of the fungus in infected hairs, and the colonial and microscopic appearances of

* Literature citations for this section will be found on pages 177 and 178.

the fungi in cultures; and made important contributions to the therapy of dermatophytosis. His classification of the dermatophytes was based on clinical manifestations for the separation of genera and largely upon the characteristics of the colony for specific separation. The three principal genera which he recognized can be defined in mycological terms and this modification of Sabouraud's classification will be followed here. His dependence upon colonial appearance to determine species led to an excessive splitting of species and his disregard of earlier specific names makes some of his names invalid. Discussions of the dermatophytes will be found in many other publications.[2, 6, 8, 9, 10, 15, 19]

Because of the complexity of the subject it will be necessary to consider the important species of dermatophytes separately. We shall therefore depart from the usual order followed elsewhere in this book and discuss first the morphological and physiological features which relate the dermatophytes to each other and the taxonomic position they occupy.

Cultural Characters. The identification of the various species of dermatophytes is made very largely by the appearance of the colonies. Since this is subject to some variation with the composition of the medium, Sabouraud insisted that cultures should be made upon his proof agar. Since the ingredients he used are no longer available or were impure products, substitutes have been required. Plaut and Grütz offered several alternative formulas which they claimed served in place of Sabouraud's medium. Weidman also proposed some satisfactory substitutes. A satisfactory medium which is constant in composition, simple to prepare, and gives satisfactory colony characteristics is described on page 55. It contains 1 per cent neopeptone and 2 per cent glucose.

The colonies may be smooth and waxy if no aerial mycelium is formed, or have a chalky surface, or velvety or woolly texture, depending upon the abundance and height of the aerial mycelium. They may be yellow or rose or violet in color, but most species are yellowish or white. They may be irregularly folded to form cerebriform masses, regularly folded in radial patterns, or they may lack folds.

These characters are not constant. Pigment production may be lost rapidly on subcultivation, and the texture of the colony is frequently altered by the gradual or sudden appearance of an abundance of sterile aerial mycelium, at first as localized tufts on various parts of the colony, but rapidly growing over the whole colony. This is a type of mutation which occurs regularly in some species of derma-

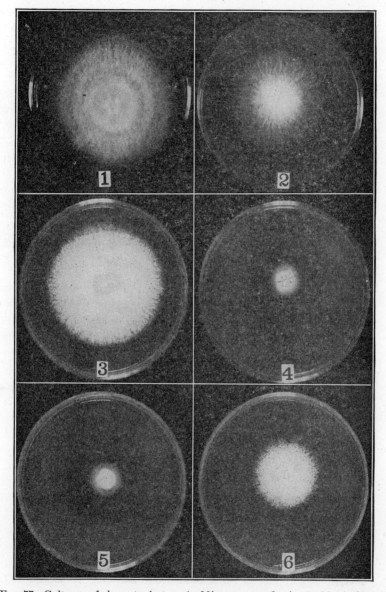

FIG. 77. Cultures of dermatophytes: 1, *Microsporum Canis;* 2, *M. Audouini;* 3, *M. gypseum;* 4, *Trichophyton sulfureum;* 5, *T. rubrum;* 6, *T. mentagrophytes.*

tophytes and once it has replaced the original type of growth the latter cannot be recovered. Old laboratory cultures are thus frequently quite atypical unless they have been properly cared for. If a strain is to be conserved in typical condition a culture should be allowed to grow for 10 days (or longer if required for sporulation by slowly growing species) and then stored at 2° to 5° C. until it is again subcultured. Transfer periods should not exceed 4 months. Strains can be conserved by leaving cultures at room temperature for several months and then, only after the culture is very dry, transferring spores from the upper end of the slant. Under these conditions the sterile overgrowth is usually dead and conidia which have not mutated but have remained viable, when transferred to new slants, will reproduce the original colony type. This method cannot be depended upon, however, and strains kept in this manner are apt to be lost. From these considerations it will be seen that the precise determination of species is a matter requiring some experience and judgment.

Morphology in Culture. In artificial cultures specific and characteristic structures of several kinds are produced. Most important of these are the conidia which are produced in large numbers by many strains and species. The conidium of the dermatophytes shows more clearly than any other single structure the close relationship between the different groups. It varies in size, shape, and abundance to some extent, and in one genus is lacking, but in general it is characteristic. The size varies from 2 by 2 microns to 3 by 5 microns. It is spherical to egg-shaped or even clavate, and has a thin smooth wall. The conidium has a broad attachment to the conidiophore and when it breaks loose from this attachment the broad base, fringed by the broken fragments of the end of the conidiophore, can be easily seen if the spore is carefully examined under high magnification. The shape of the spore in some strains of Trichophyton is almost spherical except for this basal facet. In other strains, and in Microsporum, the conidium is usually about 3 by 5 microns or larger, and is distinctly clavate, but the basal facet is like that seen in Trichophyton.

The attachment of the conidium in some species of Trichophyton is rather persistent and in some strains one can observe spores still attached to a phantom hypha in which most of the cells are empty. This characteristic has led the French taxonomists to designate these spores aleuries. In the most common species, however, the name is a misnomer because the conidia are easily detached and these conidia are obviously of the same type in all species. A second definitive type of spore is the macroconidium. Macroconidia are sometimes called spindle-spores or fuseaux, but the latter terms are descriptive of only the macroconidia of Microsporum. In *Microsporum Canis* the macroconidia are large, reaching a size of 40 by 150 microns,

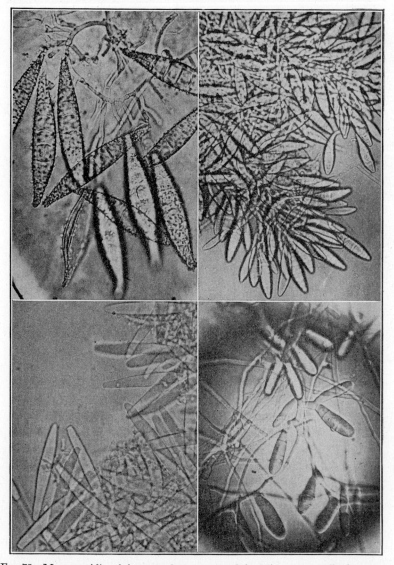

FIG. 78. Macroconidia of dermatophytes: upper left, *Microsporum Canis;* upper right, *M. gypseum;* lower left, *Trichophyton mentagrophytes;* lower right, *Epidermophyton floccosum.*

having as many as 12 or 15 crosswalls, and are truly spindle-shaped with thick, rough walls. In *M. Audouini* a few macroconidia similar to those seen in *M. Canis* may be found in some strains, but most of

Trichophyton   Epidermophyton   Microsporum

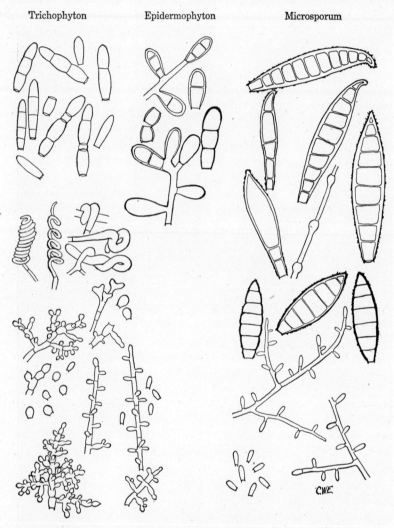

Fig. 79. Spore types in the three genera of dermatophytes.

them are smaller, have only one or a few crosswalls, and the walls are usually smooth except near the tip. In *M. gypseum* the macro-conidia are very numerous, broader in proportion to length than in *M. Canis,* and the walls are nearly smooth.

In Epidermophyton no conidia are produced and the macroconidia are clavate or egg-shaped, rounded instead of pointed at the tip, with no septa or only a few, and the walls are thick and smooth.

In Trichophyton the macroconidia, when produced, are long clavate spores with rounded end, one or several cells formed by cross septa, and the walls are smooth and thinner than in the other genera.

The macroconidia thus serve to identify the genus of dermatophyte. Macroconidia are produced in each of the three genera (although not in every strain of every species), but the type of macroconidium in each genus is distinctive.[6]

Taxonomy. Some of the dermatophytes occasionally form peculiar knots and twisted masses of hyphae which resemble the ascogonia of some Ascomycetes. These have been interpreted as abortive attempts to form asci. They have been referred to by the French authors as nodular organs. Matruchot and Dassonville [12] noted a similarity between certain of the dermatophytes and some species of Gymnoascaceae, and claimed to have produced experimentally a ringworm with a species belonging to this family of the Ascomycetes, *Ctenomyces serratus*. The Gymnoascaceae are characterized by the formation of asci, not in a compact and well-defined perithecium, but in masses surrounded by a rather loose network of protective mycelium. The clusters of conidia and specialized hyphae produced by some strains of Trichophyton resemble the loose poorly organized ascocarp of the Gymnoascaceae in a superficial way, and several authorities have therefore considered that the dermatophytes are ascomycetes. We do not believe that this point has yet been proved, and prefer to consider the dermatophytes as Fungi Imperfecti, without however denying the probability of a relationship to the Ascomycetes. The variety and variability of the spores formed by the dermatophytes has made it difficult to assign them a position in Saccardo's classification. Vuillemin groups them with his Arthrosporineae, Ota and Langeron [15] with the Conidiosporales of Vuillemin's classification.

In the hair and skin the dermatophytes sporulate only by a fragmentation of the mycelium into its component cells. The so-called spores found in the lesions are therefore to be looked upon as oidia or arthrospores. The size and arrangement of these arthrospores give some information about the identity of the fungus, but for specific identification pure cultures must be studied.

Cytology. Grigorakis studied the cytology of the ringworm fungi. The cells of the vegetative hyphae and of the macroconidia, chlamydospores, and arthrospores are multinucleate. The conidia are uninucleate. Mitotic division of the nuclei was not observed. Mitochondria and metachromatic granules were also demonstrated. Emmons confirmed the nuclear findings.

Enzymes. The biochemical activities of the skin fungi have been investigated by Tate [19] who found that all the species which he investigated were proteolytic and secreted lipase, urease, maltase, and diastase. None contained invertase, inulase, lactase, or zymase. The proteolytic enzyme resembled trypsin, acting in an alkaline medium; it did not digest coagulated egg. None of the strains studied could hydrolyze keratin. The fat-splitting activities of ringworm fungi was studied by Mallinckrodt-Haupt, who found that the species studied could grow in mineral solutions with neutral fats as the sole source of carbon, if these were of animal origin, but showed little or no growth with vegetable oils.

Main Groups of Dermatophytes. Sabouraud recognized four main groups of dermatophytes, Microsporum, Trichophyton, Epidermophyton, and Achorion. These were defined on the basis of the clinical type of lesion produced and the microscopic appearance of the fungus in the lesion, specifically, its relationship to invaded hairs. Thus Microsporum produced on the surface of a parasitized hair a mosaic pattern of small spores, Trichophyton was characterized by a linear arrangement of spores on the hair surface, Epidermophyton did not attack the hair, and Achorion produced peculiar yellow crusts and scutula on the scalp. The first three groups stand as valid genera if defined according to mycological criteria, although a considerable revision of Epidermophyton is required because of its use by some dermatologists for any fungus found growing on the glabrous skin, whether or not it was capable of invading the hair. The fourth genus, Achorion, cannot be defined as a genus of fungi by any valid method, and its species should be distributed to appropriate genera, as we shall see in a later paragraph.

Sabouraud divided the genus Trichophyton into subgenera on the basis of the position of the fungus with regard to the hairs: Endothrix species of Trichophyton growing entirely within the hairs; Ectothrix species of Trichophyton growing mainly on the surface of hairs; and Ectoendothrix or Neoendothrix species occupying an intermediate position between the two other groups.

The key to the main groups of dermatophytes presented below is based in part on Sabouraud's clinical classification and in part on mycological criteria.[6] The main groups write their own label, so to speak, on the invaded hair, and their identification is often easier if one has also seen the patient, but the final identification of species rests upon an examination of a pure culture. In using Sabouraud's system of differentiation, it is obvious that the inspection of hairs is necessary. For this purpose it is of course necessary to select diseased hairs. Selection may be facilitated by search under Woods light.[3] Too frequently a bunch of perfectly normal hairs is sent to the laboratory for diagnosis! The fungus is found in the lower part of the hair, that which is within the follicle and extends for a relatively short distance above the skin level. Hairs which have broken are of course more likely to show an extensive development of the organism than those which are not. Infections with *Trichophyton tonsurans* cause the hairs to break off flush with the skin, the stumps appearing as black dots in the follicles. These should be extracted with forceps for examination. In all cases the fungi first invade the hairs in the sheath. Whether eventually it will be found within the shaft or without would appear to depend largely upon the duration of the infection, which in turn is correlated with the degree of in-

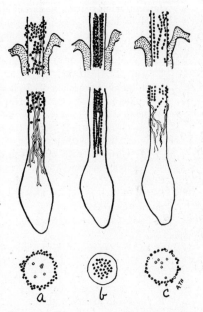

Fig. 80. Diagram showing the relations of ringworm fungi to the hairs: *a*, Microsporum; *b*, Endothrix Trichophyton; *c*, Ectothrix Trichophyton.

flammatory reaction. In any case, it is well to remember that the differentiation according to position of the fungus in or on the hair is not an absolute one. In endothrix forms there will be some spores outside the hair, in ectothrix types some within.

KEY TO THE DERMATOPHYTES

LESIONS OF THE SCALP

A. Yellow crusts or scutula present. Clinical favus.
  1. Hairs tend to split longitudinally. Colonies waxy, wrinkled, little or no aerial mycelium. Hyphae coarse, distorted, tips swollen and branched. Few conidia, no macroconidia.   *Trichophyton Schoenleini*
  2. Colonies white, downy. Conidia and macroconidia formed.
                    Trichophyton quinckeanum

3. Colonies yellowish brown with abundant aerial mycelium and very numerous macroconidia.   *Microsporum gypseum*

4. Colonies glabrous, wrinkled, reddish violet.
                                                Trichophyton violaceum

B. No scutula present. Hairs tend to break off square.

1. Suppurative reactions (as follicular abscesses), pustules (of kerion) absent (except Microsporum species of animal origin).

   a. Hairs broken off at a uniform height, several millimeters above the skin. Much scaling of the epidermis, highly contagious in most cases. Spores on outside of hairs, angular, forming a mosaic. In cultures many spindle-shaped macroconidia with thick, usually rough walls, multicellular (except *M. Audouini*).   MICROSPORUM

   b. Hairs mostly broken off flush with the skin, leaving black points. Little scaling of the epidermis. Not so contagious. In cultures conidia variable in size, macroconidia very few or lacking.

      aa. Grows entirely within the hair, both mycelium and spores.
                                        Endothrix TRICHOPHYTON

      bb. Grows mainly within the hair, but a few hyphae and spores can be found on the exterior.   *Neoendothrix* TRICHOPHYTON

2. Suppurative reactions occur. Lesions of smooth skin also frequently present. Some strains of animal origin. Fungus grows in and on the hair, spores mostly external.

   a. Spores arranged in rows, not in mosaic.
                                        Ectothrix TRICHOPHYTON

      aa. Spores in hair 5 to 8 microns in diameter.
                                        Section *Megaspores*

      bb. Spores in hair 3 to 4 microns in diameter.
                                        Section *Microides*

   b. Spores in mosaic pattern.
                                        Microsporum Canis

LESIONS OF THE SMOOTH SKIN

A. Eczema-like lesions confined to moist parts, as inner surfaces of thighs, axillary regions, between fingers or toes, soles of feet. Not found within hairs. In culture, greenish yellow, no conidia, macroconidia egg-shaped to clavate, thick, smooth walls.

                                EPIDERMOPHYTON (*E. floccosum*)

B. Lesions not as above, generally involving hands, arms, general body surface, face, neck.

1. Lesions form intricate patterns of concentric rings with marked scaling. Hairs not invaded.   *Trichophyton concentricum*

2. Lesions are reddish patches, not raised above the skin level, round to irregular in form, darker at the border, forming rings. Tending to heal in the center, new attacks may occur, forming concentric rings.

                                Generally MICROSPORUM
                                Sometimes *Endothrix* TRICHOPHYTON

3. Lesions are elevated plaques, reddish, round or oval, scaly. Pustules frequently present at the border.   *Ectothrix* TRICHOPHYTON

Favus. Favus is caused by *Trichophyton Schoenleini* in most cases but *T. violaceum* and *Microsporum gypseum* occasionally cause● clinical favus. The disease occurs not only in man but also in various lower animals, particularly mice, but also cats, dogs, chickens, and some others. The great majority of human cases are contracted by direct or indirect contact with preceding cases, and are due to *T. Schoenleini*, but some of the species infecting lower animals will also produce the disease in man.

The disease occurs particularly in the poor and the unclean. It has almost disappeared in the more advanced countries, but is prevalent in southeastern Europe and northern Africa. It occurs more frequently in children than in adults.

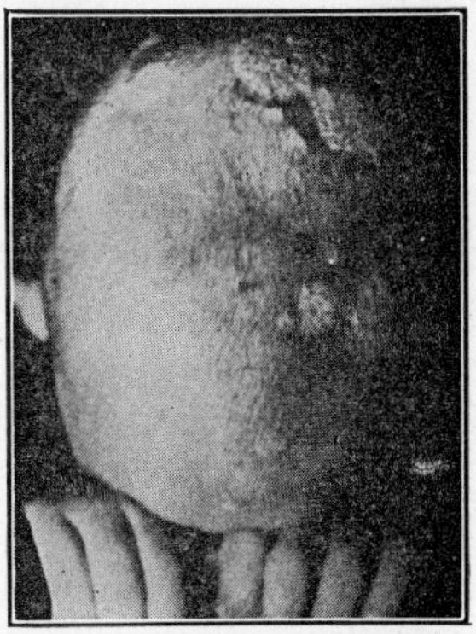

The lesions occur most frequently on the scalp, though other parts of the body surface may be affected, but in the latter case the disease has usually been carried from the scalp. The fungus grows between the outer cornified layer of the skin and the inner layer of epithelial cells (Malpighian layer) and forms a very characteristic yellow, cup-shaped mass, the scutulum. The infection begins in a hair follicle, and the hair is usually seen projecting from the scutulum. When the

Fig. 81. Favus of the scalp showing crusts or scutula.

latter is pulled off, there is left a raw, sometimes suppurating surface. By growth and coalescence of the scutula, there may be formed an extensive crusted layer on the scalp. The hairs become opaque and dull, and finally drop out, leaving bald spots.

A section through the scutulum shows a radiating feltwork of mycelium, which tends to die off in the center, leaving a granular debris, and to form spores at the periphery. The fungus also invades the shaft of the hair, forming parallel bundles of mycelium through its center.

The organism may be demonstrated by a microscopic examination of either the scutulum or a hair. A small portion of the former should be crushed under a cover slip in a 10 per cent sodium hydroxide solution; the hair should also be examined in alkali. In the lesions the mycelium is very irregular, its component cells varying considerably in size and form. The cells tend to break apart, giving the filaments an articulated appearance, and the terminal portions of the filaments give rise to a series of round arthrospores. In a preparation from a scutulum as described above, these elements become mixed together and one finds a melange of rounded cells, short oval cells, and longer and shorter fragments of mycelium. The fungus has a similar structure in the hair; one finds long, articulated filaments of cells of varying size, the terminal portions ending in a series of rounded arthrospores. A very characteristic feature is the degeneration and disappearance of the fungus in the hair, which leaves a series of air bubbles.

Cultures are obtained by inoculating minute portions of scutula or hairs on the surface of agar slants. As these cultures are likely to be contaminated by bacteria the specimens should be placed for several minutes in 70 per cent alcohol and a large number should be planted to increase the chance of obtaining some colonies reasonably pure. The particles of material are transferred to the surface of the agar with a needle, and three or four widely separated inoculations are made on a slant. The optimum temperature is 30° C. The various strains vary considerably in rapidity of growth and in colony pattern and several varieties have been named on the basis of this variability.

The colonies on agar are at first yellowish and waxy in appearance. As they grow older they become much wrinkled and develop a short whitish aerial mycelium (some strains may fail to do this). In cultures the organism is extremely pleomorphic. In slow-growing strains, the mycelium may become articulated and numerous chains of arthrospores appear as in the lesions. In more rapidly growing strains there occurs an extensive development of mycelium which is, however, very irregular; it forms in some places thick, irregular masses having little resemblance to ordinary mycelium. These are called the ameboid forms. Large yellowish thick-walled cells may appear in the course of the mycelium. Finally, filaments at the periphery of the colony end characteristically in a branched cluster of swollen cells. The latter structure is referred to as the favic chandelier.

In cultures which form a short aerial mycelium a few conidia can usually be demonstrated. These are typical of the dermatophyte conidia except that they are more variable in size and shape than in most species. A few are so large as to suggest the macroconidia seen in other species of Trichophyton.

T. Schoenleini is apparently of variable pathogenicity for lower animals. Typical scutula have been produced by inoculation of the skin in mice. Intravenous and intraperitoneal injections into rabbits produce nodular lesions of the lungs or peritoneum respectively.

Cases of favus contracted from lower animals are not nearly so frequent as the purely human form. Of these the mouse type is more frequently seen. It occurs on the smooth skin, rather than the scalp. Multiple scutula may develop, but the disease does not tend to spread and progress as in the infections with *T. Schoenleini*. The parasite of mouse favus is *T. quinckeanum*.

Ringworm. Ringworm is a parasitic infection of the skin due to various fungi belonging in the genera Trichophyton and Micro-

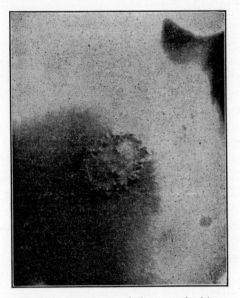

Fig. 82. Ringworm of the smooth skin.

sporum. It occurs endemically in some centers of population and at times produces small epidemics. The disease is transmissible from man to man, from lower animals to man, and, rarely, from man to animals.[1] It was formerly a very common disease, especially in children of the poorer classes. For a time in Paris special schools were maintained for children with ringworm. Partly as a result of a rapid means of treatment utilizing Roentgen rays, the disease has greatly decreased in prevalence within recent years.

The disease is transmitted by means of the spores formed in or on the skin and hairs, either by direct contact or indirectly through combs, brushes, or towels. It may be contracted from animals also by direct contact, more frequently from the walls of stalls and litter about barns. Children are frequently infected from cats and dogs with which they play. The fungus has been isolated from the litter of animal stalls; this shows that the fungus is capable of living saprophytically upon vegetable matter, as many of the other pathogenic fungi are. The spores can probably remain viable for long periods outside the animal body.

The disease may attack all parts of the skin surface. Clinically a division is made between ringworm of the hairy parts and ringworm of the smooth skin; ringworm of the nails also occurs and may constitute a reservoir of infection which is difficult to eradicate. The nature of the infection varies considerably according to the degree of inflammatory reaction of the invaded tissues. Thus a wide variety of clinical types may be recognized, but the differences are more apparent than real because fundamentally the pathologic changes are the same in all the types.

The infection begins in a hair follicle, from which focus it extends to the surrounding skin and into the hair. In the skin, in addition to redness due to congestion, there occurs scaling caused by an overproduction of epithelium in response to the irritation caused by the presence of the fungus, an exudation of fluid, and an accumulation of leucocytes. A very characteristic feature is the formation of concentric rings of inflammatory reaction. This is, of course, more apparent on the smooth skin. The formation of these rings has not been satisfactorily explained, but may be due to the same mechanism which leads to the formation of concentric rings of growth so frequently seen when molds are grown in Petri plate cultures. The infection tends to spread at the periphery and heal in the center. It is the formation of these advancing rings of inflammatory reaction which has given origin to the popular name ringworm (Latin, tinea; French, teigne).

Microsporum Ringworm. In Microsporum infection, although the mycelium invades and is found inside the hairs, the spores are formed on the exterior. There is some difference of opinion as to whether these spores are to be considered arthrospores, i.e., produced by fragmentation of the mycelium, or whether they are conidia. But they occur in irregular clusters not in chains, and are closely packed together on the surface, forming a sort of mosaic. The individual cells are polyhedral in form, not rounded or cylindrical. In Trichophyton infection, for comparison, the mycelium may be within or without the hair, or both, and the spores are formed in both places, but they are definitely produced by a fragmentation of the mycelium, and as a result appear in regular parallel rows or chains.

Ringworm due to members of the genus Microsporum is sometimes referred to as microsporosis, to distinguish it from ringworm caused by Trichophyton. Microsporosis is in the majority of cases a ringworm of the scalp, called tinea capitis by the dermatologists. It occurs most frequently in children; in stubborn and untreated cases caused by *Microsporum Audouini* it may persist for some years, but usually disappears at puberty. It is the most contagious of the ringworms. During epidemics such as those recently seen in several cities in eastern United States *M. Audouini* causes a very high percentage of ringworm of the scalp. In other parts of the United States *M. Canis* is of more frequent occurrence and may exceed *M. Audouini*.

In infections caused by *M. Audouini* the lesion consists of a reddened scaling area which tends to spread in the characteristic ring form. A number of such patches may form and coalesce to give an irregular area. There is marked scaling of the epidermis. The hairs tend to break off transversely at a height of 2 to 6 mm., leaving the stumps somewhat thickened, whitish, and opaque. Thus there appear a number of very characteristic irregular (moth-eaten) bald patches covered by the short stumps of the diseased hairs, which are fairly uniform in height. Generally inflammatory reactions are not pronounced. In infections caused by *M. Canis* inflammatory reactions are more often present. One can therefore frequently predict, from the clinical appearance, which of the two fungi is the cause of the lesion, but there are so many exceptions to the general rule that it is not a dependable method of determining the etiology.

The diagnosis may be established by examining an epilated hair in a drop of sodium hydroxide solution. There will be found on the outside a sheath of spores closely packed together to form a polyhedral or mosaic pattern, and in the interior of the hair shaft septate hyphae which tend to break up into arthrospores toward the distal end of the hair stub, and which terminate in growing hyphal tips (frequently dichotomously branched) toward the root of the hair.

The spores germinate readily on Sabouraud's medium and give rise to a rather fine septate mycelium. After a few days the mycelium becomes distended here and there, the swollen cells developing into chlamydospores. These are very characteristic of the mycelium of Microsporum. The aerial mycelium is frequently peculiarly twisted, and gives rise to numerous lateral branches of short length and finally, on some of the branches, clavate conidia borne as lateral buds on conidiophores or undifferentiated hyphae. In *M. Canis* very numerous large, multicellular, spindle-shaped, rough, and thick-walled macroconidia are also borne on the hyphae. The macroconidia of *M. Audouini* are smaller, have fewer cells, and appear to be depauperate forms of the type. These macroconidia are so different from the clavate macroconidia of Trichophyton with smooth, thin walls, rounded tips, and few cells, that there is usually little difficulty in deciding which type is under observation.

A number of species of Microsporum have been described. Castellani recognized sixteen, of which four were of human origin, the remainder of animal origin. The important species are *M. Audouini*, seen only in man; *M. Canis* (*M. lanosum, M. Felineum*), and *M. gypseum*, from animal sources. Most of the other described species are only varieties of the first two named. These two species may be differentiated by the characters tabulated below (adapted from Plaut and Grütz).

Microsporum Audouini	*Microsporum Canis*
Highly contagious, causing school epidemics.	Less contagious, may cause family epidemics.
Of long duration, resistant to treatment.	Of shorter duration, about 1 year.
Only the head usually involved, exceptionally areas in the immediate vicinity.	Frequently also skin lesions at a distance from the head.
Inflammatory reactions mostly lacking if untreated.	Inflammatory reactions often present without any irritation from treatment.
Cultures grow slowly.	Cultures grow more rapidly and colonies attain a larger size.
Colonies remain grey or white with a reddish color visible in reverse of culture.	Colonies become tobacco brown to reddish in center.
Only rarely transmissible to animals from cultures.	Rabbits and guinea pigs easily infected from cultures.

Further differentiation may be made on the basis of colony structure. In *M. Audouini* there is often a small central knob elevated above the surface of the colony. In some strains the latter is marked radially by four to six deep clefts. The whole surface has a velvety texture. In *M. Canis* there is a central flat area surrounded by an elevated zone of aerial mycelium with usually no folding. The surface has a woolly texture.

Endothrix Species of Trichophyton. The pure endothrix species of Trichophyton are from human sources. Their infections occur mainly in the scalp, the majority of the cases of ringworm of the scalp not due to Microsporum being caused by members of this group of molds. They produce persistent infections without much inflammatory reaction. Although most cases occur in younger life, the infection does not, like microsporosis, tend to disappear at puberty, but may persist into adult life. Trichophytosis (endothrix) of the scalp is differentiated from microsporosis by the fact that the organism is found almost exclusively within the hair, the spores being arranged in chains. The hairs tend to break off at the skin level rather than a few millimeters above, leaving a smooth bald spot with few hair stumps and little scaling of the skin. In addition the disease almost always involves some part of the smooth skin as well. The disease is sometimes referred to by its French name, peladoide.

Many endothrix species of Trichophyton have been described, but most of these names apply to minor variants of two or three species. The important species are *Trichophyton tonsurans* (*T. crateriforme*), *T. Sabouraudi* (*T. acuminatum*), and *T. violaceum*.

T. tonsurans produces large irregular bald patches, the hairs breaking off flush with the skin early after infection. The skin of the scalp in these bald patches may appear quite healthy. Some hair stumps may be present. They are dark in color, thicker than the normal hairs, and pull out with some difficulty. Microscopic examination reveals the chains of spores in the interior of the hair. They are round, oval, or cylindrical in form and are produced by simple fragmentation of the mycelium into its component cells. They are much larger than the spores of Microsporum and have thick walls. In addition to the bald patches of the scalp, ring-shaped lesions frequently develop on the face, neck and hands.

The colonies on Sabouraud's agar are acuminate, i.e., there is a conical peak projecting from the center of the colony. The closely related *T. Sabouraudi* forms a colony similar in appearance except that there is a central depression. The peripheral portion of the colony is folded into ridges. The colony is creamy white in color, becoming brownish in some strains; the surface is covered with a fine powdery coat of short hyphae and conidia. The conidia are spherical to pear-shaped or clavate in some strains, borne laterally and at the tips of conidiophores or on only slightly differentiated hyphae. Chlamydospores are formed in abundance in the vegetative mycelium.

T. violaceum is found in northern Africa, southern Europe, Russia, and America. It produces lesions of the scalp of the same general character as the species just described. In the hair the spores are not so regularly in chains, and they are rounded. The colonies are of the acuminate type, but when first isolated they are of a deep violet color. Many strains lose the pigment upon continued cultivation. Colorless sectors frequently appear in the pigmented colonies, together with sectors of transitional color. A number of varieties have been named according to these various differences. Few spores are formed in the cultures. Some strains, after cultivation, lose the

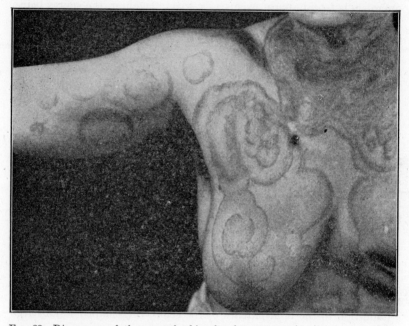

Fig. 83. Ringworm of the smooth skin showing concentric rings, approaching the imbricate type.

typical glabrous wrinkled appearance and produce a short aerial mycelium. On this mycelium a few typical dermatophyte conidia can sometimes be found. Fungi of the endothrix group have a low degree of virulence for laboratory animals producing no lesions or only localized lesions which soon heal.

Neoendothrix Species of Trichophyton. Neoendothrix species of Trichophyton are transitional between the ectothrix and endothrix groups as far as the relationship of the fungus to the hair is concerned. The condition in the early invasion of the hair by an endothrix species in which there are hyphae outside the hair shaft as well as within persists in this group. The infections produced are also transitional between those caused by the human and animal types of Trichophytons; they show some tendency to inflammatory reaction, but it is not so marked as in the ectothrix species. Infections by these transitional species are seen in subtropical America, Germany, and Austria.

There is one main species, *Trichophyton epilans* (*T. cerebriforme, T. plicatile*). It produces ringworm of the scalp, the beard, and the smooth skin, with varying degrees of inflammatory reaction. Plaut reports isolating it from cats. It may be inoculated on guinea pigs. The colony resembles *T. tonsurans* but is yellower and the surface is more wrinkled and folded.

Ectothrix Species of Trichophyton. Ectothrix species of Trichophyton are clinically sharply differentiated from the endothrix

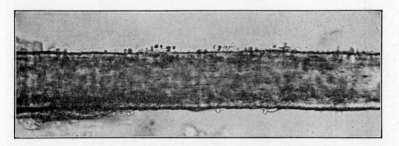

Fig. 84. A hair from ringworm of the scalp. This is a small-spored Ectothrix Trichophyton. The spores are seen on the surface of the hair.

types by the more pronounced inflammatory reaction which they produce in the skin. This would seem to indicate a greater virulence. These acute types of trichophytosis tend to heal more rapidly than those with a less pronounced inflammation. Whereas with Microsporum and Trichophyton infections the skin changes are usually limited to congestion of the advancing border and scaling of the epidermis, with infections from the ectothrix species there is also an exudation of serum and leucocytes into the skin which leads to more or less bogginess and infiltration of the deeper tissues. Not infrequently pus oozes in small droplets from the mouths of the hair follicles, or distinct pustules may appear. In more acute forms certain areas of skin may become elevated and feel quite boggy when palpated, as though an abscess of some size were developing, and pus oozes from the hair follicles when the skin is squeezed. Such a lesion is called a kerion. Suppurative lesions of the beard are referred to as sycosis.

The ectothrix species are divided into two groups, those with small spores in the lesions (about 3 microns in diameter) and those with large spores (5 to 7 microns in diameter). Species of the first group grow more rapidly in artificial culture than those of the second.

The small-spored species may be confused with Microsporum if the differentiation is made solely on a hasty examination of the hairs, for they present the same general appearance—a few articulated hyphae within the hair and numerous spores on the surface forming a sheath. However, these spores, unlike those of Microsporum, are

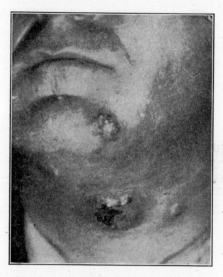

Fig. 85. A suppurating ringworm of the beard ("sycosis"). This is due to an Ectothrix Trichophyton.

produced by a fragmentation of hyphae and therefore tend to be arranged in chains rather than in an irregular mosaic. The spores of the two fungi are about of a size. In microsporosis one rarely sees as much inflammatory reaction with a tendency to deep infiltration of the skin as is characteristic of the small-spored ectothrix species of Trichophyton.

In adults the small-spored ectothrix species cause infections of the beard region, the smooth skin, especially the extensor surfaces of the forearms, and the feet. In children lesions of the scalp, face and hands occur. The lesions, when on the smooth skin, are usually of the circular type characteristic of ringworms.

The small-spored group form white, cream-colored, yellow, or pink colonies which vary from granular, stellate colonies to snow-white, floccose, "powder-puff." colonies. Many species have been described and differentiated on the basis of colony type. The most common of these are *Trichophyton gypseum, T. interdigitale, T. pedis,* and *T. niveum.* This represents a considerable range in colony type, but when many strains are compared intermediate types can be demonstrated readily.[14] The fungi of this group seem to be actually variants of a single species. The oldest name for this species is *T. mentagrophytes* and this is accepted here as the valid name.[6]

The members of this group will readily infect guinea pigs. They have been found causing infections of various domestic animals, especially horses but also cats and dogs.

The large-spored ectothrix species are also divided into two groups, those with downy colonies, and those with faviform (i.e., resembling *T. Schoenleini*) colonies. This difference is due to the amount of aerial hyphae, which is formed early and abundantly in the former, later and less abundantly in the latter. The colonies of the faviform group have the waxy appearance of those of the favus parasite. Cultures of the downy type produce conidia as the only fruiting bodies; cultures of the faviform type fail to produce these, forming only mycelium and chlamydospores.

All the large-spored ectothrix species may produce ringworm of the smooth skin, scalp, or beard. They occur more commonly in adults than children. They also occur on a variety of domestic animals. The most important species, *T. faviforme,* is a pathogen of cattle which readily attacks man.

Tinea Imbricata. *Trichophyton concentricum* is the etiological agent of a variety of ringworm occurring in China, the Malay peninsula, various Pacific islands, and in Central America, known as Tokelau ringworm or tinea imbricata. The concentric rings so characteristic of the tineas reach their highest development in this disease. There is much more scaling of the epithelium than in the other ringworms, and as a result there is produced on the skin a complicated pattern caused by the confluence of concentric rings of scales.

The fungus grows within the epithelium between the superficial and deeper layers. It appears in the scales much as does Epidermophyton. Cultures are obtained with great difficulty, partly because many of the very numerous hyphae which can be demonstrated in the scale seem to be dead, and partly because the bacterial infection of the scales is usually so high. The scales can be soaked first in 70 per cent alcohol and a large number of plants made. The colonies are at first like those of *T. Schoenleini.* Few spores are formed in cultures.

Dermatophytosis of the Feet. During recent years dermatophytosis of the feet (athlete's foot) has attracted increasing attention.[16, 20] The condition was probably overlooked for many years, but there may also be an increase over the occurrence fifty years ago. According to Mitchell,[13] this was due in part to the demobilization of a considerable number of soldiers at the end of World War I who were suffering from this infection and tinea cruris. Perhaps a greater factor has been the increased participation of the population

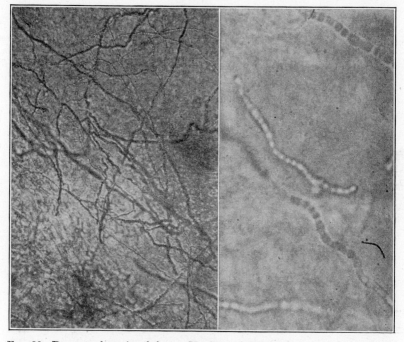

FIG. 86. Dermatophytosis of foot. Hyphae of *Trichophyton mentagrophytes* in epidermal scales, unstained.

in athletics and golf. It is popularly believed that the infection is contracted by going barefoot in dressing rooms and showers where infected desquamated epithelium may be picked up.[1] The infection is extraordinarily prevalent among college students. Legge, Bonar, and Templeton [11] found the disease in 78 per cent of the men and 17 per cent of the women in a survey at the University of California. The much lower incidence in the women was attributed to the use of rubber bathing slippers. The clinical diagnosis should be confirmed by laboratory examination.[4, 18]

The condition begins in the folds between the toes or on the sole. The lesions begin (frequently rather suddenly) as a series of small blisters, which tend to coalesce. This is followed by scaling and the development of eczema-like lesions. The condition may yield to treatment, but tends to recur, especially during the summer months. Recurrence is probably more important in the incidence of infection than reinfection. The sudden appearance of a lesion after unusual amounts of walking or standing may be due merely to the sudden activation of an old quiescent lesion in the epidermis or on a toe nail. The presence of fungi has been demonstrated in skin showing no evidence of clinical dermatophytosis or in skin at some distance from an apparent lesion. The lesions in the nails are particularly difficult to clear up completely and treatment is often stopped in the belief that cure has been achieved when actually there is still a focus of infection in a toe nail.

A variety of fungi have been isolated. Although some of the cases have been definitely associated with tinea cruris and *Epidermophyton floccosum* has been isolated from a considerable number of cases (20 per cent in Mitchell's series), it is now apparent that the majority of cases are caused by various varieties of *Trichophyton mentagrophytes* (*T. gypseum, T. interdigitale, T. pedis*) and *T. rubrum*.

Epidermophyton. The genus Epidermophyton contains a single species, *Epidermophyton floccosum* (*E. inguinale, E. cruris*). The

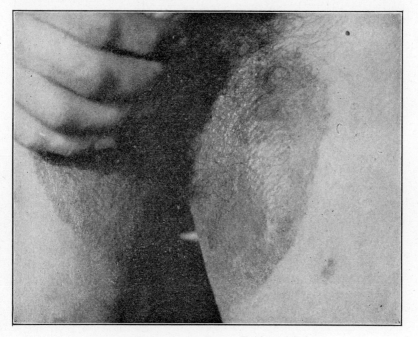

Fig. 87. Tinea cruris, due to Epidermophyton.

use of the name Epidermophyton for other species found on the feet, merely because they are not seen in hairs, is incorrect. *E. floccosum* is found on the feet as a cause of athlete's foot but it is most important as the cause of tinea cruris or eczema marginatum. It occurs on the smooth skin in those parts which are likely to be moist, most frequently the inner surfaces of the thighs, but also in the axillae, the folds of the buttocks, or under the breasts. It is more frequent in warm climates and is especially prevalent in India, where it is apparently one of the conditions known as dhobie itch. It has been responsible for epidemics aboard ship. The affection is somewhat different from the other ringworms especially in that it does not tend to heal in the center as it spreads at the periphery.

The fungus is found in scales of epidermis as septate hyphae breaking up into chains of oval or round arthrospores. In artificial cultures, reproduction takes place entirely by macroconidia, which are not spindle-shaped as in Microsporum, but are clavate or egg-shaped. The walls are thick and smooth. The distal end is rounded. The macroconidium may be one-celled or may have one or more septa. No small conidia are produced. The color of the colony is a characteristic greenish yellow. Cultures rapidly become overgrown with the white sterile mutant mentioned earlier.

Saprophytic Skin Fungi

Pityriasis Versicolor. Pityriasis versicolor is one of the commonest of the dermatophytoses. It is characterized by a brownish discoloration of the skin and it occurs most frequently on the trunk. It causes a light branny scaling and, in some cases, slight itching. In non-pigmented areas of the skin the lesion is darker than the surrounding skin. In exposed skin which is tanned the lesion is often lighter than the other skin, apparently because the fungus interferes with the normal sun-tanning.

The causative organism, *Malassezia furfur*, may be found in large numbers in scales of the epidermis mounted in hydroxide solution. It appears as short irregular strands of branched hyphal fragments accompanied by large numbers of round spores varying considerably in size. When stained with carbol fuchsin the spores are seen to contain several deeply stained bodies of globular form in a less deeply stained protoplasm. The spores tend to be arranged in clusters and are perhaps produced from the hyphae as spores.

Although some investigators have claimed to cultivate the fungus it is evident that most of the fungi isolated in culture have been contaminants.

Erythrasma. Erythrasma is an affection of the moist skin areas of the axillae and groin. It is characterized by a brownish to reddish discoloration. The fungus appears in the epidermal scales as very minute (about 1 micron in diameter) branched hyphae and spores. It is generally referred to as *Microsporon minutissimum*, but there seems to be little doubt that it is one of the actinomycetes.

Piedra. Piedra, or trichosporosis, is an affection of the hairs, not actually a dermatophytosis, occurring in tropical climates. Masses of fungus mycelium grow as little hard knobs on the hairs. Black piedra is caused by an Ascomycete, *Piedraia Hortai*. White piedra is caused by *Trichosporon Beigelii*. Both fungi are most common in tropical regions of high humidity.

LITERATURE

1. Bonar, L., and A. D. Dreyer, Studies on ringworm funguses with reference to public health problems, *Am. J. Pub. Health,* **22,** 909 (1932).
2. Catanei, A., Études sur les teignes, *Arch. inst. Pasteur,* **11,** 267 (1933).
3. Davidson, A. M., and P. H. Gregory, Note on an investigation into the fluorescence of hairs infected by certain fungi, *Can. J. Research,* **7,** 378 (1932).
4. ———, The so-called mosaic fungus as an intercellular deposit of cholesterol crystals, *J. Am. Med. Assoc.,* **105,** 1262 (1935).
5. Emmons, C. W., Pleomorphism and variation in the dermatophytes, *Arch. Dermatol. Syphilol. (Chicago),* **25,** 987 (1932).
6. ———, Dermatophytes: natural grouping based on the form of the spores and accessory organs, *Arch. Dermatol. Syphilol. (Chicago),* **30,** 337 (1934).
7. Emmons, C. W., and A. Hollaender, The action of ultraviolet radiation on dermatophytes. II. Mutations induced in cultures of dermatophytes by exposure of spores to ultraviolet radiation, *Am. J. Botany,* **26,** 467 (1939).
8. Gregory, P. H., The dermatophytes, *Biol. Rev., Cambridge Phil. Soc.,* **10,** 208 (1935).
9. Guiart, J., and L. Grigorakis, La classification botanique des champignons des teignes, *Lyon méd.,* **141,** 369 (1928).
10. Kaufmann-Wolff, M., Über Pilzerkrankungen der Hände und Füsse, *Dermatol. Z.,* **21,** 385 (1914).
11. Legge, R. T., L. Bonar, and H. J. Templeton, Epidermomycosis at the University of California, *Arch. Dermatol. Syphilol. (Chicago),* **27,** 12 (1933).
12. Matruchot, L., and C. Dassonville, Sur le champignon de l'herpes (Trichophyton) et les formes voisines, et sur la classification des Ascomycetes, *Bull. soc. mycol. France,* **15,** 240 (1899).

13. MITCHELL, J. H., Further studies on ringworm of the hands and feet, *Arch. Dermatol. Syphilol.* (*Chicago*), **5**, 174 (1922).
14. NEAL, P. A., and C. W. EMMONS, Dermatitis and coexisting fungous infections among plate printers, *Public Health Bull. 246*, 1939.
15. OTA, M., and M. LANGERON, Nouvelle classification des dermatophytes, *Ann. parasitol.*, **1**, 305 (1923).
16. PECK, S. M., Epidermophytosis of the feet and epidermophytids of the hands, *Arch. Dermatol. Syphilol.* (*Chicago*), **22**, 40 (1930).
17. SABOURAUD, R., *Maladies du cuir chevelu. III. Les maladies cryptogamiques. Les teignes*, Masson et Cie., Paris, 1910.
18. SWARTZ, J. H., and N. F. CONANT, Direct microscopic examination of the skin, *Arch. Dermatol. Syphilol.* (*Chicago*), **33**, 291 (1936).
19. TATE, P., The dermatophytes or ringworm fungi, *Biol. Rev.*, Cambridge *Phil. Soc.*, **4**, 41 (1929).
20. WISE, F., and J. WOLF, Dermatophytosis and dermatophytids, *Arch. Dermatol. Syphilol.* (*Chicago*), **34**, 1 (1936).

BLASTOMYCOSIS

(American Blastomycosis, Gilchrist's Disease)

Blastomycosis was first described in 1894 by Gilchrist.[6] * In a second case reported by Gilchrist and Stokes [7] the fungus causing it was isolated in culture. It was thoroughly studied by Ricketts.[9] Martin and Smith [8] have more recently published a very useful review of the disease and reported in detail several cases. Although not common, it has been reported frequently enough from many parts of the United States to establish it as one of the most important of the systemic mycoses.

Clinical. In about half the reported cases of blastomycosis the first complaints were of pulmonary involvement. In a considerable number of the remaining cases the first observed lesions were subcutaneous nodules. The distribution of these lesions does not appear to be related to trauma or exposure and it is probable that the primary lesion was actually in the lung and that there was blood stream dissemination of the fungus. Primary blastomycosis of the lungs frequently bears a striking resemblance to pulmonary tuberculosis in its course and symptoms, and is often so mistakenly diagnosed, the first indication of the true nature of the disease being a rather sudden generalization of the infection with the development of subcutaneous abscesses.

In systemic blastomycosis the lungs are involved in 95 per cent of the cases and it is probable that in most of these instances the primary lesion was in the lungs. Pulmonary blastomycosis may

* Literature citations for this section will be found on page 186.

resemble miliary tuberculosis or there may be a few large nodules or abscesses. Small cavities are sometimes found. There may be diffuse or focal consolidation. The bones and joints, spleen, kidneys, prostate and central nervous system are frequently involved. Lesions are found in other organs less frequently. In most cases of systemic blastomycosis skin lesions eventually develop.[8, 11]

Dissemination by way of the blood stream leads to a development of multiple abscesses throughout the body. These are particularly prone to occur in the subcutaneous tissues, but may also develop in the muscles, under the periosteum of the bones, or in the viscera. The subcutaneous abscesses are quite characteristic and quite different from the primary skin lesions. They develop painlessly and without much local heat or redness; they are soft and fluctuant, and when opened discharge a considerable amount of pus from which the fungus may be cultivated. The generalized form of the disease is accompanied by a septic type of fever curve and is usually fatal.

Finally there are cases of primary cutaneous blastomycosis occurring most commonly on the face, hands, wrists, arms, or lower legs, where exposure to trauma or repeated irritation may be important factors in permitting entrance of the fungus through the skin. In many of these cases there has been a definite history of injury preceding the development of the skin lesion.

In primary cutaneous blastomycosis lesions frequently begin as pustules which ulcerate and do not heal. There is usually a single lesion although satellite lesions may follow autoinoculation by scratching. The primary skin lesion may be a papule. Around this secondary nodules develop, slowly enlarge, and coalesce. These break down and discharge pus through a number of small fistulae. As the disease progresses there gradually develops a large elevated mass of tissue with an irregular ulcerated surface that resembles somewhat a breaking down cancer, sometimes a tuberculous ulcer. Slight pressure on the mass will cause pus to ooze from a number of minute openings. There is a considerable development of granulation tissue which may be covered with a yellowish oozing crust but which frequently becomes verrucous. The border of the typical skin lesion is elevated and slopes sharply to the normal skin. This active border advances slowly, obliterating the normal structures. The older part of the lesion heals, but the resultant scarring is often very disfiguring.

The microscopic appearance of the tissue presents some resemblance to both tuberculosis and cancer. The inflammatory reaction, particularly in the subcutaneous fibrous tissue, is largely gran-

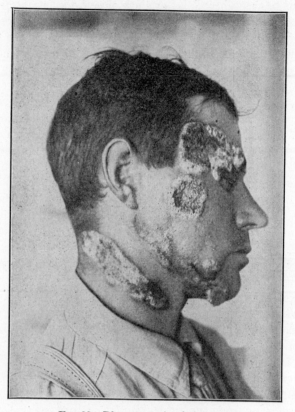

Fig. 88. Blastomycosis of the skin.

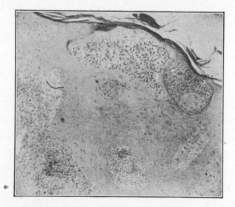

Fig. 89. Blastomycosis (Gilchrist's disease) of the skin.

ulomatous in nature, there being much new-formed connective tissue and considerable infiltration with mononuclear leucocytes. Giant cells may be formed, and the epithelial tissue, in response to irritation, undergoes considerable proliferation and may send long, finger-like processes down into the inflammatory tissue, much as in epithelioma. A very constant and characteristic feature of the microscopic pathology is the occurrence of minute abscesses, i.e., spaces filled with polymorphonuclear leucocytes, in the epithelium proper. In these miliary abscesses the parasites are found extracellularly and within giant cells. Baker[2] has recently analyzed the tissue reactions in twenty-three cases.

Diagnosis. The diagnosis of blastomycosis is made by the demonstration of the fungus in tissues or pus. This is necessary because of the similarity of the lesions to those of other granulomatous processes. The size of the fungus makes it relatively easy to find in tissue sections or when pus is mixed with a drop of 10 per cent sodium hydroxide and examined unstained under a cover slip. Martin described a complement-fixation test which appeared to be specific. However, a negative test does not exclude the diagnosis because complement-fixing antibodies are absent from the blood in some cases.

Treatment and Prognosis. In the treatment of cutaneous blastomycosis sodium iodide intravenously and potassium iodide by mouth have been fairly successful. Tincture of iodine is also applied locally. Currettage of the lesions and x-ray therapy as well as radium have also cured some cases. Occasionally no treatment is effective.

In systemic blastomycosis iodides not only fail to arrest the disease but may cause a rapid spread of the lesions. Martin and Smith[8] recommend partially desensitizing the patient by injecting subreacting doses of a skin-testing material prepared from the fungus and gradually increasing the dose until little or no reaction is elicited. Iodides can then be safely administered and sometimes they cure the infection. The prognosis in systemic blastomycosis, however, remains extremely bad.

Parasitic Growth Phase. Cells of the parasitic growth phase vary from 3 to 24 microns in size, the usual range being 8 to 10 microns. The fungus cell has a thick wall which is sometimes described by the rather ambiguous term, double contoured, because its inner and outer limits can be observed. The cell may bud in a manner resembling that of the yeasts or it may elongate or become dumb-bell-shaped and be divided by a crosswall at the point of constriction. When a bud is formed it at first has a thinner wall than the parent cell. Usually a cell bears a single bud, but one can also find two or more buds arising from one end of a cell or observe a chain of cells representing buds which have failed to separate. The opening between the parent cell and the young bud (and the plane of attachment between two mature cells) has a greater diameter than is seen in the typical budding of yeasts where the bud is typically pinched off and successive buds form at or near the same spot.

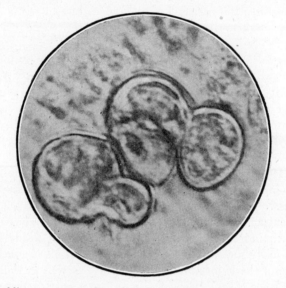

Fig. 90. Budding yeast-like cells of *Blastomyces dermatitidis*, in a wet preparation of pus from a case of blastomycosis.

The cells of *Blastomyces dermatitidis* are larger and have thicker walls than those of *Candida albicans* and the yeasts. They lack the conspicuous capsule produced by *Cryptococcus neoformans* and are less uniform in shape than the spherical cells of that fungus. *B. dermatitidis* has sometimes been confused with *Coccidioides immitis*, but careful search will reveal budding or pseudobudding which is never observed in the latter. No endospores or ascospores are formed by *B. dermatitidis*.

Cultures. The fungus grows slowly, but if primary cultures are not too heavily contaminated it can be isolated in culture readily. Pus can be spread on blood agar plates and incubated at 37° C., wherupon the fungus grows in a manner closely resembling its parasitic growth phase. Colonies are yellowish white to tan, somewhat mealy or waxy, and of a vermiculate or worm-cast type. A micro-

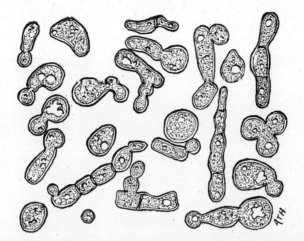

FIG. 91. *Blastomyces dermatitidis* in a young culture, showing transitions from the yeast-like form to mycelium.

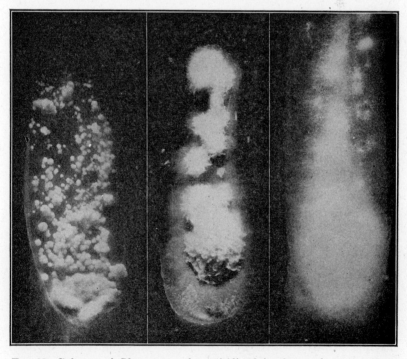

FIG. 92. Cultures of *Blastomyces dermatitidis:* left, the mealy type; center, the prickly type; right, the woolly type.

scopic examination of such a colony shows many cells which closely resemble those found in tissue, others which are perhaps twice as long as thick and divided into two cells by a central septum, and some which form thick, abortive hyphae. An examination of these types and transitional forms illustrate clearly the morphological differences between the budding cells of *Blastomyces dermatitidis* and those of the true yeasts.

When pus containing the fungus is streaked on Sabouraud agar and incubated at room temperature or 30° C. the parasitic growth phase produces branching hyphae and the resultant colony is that

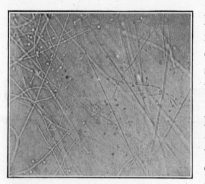

FIG. 93. *Blastomyces dermatitidis.* Conidia in culture.

of a mold. Three types of growth have been described. Colonies may be somewhat friable (the so-called mealy type), they may consist of a glabrous moist growth on the agar surface with coremia (upright composite strands of hyphae forming spine-like aggregates at the center of the colony), or they may be tangled masses of dry, aerial hyphae. Some colonies are pure white whereas others become brown in age. These variations are sometimes related to strain differences and may also be observed in a single strain when it is kept in the laboratory over a period of years. Thus the mealy type is most apt to appear in newly isolated strains and microscopic examination will show the presence of pseudobudding forms and abortive hyphae. The presence of contaminating bacteria which may be carried along undetected for many culture generations often modifies the growth habit.

Conidia. Gilchrist and Stokes,[7] in their original description of the fungus, and many subsequent observers have described the conidia which develop in cultures. These structures are quite variable in size and shape, depending to some extent upon the individual strain. They are spherical to pyriform or oval and range in size from 2 microns in diameter to 3.5 by 5 microns. Some are sessile, budding directly from the hyphae, and others are on lateral stalks of conidiophores 1 to 10 microns long. The walls are smooth. Conidia may be rare, and in strains kept for many years in the laboratory none may be found.

Animal Inoculations. Laboratory animals are somewhat resistant to infection so that animal inoculation is not a useful method of laboratory diagnosis. However, when large numbers of spores from a culture are injected typical lesions result, and this is a useful method of confirming the identify of a culture. Spring[10] found that mice are the most susceptible of the common laboratory animals, guinea pigs being more resistant, and rabbits practically immune. When the animals are inoculated intraperitoneally, small caseous nodules develop on the peritoneal surfaces which contain the budding fungus cells. These are more numerous in mice than in other animals. The type of tissue reaction in experimentally inoculated animals varies with the virulence of the strain and the resistance of the animal, from frank abscesses to lesions like tubercles, including giant cells. Benham[3] stated that dogs and monkeys are most susceptible. DeMonbreun[5] produced in monkeys cutaneous blastomycosis of the type seen in man. Baker[1] discussed experimental blastomycosis in mice. Spontaneous blastomycosis in dogs has been reported.

Taxonomy. Both the name of the disease and that of its etiological agent are misnomers. Blastomycosis is used in Europe to designate any disease caused by a budding yeast-like fungus. Whether or not this terminology is justified, it has been the source of considerable confusion. Although *Blastomyces dermatitidis* produces buds of a sort in its parasitic growth phase, it is unlike the yeasts both in tissue and in culture, as already pointed out.

B. dermatitidis, likewise, is an incorrect name for the fungus because that generic name properly belongs to an unrelated group of fungi. Nevertheless, both names are generally recognized, and because of their familiarity we continue to use them here.

Misinterpretation of oil droplets and stored food particles within chlamydospores and other structures have led some observers to place *B. dermatitidis* among the Ascomycetes. It is properly classified among the Fungi Imperfecti. Although its relationships are not known, its resemblance in culture to *Histoplasma capsulatum* should be pointed out. Skin tests indicate an immunological cross reaction between these two fungi.

Several species names have been proposed for the fungus causing blastomycosis. A critical examination of the strains named shows that some of them are varieties of *B. dermatitidis* characterized by minor differences which do not deserve specific differentiation. It is evident that in other cases the multiplication of names has been due to failure to differentiate *B. dermatitidis* from Coccidioides or other fungi.

Conant and Howell [4] have recently transferred the fungus causing South American blastomycosis (paracoccidioidal granuloma) to this genus. Aside from the recognized error in the use of Blastomyces it seems reasonable to range the South American fungus, B. brasiliensis, alongside B. dermatitidis.

Geographical Distribution. Blastomycosis is an American disease. It appears to be most common in the Mississippi Valley and it has been called the Chicago disease because of the number of cases observed in that area. However, it has a wide distribution on this continent; it has extended into Canada. Presumptive cases have been reported from England.

Habitat in Nature. The occurrence of the fungus outside the animal body is not known. Circumstantial evidence suggests that it grows as a saprophyte in soil or dead vegetation.

LITERATURE

1. BAKER, R. D., Experimental blastomycosis in mice, Amer. J. Path., **18**, 463 (1942).
2. ———, Tissue reactions in human blastomycosis, Amer. J. Path., **18**, 479 (1942).
3. BENHAM, R. W., The fungi of blastomycosis and coccidioidal granuloma, Arch. Dermatol. Syphilol. (Chicago), **30**, 385 (1934).
4. CONANT, N. F., and A. HOWELL, JR., Etiological agents of North and South American blastomycosis, Proc. Soc. Exptl. Biol. Med., **46**, 426 (1941).
5. DeMONBREUN, W. A., Experimental chronic cutaneous blastomycosis in monkeys, Arch. Dermatol. Syphilol. (Chicago), **31**, 831 (1935).
6. GILCHRIST, T. C., A case of blastomycetic dermatitis in man, Johns Hopkins Hosp. Repts., **1**, 269 (1896).
7. GILCHRIST, T. C., and W. R. STOKES, A case of pseudo-lupus vulgaris caused by a blastomycete, J. Exptl. Med., **3**, 53 (1898).
8. MARTIN, D. S., and D. T. SMITH, Blastomycosis, Am. Rev. Tuberc., **39**, 275, 488 (1939).
9. RICKETTS, H. T., Oidiomycosis (blastomycosis) of the skin and its fungi, J. Med. Research, **1**, 373 (1901).
10. SPRING, D., Comparison of seven strains of organisms causing blastomycosis in man, J. Infectious Diseases, **44**, 169 (1929).
11. STOBER, A. M., Systemic blastomycosis, Arch. Internal Med., **13**, 509 (1914).

South American Blastomycosis

(Paracoccidioidal Granuloma)

Historical. Lutz [3] * in 1908 and Splendore [5] in 1909 described a highly fatal disease observed in Brazil and characterized by skin

* Literature citations for this section will be found on page 189.

and mucous membrane lesions and systemic involvement in which budding cells were observed in the pus. Splendore in 1912 named the fungus *Zymonema brasiliense.* In many of the early studies the disease was confused with coccidioidomycosis; Almeida [1] in 1929 summarized the characteristics of the two mycoses and clearly pointed out their clinical differences, the fundamental morphological differences between the fungi, and the lower virulence of this fungus for experimentally infected guinea pigs.

Clinical. Unlike coccidioidomycosis, the primary lesions are most often in the mucous membranes of the mouth and nostrils and involvement of the gastrointestinal tract is usual. The lesions are ulcers which increase in size by peripheral spread and by the coalescence of satellite lesions. They cause a rapid and extensive destruction of the tissues. Skin lesions are crusted or nodular and resemble those of American blastomycosis. The regional lymph nodes become enlarged, break down, and drain through sinuses which penetrate the skin. Hematogenous spread of the organism follows. In some cases the first evidence of infection is enlargement of the lymph nodes in the neck.

Primary lesions may appear in the gastrointestinal tract in the region of the cecum or appendix, where ulcers develop. The infection spreads by peripheral enlargement of the lesions and by way of the blood stream. The lungs, spleen, liver, and other organs are involved when the disease becomes generalized.

Diagnosis. The clinical aspects of the disease and the location and appearance of the lesions are fairly distinctive. In the laboratory diagnosis the fungus should be demonstrated in the lesions or a culture should be obtained.

Treatment and Prognosis. The disease does not yield to iodides and other antimycotic treatment and is almost invariably fatal in the diagnosed cases.

Appearance of the Fungus in Tissues. The fungus is found in pus and in the tissues as a spherical cell 10 to 60 microns in diameter. It reproduces by budding. Some cells produce one or a few buds and resemble *Blastomyces dermatitidis.* Cells considered typical of this fungus produce many small buds. In optical section these appear as a crown of small (1 to 4 microns) spherical or elongated projections from the cell wall.

Appearance in Culture. The fungus grows slowly. When cultures are incubated at 37° C. the fungus reproduces by a process of multiple budding similar to that seen in tissues. At room temperature it produces hyphae which bear conidia similar to those seen in *Blastomyces* *dermatitidis* except that they are less uniform in size and shape and are not so well differentiated from the chlamydospores which are also present. Strains vary, some producing a glabrous, wrinkled, or vermiculate colony, others extending more widely over the agar surface and being covered with short white aerial hyphae.

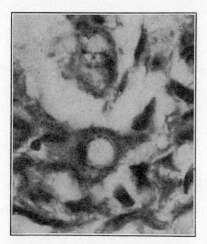

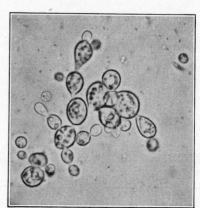

FIG. 94. *Blastomyces brasiliensis* in liver tissue (×1100), showing peripheral small buds from parent cell. Occasionally larger buds are formed. Photomicrograph by Dr. N. F. Conant.

FIG. 95. *Blastomyces brasiliensis* from beef infusion agar, 37°, ×700. Sometimes multiple budding with large peripheral cells is seen, like that sometimes found in tissues. On Sabouraud agar at room temperature, morphology is mycelial, very like that of *B. dermatiditis.* Photomicrograph by Dr. N. F. Conant.

Taxonomy. Since Splendore named the fungus *Zymonema brasiliense* it has been known under a variety of names, most familiar of which is *Paracoccidioides brasiliensis* Almeida. Conant and Howell [2] have called attention to the similarities between this fungus and *Blastomyces dermatitidis* and have transferred it to the genus Blastomyces. Moore [4] described two additional species, but there is some doubt whether these are more than minor and unstable variations of *B. brasiliensis.*

Geographical Distribution. The mycosis appears to be most common in Brazil and particularly in the state of São Paulo, but it is known also in Argentina and other South American countries.

Habitat. The habitat in nature of *Blastomyces brasiliensis* is unknown. There is some evidence of direct transmission of the fungus from man to man.

LITERATURE

1. ALMEIDA, F. P. DE, Estudo comparativo do granuloma coccidioidico nos Estados Unidos e no Brasil, *Ann. med. São Paulo,* **4,** 91 (1929).
2. CONANT, N. F., and A. HOWELL, The similarity of the fungi causing South American blastomycosis (paracoccidioidal granuloma) and North American blastomycosis (Gilchrist's disease), *J. Investigative Dermatol.,* **5,** 353 (1942).
3. LUTZ, A., Uma mycose pseudococcidica localisada na bocca e observada no Brasil, *Brasil med.,* **22,** 121, 141 (1908).
4. MOORE, M., Blastomycosis, coccidioidal granuloma and paracoccidioidal granuloma, *Arch. Dermatol. Syphilol. (Chicago),* **38,** 163 (1938).
5. SPLENDORE, A., Sobre um novo caso de blastomycose generalizada, *Rev. soc. sci. São Paulo,* **4,** 52 (1909).

HISTOPLASMOSIS

From 1906 to 1909 Darling, in a series of papers,[2, 3] * reported his discovery of a new disease which he had found while searching the pathological material at the Ancon Hospital, Canal Zone, for kala-azar. He recognized in this material features which differentiated the organism from Leishmania, but he believed it to be a protozoan and he erected for it a new genus, Histoplasma, calling the organism *Histoplasma capsulatum* and the disease histoplasmosis. As additional material was studied it became apparent that the organism was a fungus rather than a protozoan, but not until 1934 when Dodd and Tompkins [5] observed the fungus in blood smears taken before death and DeMonbreun [4] isolated it in culture was its complete life cycle known. In the same year Hansmann and Schenken [7] also isolated the fungus in culture although, because of certain clinical features of their case, they did not identify it with histoplasmosis. Since these important advances in the knowledge of the fungus several cases have been diagnosed before death and the fungus isolated in culture. A study of this material has demonstrated some variability in the various strains of the fungus, and considerable variation in the clinical aspects of the disease.

Clinical. Darling, from his study of preserved material and a review of case records, described the mycosis as one characterized by irregular fever, emaciation, leukopenia, anemia, and splenomegaly. The study of additional cases has demonstrated that some of these features may be lacking in some cases and that there may be other manifestations not at first recognized.[8, 9, 10, 11, 12] There may be papular or ulcerative skin and mucous membrane lesions, the naso-oral

* Literature citations for this section will be found on page 193.

cavity commonly presents lesions, and vegetative endocarditis and ulcerative enteritis have been reported.

Diagnosis. Histoplasmosis should be suspected in undiagnosed cases presenting the foregoing characteristics. Its diagnosis depends upon the laboratory demonstration of the fungus in cells of the reticuloendothelial system or its isolation in culture. Histoplasma may be present in the circulating blood, and it can be demonstrated

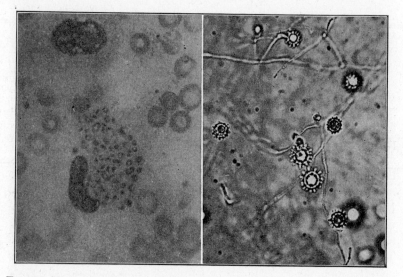

FIG. 96. Histoplasmosis: left, *Histoplasma capsulatum* in blood smear (impression smear of liver of hamster with experimental histoplasmosis, Giemsa stain, ×900); right, spores ("chlamydospores") of *H. capsulatum*.

during life in smears of blood or of sternal bone marrow stained by Giemsa's or Wright's methods. Mucous membrane lesions of the oral cavity, when present, are probably better sources of material for smears. For its isolation in culture blood, sternal bone marrow, or material from ulcers should be spread on the surface of Sabouraud agar slants which should then be incubated at 30° C. or on blood agar incubated at 37° C. A skin-testing antigen can be prepared by growing the fungus for 3 months on the synthetic broth medium used in the preparation of coccidioidin. When 0.1 ml. of a dilution of 1:1000 of the sterile filtrate from such a culture is injected intracutaneously into the patient or into infected guinea pigs the tuberculin type of delayed reaction is observed. The antigen is known to cross-react with blastomycosis and occasionally with other mycoses and its usefulness as a diagnostic test remains to be proved. An antigen has also been prepared from glucose broth.[6, 12, 13]

Prognosis and Treatment. With very few exceptions, recognized cases of histoplasmosis have terminated in death. There is some evidence indicating that the disease occurs in a mild and unrecognized form. Some apparently healthy individuals react strongly to intradermal injections of histoplasmin, and lesions have been found by accident in individuals apparently dying of other causes. However, treatment of diagnosed cases has been ineffective. Meleney[10] recommends the use of the organic salts, the trivalent organic preparations, and the pentavalent preparations of antimony.

Morphology in Tissue. In tissue the fungus is a small oval budding cell measuring about 3 by 5 microns including the capsule. It appears principally within cells of the reticuloendothelial system. Extracellular fungi are also numerous when infection is heavy. The stainable protoplasm of the fungus cell in most pathological preparations is in a cup-shaped mass at one end of the cell. This no doubt represents shrinkage in part and the presence of a normal cell vacuole in part. The minute nucleus is not apparent. Each cell may be surrounded by a narrow capsule.

Morphology in Culture. When *Histoplasma capsulatum* is grown in culture on blood agar at 37° C. it produces budding cells like those seen in tissues.[1, 4] Under these conditions of culture newly isolated strains may grow exclusively in the budding form.

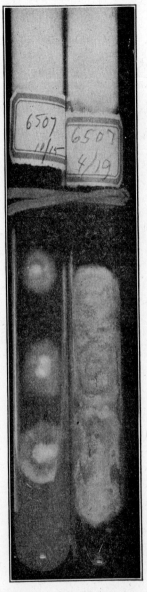

Fig. 97. *Histoplasma capsulatum.* Young and old cultures on modified Sabouraud agar medium.

However, many old strains and all strains when grown on American Sabouraud agar or other common media at 30° C. or at room temperature revert to a hyphal type of growth and appear as white or brownish cottony molds. On the hyphae of such a culture two types of spores are commonly formed. There are small spherical conidia 1 to 3 microns in diameter borne on lateral conidiophores of varying length but usually not exceeding 4 or 5 microns. These conidia may be smooth, in which case they are practically indistinguishable from the conidia of *Blastomyces dermatitidis*. Other conidia, and particularly the larger ones, have a rough or spiny outer wall. In many cultures and at early stages of sporulation there are conidia intermediate between these rough-walled conidia and a larger type of spore to be described.

It is the second type of spore which characterizes *H. capsulatum*. It is large, varying in size and shape from a spherical cell 10 to 15 microns in diameter to a clavate cell reaching a size of 12 by 20 microns. The outer wall is adorned with warty, finger-like, or occasionally spiny excrescences which give it a distinctive appearance. The variation in size and shape of these excrescences and their homogeneous structure suggest that they are produced by the proliferation of the cell wall itself. They are not asci, as suggested by some investigators. The spores bearing these external structures are usually called chlamydospores, but one can find intermediate forms which seem to relate them closely to the smaller conidia in a single series. No ascomycetous form is known. When these conidia are injected into an experimental animal they give rise to buds which reproduce the budding life cycle characteristic of the parasitic phase of growth.

Taxonomy. The fungus was described and named in the mistaken belief that it was a protozoan. However, since the genus was erected for this organism and has never actually included protozoa the name is valid. There are some differences between the various strains of the fungus so far isolated but these are insignificant and do not merit specific separation. A single species, *Histoplasma capsulatum*, is recognized.

Geographical Distribution. The distribution appears to be circumglobal. Reports have come from the United States, Central and South America, Europe, Russia, Java, and Africa.

Habitat. The natural habitat of the fungus is unknown. It has been reported in several cases from dogs, but there is not yet sufficient evidence to incriminate dogs as a reservoir.

LITERATURE

1. CONANT, N. F., A cultural study of the life-cycle of *Histoplasma capsulatum* Darling 1906, *J. Bact.*, **41**, 563 (1941).
2. DARLING, S. T., A protozoan general infection producing pseudotubercles in the lungs and focal necrosis in the liver, spleen and lymph nodes, *J. Am. Med. Assoc.*, **46**, 1283 (1906).
3. ———, The morphology of the parasite (*Histoplasma capsulatum*) and the lesions of histoplasmosis, a fatal disease of tropical America, *Jour. Exptl. Med.*, **11**, 515 (1909).
4. DEMONBREUN, W. A., The cultivation and cultural characteristics of Darling's *Histoplasma capsulatum*, *Am. J. Trop. Med.*, **14**, 93 (1934).
5. DODD, K., and E. H. TOMPKINS, A case of histoplasmosis of Darling in an infant, *Am. J. Trop. Med.*, **14**, 127 (1934).
6. EMMONS, C. W., B. J. OLSON, and W. W. ELDRIDGE, Studies of the role of fungi in pulmonary disease, I. Cross reactions of histoplasmin, *Public Health Repts.*, **60**, 1383 (1945).
7. HANSMANN, G. H., and J. R. SCHENKEN, A unique infection in man caused by a new yeast-like organism, a pathogenic member of the genus Sepedonium, *Am. J. Path.*, **10**, 731 (1934).
8. HENDERSON, R. G., H. PINKERTON, and L. T. MOORE, *Histoplasma capsulatum* as a cause of chronic ulcerative enteritis, *J. Am. Med. Assoc.*, **118**, 885 (1942).
9. HUMPHREY, A. A., Reticuloendothelial cytomycosis (histoplasmosis of Darling), *Arch. Internal Med.*, **65**, 902 (1940).
10. MELENEY, H. E., Histoplasmosis (reticulo-endothelial cytomycosis): a review, *Am. J. Trop. Med.*, **20**, 603 (1940).
11. MOORE, M., and L. H. JORSTADT, Histoplasmosis and its importance to otorhinolaryngologists. A review with report of a new case, *Ann. Otol. Rhinol. Laryn.*, **52**, 779 (1943).
12. PARSONS, R. J., and C. J. D. ZARAFONETIS, Histoplasmosis in man, *Arch. Internal Med.*, **75**, 1 (1945).
13. VAN PERNIS, P. A., M. E. BENSON, and P. H. HOLINGER, Specific cutaneous reactions with histoplasmosis, *J. Am. Med. Assoc.*, **117**, 436 (1941).

SPOROTRICHOSIS

The genus Sporotrichum is characterized by the production of pear-shaped conidia on minute apiculate processes. The first conidia produced by a culture are usually borne at the tips of short simple conidiophores. As the culture ages the conidia are borne laterally on the conidiophores and on the undifferentiated hyphae. Thus, in an old culture there are very numerous dark or smoky-colored conidia borne at the tips of conidiophores and forming sleeve-like masses around conidiophores and hyphae.

Clinical. There are two portals of entry, through wounds and through the alimentary tract. The great majority of human cases have been primarily wound infections, but a few cases presenting a generalized infection without any primary focus have been interpreted as an invasion through the mucous membrane of the intestinal tract. Davis[3] * was thus able to produce a generalized infection in rats by feeding the organism. A few cases have been reported in which apparently a primary involvement of the lungs occurred. In most of the cases the lesions will be seen in the skin and subcutaneous tissues. Foerster[6] reports that 111 of 146 cases were primary on the hands.

The clinical picture of a typical case is so striking that, once seen, the disease will always be readily recognized.[5, 6, 7, 11] There will be

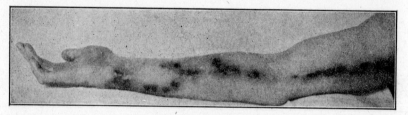

Fig. 98. Sporotrichosis.

seen extending in a line upon the surface of an extremity, a series of hard, elevated, reddened lumps, the older lesions presenting a fistula from which pus may be expressed. At first glance the lesions look like boils but are not hot and tender, and there is practically no constitutional reaction. The firmness of the nodules suggests a syphilitic gumma. Between the lesions the course of the subcutaneous lymph vessels can frequently be traced as reddened lines. Although in the majority of cases the infection spreads from the primary lesion by way of the lymph vessels, it seldom goes beyond the regional lymph nodes. Cases of generalized infection by way of the blood stream occur but are relatively rare. Metastatic lesions may occur in the lungs, liver, and especially frequently in the testicles. One gains the impression that such generalized cases are more frequent in Europe than in America. In some cases the disease may be transmitted from the arm to some other part of the skin surface by contact.

Diagnosis. The disease may present so close a resemblance to tertiary syphilis that it has undoubtedly been frequently misdiagnosed for that disease. An incorrect diagnosis subjects the patient needlessly to a prolonged course of treatment without any benefit

* Literature citations for this section will be found on page 199.

unless iodides are administered. A correct diagnosis with proper treatment (internal administration of iodides) leads to a prompt and permanent cure. Since iodides are commonly used in the treatment of tertiary syphilis, one may make an erroneous diagnosis of syphilis in a case of sporotrichosis, and believe that the diagnosis has been confirmed by the results of specific treatment.

The diagnosis is established by demonstrating the organism in the pus. In the body tissues and exudates the parasite appears as a small, single-celled, spindle-shaped organism. It is most frequently seen within the polymorphonuclear leucocytes. It reproduces by budding at one end of the cell. In size the cells are comparable to those of some of the larger bacteria, but they are easily recognized by their characteristic cigar shape. They have sometimes been incorrectly referred to as spores, but they are quite different from the spores formed in cultures. They are the only structures formed in animal tissue; no mycelium develops. They are far from being numerous in pus

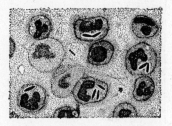

FIG. 99. Smear of pus from sporotrichosis, showing the parasites within the leucocytes.

from human cases, and may be found only after prolonged search. They are best looked for in smears stained by Gram's method, although many of the cells are Gram-negative.

Although these bacillus-like cells are never found in ordinary cultures, according to Davis [3] they are formed in cultures in blood or blood serum, especially if air is excluded or if sterile tissue is added.

Cultures. Cultures are of more value in diagnosis than are smears. Pure cultures may be readily obtained if made from pus aspirated from the younger lesions which have not yet opened; with more difficulty from those which have developed fistulae, for in these latter there is always considerable secondary infection with bacteria. The fungus will not grow readily on dextrose-tartaric agar, and the medium of choice is Sabouraud agar.

The character of the growth on agar is strikingly different from that of most molds. At first it is soft and creamy in texture, the surface moist and shiny, whitish in color, and resembles more a culture of bacteria. As the culture grows older, it becomes darker in color, first a light tan which gradually deepens to a coffee brown and may eventually become quite black. The mass becomes firmer in texture, tending to pull off the agar in rather elastic flakes, and the surface becomes more and more wrinkled. Some strains remain smooth, moist and shiny without developing the cottony masses of aerial mycelium seen in most molds. Other strains develop a short black aerial mycelium which may be more abundant on some media such as prune agar, and which may be aggregated into coremia-like structures which give the surface of the colony a spiny appearance.

If some of this growth is examined under a microscope there are found a tangled mass of branched mycelium and a large number of pear-shaped conidia which are almost all freed from the hyphae when material is mounted for examination in the usual manner. To

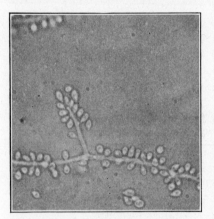

FIG. 100. *Sporotrichum Schenckii.*
Conidia in culture.

see their normal relationship it is necessary to prepare slide cultures. This was done by de Beurmann and Gougerot[5] by placing sterile slides in wide test tubes with a small amount of dextrose broth into which the organism was inoculated. As it grew, the mold would climb the slide for a short distance, and the slide was then removed and the growth fixed and stained. The methods of slide culture preparation described in Chapter I are preferable. In such a preparation some of the conidia

will remain in place at the tips and along the sides of simple conidiophores and on the undifferentiated hyphae. Each conidium is attached by a very narrow stalk which, when it breaks, remains in part on the pointed end of the conidium and in part as an apiculate scar on the hypha from which the conidium fell. This stalk may appear almost thread-like in specimens which have been dehydrated and stained. Conidia which have fallen to the surface of the culture frequently bud to produce secondary conidia which are borne on narrow sterigmata. Chlamydospores are also produced on the mycelium.

Both cultural and morphological characters are subject to considerable variation. Of the former, the degree of pigmentation is most variable. Some strains may never develop more than a light tan color, others may darken very rapidly. The same strain may form more pigment on some media than on others, or on the same medium may remain colorless at one time and become pigmented in a later transfer. An inoculation of a pure culture on agar may show pigmentation in one portion of the colony and none in another.

Taxonomy. On the basis of these rather variable cultural characters a number of different species of pathogenic Sporotrichum have been described. Buschke and Langer recognized thirteen. It would seem, however, that the differences upon which these species were made are well within the limits of variability of a single strain. Greatest stress has been placed upon the differentiation between the American species, *Sporotrichum Schenckii,* and the variety described in Europe as *S. Beurmanni.* These have been separated mainly on the ground of pigment formation, *S. Schenckii* being light and *S. Beurmanni* dark; on the degree of spore formation, *S. Schenckii* forming fewer lateral conidia; and on sugar fermentations, *S. Schenckii* producing acid from lactose, not sucrose, whereas *S. Beurmanni* is said to ferment sucrose but not lactose. Davis,[4] however, has shown that both pigment formation and spore formation are too variable to be used for differentiation because it depends more on the nature of the medium and rapidity of transfer than on the strain. Meyer [8] similarly found that sugar fermentations are highly variable. It would seem, therefore, that although different strains may appear somewhat unlike, there is no valid reason for recognizing more than one of these species, *S. Schenckii.*

Animal Inoculations. Although various laboratory animals are susceptible to infection, rats are particularly so. In addition to making cultures, inoculation into a male white rat is a procedure of considerable diagnostic value. The inoculation should be made into the peritoneal cavity. There occurs a generalized peritonitis with minute nodules on all the peritoneal surfaces, and in addition a very pronounced inflammation of the testis, which may be determined without sacrificing the rat. Unlike human lesions, those in the rat contain the typical cigar-shaped cells in great abundance, and these may be found readily in Gram-stained smears.

The agglutination reaction with spores of Sporotrichum has been discussed in Chapter VI. This reaction, introduced by Widal and his coworkers, is of considerable diagnostic value; though cross reactions occur with thrush and actinomycosis, these diseases are not likely to be confused with sporotrichosis. The best diagnostic procedure is the isolation of the organism in culture, or by inoculation of a rat. Davis [2] was unable to differentiate various strains of Sporotrichum, including some of equine origin, by means of agglutination reactions. Cutaneous reactions are positive but are considered less specific than agglutination. Moore and Davis [9] got no reaction with an extract of the organism of blastomycosis in a case of sporotrichosis.

Geographic Distribution. The disease, first recognized in this country by Schenck,[11] and shortly afterwards in France by de Beurmann,[5] has since been found in all parts of the world. The great majority of the reported cases have occurred in France, the United States, and South America. There is some evidence of a limited geographical distribution. Thus Ruediger [10] found five sixths of the cases reported in America by 1912 had occurred in the valley of the Missouri River. According to Foerster [6] (1926) 130 out of 148 cases reported in the United States were in the valleys of the Mississippi or its tributaries, and a large proportion of these in the Missouri Valley. Meyer also found that outside of Pennsylvania most of the cases of equine sporotrichosis occurred in the Missouri Valley.

This geographical distribution may be due to a greater prevalence of the parasite in this region; to a larger proportion of the population (agricultural) being engaged in occupations which expose them to infection; or (and this seems the more likely) to the fact that the medical profession in these districts have been on the lookout for such cases. In recent years more and more cases have been reported from other parts of the world. This increasing number of cases reported is also probably due to an increased alertness of the medical profession rather than an actually greater prevalence of the disease.

Habitat in Nature. The infection may occur in various ways, but in a large proportion of cases it is clear that the fungus has been introduced into the tissues from or on vegetable matter of one sort or another. Thus Foerster [6] noted that 14 of his 18 cases followed wounds of the upper extremities by barberry thorns. The fungus has been found growing free in nature upon a grain by Sartory; it has been isolated at the National Institute of Health from sphagnum moss, which was responsible for several cases among florists; Lurie isolated it from the timbers of a gold mine in South Africa and from miners exposed to that source; and from the histories of numerous cases, we must assume that it is a fairly common saprophyte upon vegetable matter and in soil. Many cases have occurred in farmers, in some cases following wounds caused by agricultural implements.

Benham and Kesten [1] demonstrated the saprophytic growth of *Sporotrichum Schenckii* on experimentally inoculated barberry thorns and in the buds of carnations. They refer to the latter as the transmission of sporotrichosis to plants, but it is doubtful if that interpretation of the results is justified. Spores of *S. Schenckii, S. Poae* (a pathogen of carnations), *S. pruinosum* (a saprophyte), *S. Gougeroti, S. Councilmani,* and *Penicillium brevi-compactum,* and sterile water controls were injected into young buds of carnation. From 23 per cent (sterile water controls) to 87 per cent (*S. Poae*) of the buds failed to open normally. *S. Schenckii* was recovered from 3 of 18 buds inoculated with the fungus, together with 3 other contaminating fungi. The experiment demonstrated the ability of the fungus to grow on dead or damaged plant tissue.

The disease also occurs spontaneously in certain of the lower animals, notably horses and rats. A number of human cases have been contracted either directly (by bites) or indirectly from such lower animals. There have been two accidental laboratory infections, one from an equine strain, the other from a culture of human origin. In at least one case there has been direct transmission from man to man.

LITERATURE

1. BENHAM, R. W., and B. KESTEN, Sporotrichosis: its transmission to plants and animals, *J. Infectious Diseases*, **50**, 437 (1932).
2. DAVIS, D. J., Interagglutination experiments with various strains of Sporotrichum, *J. Infectious Diseases*, **11**, 140 (1913).
3. ———, Morphology of *Sporotrichum Schenckii* in tissues and artificial media, *J. Infectious Diseases*, **12**, 452 (1913).
4. ———, *The identity of American and French sporotrichosis*, Univ. Wisconsin Studies, pp. 105–131, 1917.
5. DE BEURMANN, L., and E. GOUGEROT, *Les Sporotrichoses*, Alcan, Paris, 1912.
6. FOERSTER, R. H., Sporotrichosis, an occupational dermatosis, *J. Am. Med. Assoc.*, **87**, 1605 (1926).
7. HOPKINS, J. G., and R. W. BENHAM, Sporotrichosis in New York State, *N. Y. State J. Med.*, **32**, 595 (1932).
8. MEYER, K. F., and J. A. AIRD, Various Sporotricha differentiated by the fermentation of carbohydrates, *J. Infectious Diseases*, **16**, 399 (1915).
9. MOORE, J. J., and D. J. DAVIS, Sporotrichosis following a mouse bite, with immunological data, *J. Infectious Diseases*, **23**, 252 (1918).
10. RUEDIGER, G. F., Sporotrichosis in the United States, *J. Infectious Diseases*, **11**, 193 (1912).
11. SCHENCK, B. R., On refractory subcutaneous abscesses caused by a fungus possibly related to the Sporotricha, *Bull. Johns Hopkins Hosp.*, **9**, 286 (1898).

CHROMOBLASTOMYCOSIS

(Dermatitis Verrucosa, Chromomycosis)

Historical. The first reports of chromoblastomycosis were made in 1915 by Lane [9] and Medlar [10] * in Boston. They adopted for the fungus they isolated a name given it by Thaxter, *Phialophora verrucosa* Medlar. In 1920 Pedroso and Gomes,[11] in Brazil, reported

---

* Literature citations for this section will be found on pages 205 and 206.

a case observed nearly ten years earlier. They assumed that the fungus was the same as that isolated from the Boston case, but further studies showed that this was not true. In 1922 Brumpt[2] named the South American strain *Hormodendrum Pedrosoi.* The disease has since been observed in many parts of the world.

Clinical. In the first reported case of chromoblastomycosis the lesion was on the buttocks. Lesions have been reported on the hands, arms, face, neck, and shoulders, but the commonest location is on the foot and lower leg. There is frequently a history of trauma such as penetration by a thorn, and the disease is seen most often in barefooted agricultural laborers in tropical or subtropical countries. The primary traumatic lesion may appear to heal and then ulcerate or, in the absence of known injury, the primary lesion may be a pustule or a papule which slowly increases in size. There may be considerable infiltration and some serous oozing in the early lesion. In most cases the lesion soon becomes dry and somewhat verrucous, violaceous, and sharply limited by a raised margin. In these early stages there is such a close clinical resemblance to American blastomycosis that a differential diagnosis cannot be made without laboratory examination. However, the lesion does not continue to spread peripherally as in blastomycosis. Its surface becomes more verrucous and raised and in many cases of some years' duration the continued growth produces few or many large cauliflower-like masses on short pedicels. The nodular surfaces of these tumors may be covered by a smooth epidermis, but the skin is thin, and exposed lesions which are bruised or rubbed frequently ulcerate. Other lesions are crusted or rough and scaly. This is the classical appearance of the disease but the character of the lesion is modified by its location. The pedicellate lesions are seen rarely except on the lower leg and foot, and not in the latter location if the pressure of a shoe limits their development.

Satellite lesions develop, probably as the result of autoinoculation by scratching. There may be some spread by way of the lymphatics. In a few cases there appears to have been hematogenous spread. The secondary lesions may be numerous and over a period of several years involve most of the lower leg. Several of the reported cases have been of 20 years' duration.

The lesions are relatively painless unless there is ulceration and secondary infection, but there may be severe pruritis. Blockage of the lymphatics causes elephantiasis, and many patients complain mostly of the disability caused by this deformity.[3, 9, 10, 11, 12]

Diagnosis. The early lesions closely resemble those of North American blastomycosis and must be differentiated by laboratory methods. The older verrucous lesions are more diagnostic. Examination of sections made from the lesion will reveal the brown, thick-walled chlamydospores of the fungus. In some cases one can peel off some of the epidermal scales at the edge of the lesion and mount them in 10 per cent sodium hydroxide under a cover slip as in examining for dermatophytosis. In such preparations the fungus can sometimes be found growing as brown hyphae in these superficial scales.

The laboratory diagnosis is not complete without the isolation of the fungus in culture, because any one of at least three fungi may cause the disease and there is no correlation

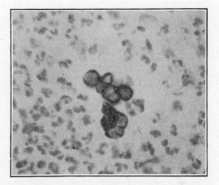

Fig. 101. Chromoblastomycosis. Chlamydospores of *Phialophora Pedrosoi* in tissue.

between a particular clinical type of lesion and one of the fungi causing chromoblastomycosis.

Prognosis and Treatment. The prognosis for cure of chromoblastomycosis is poor but the disease does not become systemic and does not endanger life. Early lesions may be excised or destroyed by electrocoagulation. They sometimes heal under irradiation or after administration of iodides. Some success has been reported in the use of copper sulphate iontophoresis.

Appearance of Fungus in Tissue. In the superficial epidermal scales the fungus may be found in the form of septate branching hyphae with thick brown walls. In the subcutaneous tissues however it is present in a more characteristic form as small clusters of chlamydospores. The disease was called chromoblastomycosis because the origin of these clusters was interpreted as a budding process. Actually, true budding does not occur, although something approaching budding is seen in some cells. In most cases the cell elongates and is divided by a septum. This elongation and septum formation takes place in any plane so that there results a small cluster of cells with thick, dark brown walls. If growth of the fungus is rapid these clusters may contain several cells and in such cases they differ only in size from the granules seen in some types of mycetomas. These clusters of fungus cells may be in giant cells or surrounded by polymorphonuclear leucocytes.

Appearance of Fungus in Culture. Examination of sections of the lesion does not indicate that more than a single species of fungus is involved in the etiology of chromoblastomycosis. However, when cultures are made, one of three fungi may be isolated. One is *Phialophora verrucosa*, first isolated in Boston from the first reported case,[9, 10] and since isolated from other North American and

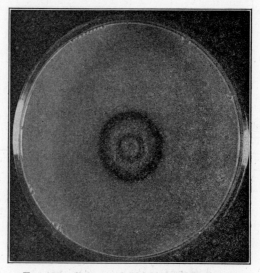

Fig. 102.   Culture of *Phialophora Pedrosoi*.

from South American cases; one is *P. Pedrosoi*,[11] first isolated in Brazil and since isolated from cases in many parts of the world; and one is *P. compactum* isolated in Puerto Rico by Carrión.[3] The second species is the most commonly found.

There are some strains of both *P. verrucosa* and *P. Pedrosoi* whose individual differences are manifested by colony characteristics but in general these two species are indistinguishable in colony appearance. Microscopic examination shows a difference in method of sporulation, but careful study shows that even here there is an evident relationship and the differences are quantitative and not qualitative. This point will be discussed further in the paragraph on taxonomy.

P. verrucosa produces short lateral or terminal conidiophores which may be of nearly uniform diameter or may be enlarged midway to form a bottle-shaped or vase-shaped cell (Fig. 103). This conidiophore terminates in a flaring cup and the spores are formed by a budding process in the bottom of the cup. As spores are successively formed in this manner they are held together in a spherical mass by

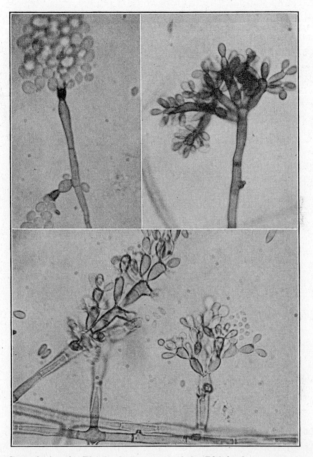

Fig. 103. Sporulation in Phialophora: upper left, *Phialophora verrucosa;* upper right, *P. Pedrosoi;* lower, both types of sporulation in *P. Pedrosoi.* In part from Emmons and Carrión, *Mycologia,* **29,** 329 (1937).

some adhesive substance so that a ball of spores is often observed at the mouth of the conidiophore. The depth of the cup in an old conidiophore makes this a semi-endogenous type of sporulation. This is the typical manner of sporulation in *P. verrucosa,* but careful examination of some strains has shown that rarely a few conidiophores bear conidia terminally and laterally in a manner similar to that seen in *P. Pedrosoi.*

P. Pedrosoi is more variable than *P. verrucosa* in its manner of sporulation. The conidiophore is a lateral or terminal branch of nearly uniform diameter which bears at its tip one or more conidia. These arise as buds at the tip and each is capable of proliferation by budding to produce one or more secondary spores. These in turn can produce tertiary spores, and so on. This results in an arborescent system of branching chains of conidia. In such spore heads the first spores formed are modified as the complex system develops so that they become shield-shaped. This is the type of sporulation typical of Cladosporium and the fungus has, indeed, been commonly classified in the genus Hormodendrum which is a synonym of Cladosporium.

Most spore heads of *P. Pedrosoi* are small, and the chains of spores are limited in length to two or three. In fact, branching chains of spores are difficult to demonstrate, both because they may be actually very few or lacking in the culture and because when present they almost invariably break up when mounted for examination. Most of the conidiophores bear, instead of branching chains of conidia, a large number of spores which are sessile and clustered about the tip and for some distance below it, forming a sort of sleeve of conidia. Such conidiophores are characteristically crooked and gnarled near the tip where the conidia are borne and, when the latter are shed, show scars where the conidia were attached. Some of the conidia may bear secondary spores. Various combinations of these two types of sporulation are commonly observed in most strains. Carrión [4] has grouped strains into named varieties characterized by the predominance of one or another type.

A third type of sporulation which appears to be identical with that characterizing *P. verrucosa* was first observed in *P. Pedrosoi* by Carrión and Emmons,[5, 8] who pointed out the significance of this observation in elucidating the relationship between these two etiological agents of one disease. The phialophores are rare in *P. Pedrosoi* but have been found in practically all strains examined. They are isolated or grouped in clusters on the mycelium, or they are borne as integral parts of the Cladosporium type of spore head.

Taxonomy. Three species are recognized, *Phialophora verrucosa*, *P. Pedrosoi*, and *P. compactum.*[7] *P. Pedrosoi*, because of the variability in its manner of sporulation, has been variously placed in the genera Hormodendrum, Trichosporium, Acrotheca, Fonsecaea, Gomphinaria, Botrytoides, Hormodendroides, and Phialoconidiophora. Binford and coworkers [1] emended the genus Phialophora to include this species, believing that the similarities between *P. verrucosa*, *P. Pedrosoi*, and *P. compactum*, their production of conidia by identical methods, and their common relationship to a single mycosis justified placing them together in one genus. If their obviously close relationship is so indicated the valid generic name is Phialophora.

Material studied from two widely separated geographical sources, Java † and Canada,‡ indicates that a fungus which resembles *Pullularia pullulans* is sometimes etiologically related to chromoblastomycosis. We believe these fungi to be aberrant strains of *P. Pedrosoi* (see discussion of black yeasts, page 111).

Geographical Distribution. Chromoblastomycosis is best known from Brazil, United States (particularly Puerto Rico), and Cuba, but it has also been reported from other areas in South and Central America, the Caribbean, Java, Russia, Africa, and Japan.

Habitat in Nature. Conant [6] showed that *Phialophora verrucosa* occurs in decaying wood where it had been described under the name *Cadophora americana.* The close resemblance between *P. Pedrosoi* and saprophytic species of Cladosporium and the story of trauma in many cases of chromoblastomycosis leaves little doubt that *P. Pedrosoi* is also normally a saprophyte of soil and decaying vegetation.

LITERATURE

1. BINFORD, C. H., G. HESS, and C. W. EMMONS, Chromoblastomycosis, *Arch. Dermatol. Syphilol. (Chicago)*, **49**, 398 (1944).
2. BRUMPT, E., *Précis de parasitologie.* Masson et Cie., Paris, 3rd ed., p. 1105, 1922.
3. CARRIÓN, A. L., Chromoblastomycosis. Preliminary report of a new clinical type of the disease caused by *Hormodendrum compactum,* nov. sp., *Puerto Rico J. Pub. Health Trop. Med.*, **10**, 543 (1935).
4. ———, Chromoblastomycosis, *Mycologia*, **34**, 424 (1942).
5. CARRIÓN, A. L., and C. W. EMMONS, A spore form common to three etiologic agents of chromoblastomycosis, *Puerto Rico J. Pub. Health Trop. Med.*, **11**, 114 (1935).
6. CONANT, N. F., The occurrence of a human pathogenic fungus as a saprophyte in nature, *Mycologia*, **29**, 597 (1937).
7. CONANT, N. F., and D. S. MARTIN, The morphologic and serologic relationships of the various fungi causing dermatitis verrucosa (chromoblastomycosis), *Am. J. Trop. Med.*, **17**, 553 (1937).
8. EMMONS, C. W., and A. L. CARRIÓN, The Phialophora type of sporulation in *Hormodendrum Pedrosoi* and *Hormodendrum compactum, Puerto Rico J. Pub. Health Trop. Med.*, **11**, 703 (1936).

† Courtesy of Dr. C. Bonne.
‡ Courtesy of Dr. L. Berger.

9. LANE, C. G., A cutaneous disease caused by a new fungus (*Phialophora verrucosa*), *J. Cutaneous Dis.*, **33**, 840 (1915).
10. MEDLAR, E. M., A new fungus, *Phialophora verrucosa*, pathogenic for man, *Mycologia*, **7**, 200 (1915).
11. PEDROSO, A., and J. M. GOMES, Sobre quatro casos de dermatite verrucosa produzida pela *Phialophora verrucosa*, *Ann. paulistas med. cirurgia*, **9**, 53 (1920).
12. WEIDMAN, F. D., and L. H. ROSENTHAL, Chromoblastomycosis; a new and important blastomycosis in North America, *Arch. Dermatol. Syphilol. (Chicago)*, **43**, 62 (1941).

ASPERGILLOSIS

Aspergillus fumigatus is an important pathogen, especially for birds. One of the earliest definite records of mycotic infection in animals concerns aspergillosis of the air sacs in birds. The disease is common enough in domesticated birds, pigeons, chickens, and ducks to be of some economic importance. Under the name brooder pneumonia it sometimes occurs in epidemic form in little chicks. Autopsies of wild birds found dead have revealed many cases in all orders of birds, not only seed eaters, but also insect-eating birds and aquatic species. Fox,[1] * in autopsies at the Philadelphia Zoological Garden, found cases in practically all the groups of birds, the disease being responsible for death in from 0.6 per cent of the cases (pigeons) to 40 per cent of the cases (penguins). The fungus is also known to invade birds' eggs during incubation and to infect the embryos.

Three types of infection occur in birds: infection of the air sacs, a pneumonic form in the lungs, and a nodular form in the lungs. The first type is a superficial infection of the epithelium lining the air sacs, which may pass into the wings or into the abdominal cavity. The wall of the sac becomes much thickened, a thick mat of mycelium covers its surface, and spores usually develop, so that the inner surface of the sac wall has a green color. In the pneumonic form a diffuse infiltrative lesion develops, the lung tissue is consolidated, and it has a grayish white color. In the nodular form, isolated masses of infiltrated tissues occur, with necrosis in the center, much resembling advanced tubercles in their gross appearance. In those lesions developing in internal tissues not freely exposed to the air no spores develop.

The disease in domestic birds, especially when it occurs in epidemic form, can usually be traced to feeding moldy grain. It may be due to damp quarters in which straw or other material has become moldy.

* Literature citations for this section will be found on page 210.

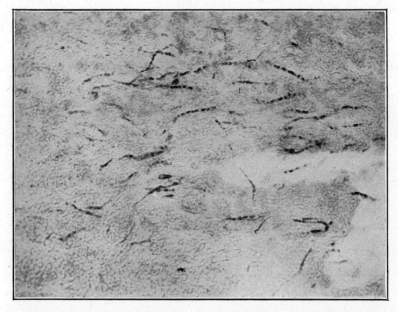

FIG. 104. Section through the lung of a grouse (*Bonasa umbellus*) dead of spontaneous aspergillosis, showing filaments of mycelium. Gram-Weigert stain.

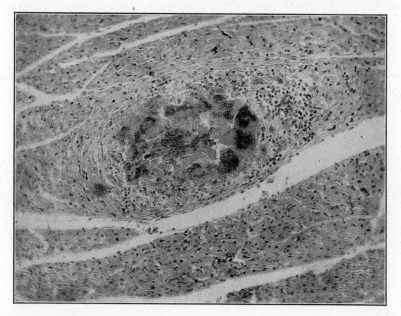

FIG. 105. Histological tubercle in the heart muscle of a pigeon inoculated intravenously with spores of *Aspergillus fumigatus*.

Infection of the eggs is usually due to moldy nesting material. Experiments have shown that if the eggs are carefully cleaned of their fatty coating, infection will not take place. The infected eggs may be detected by candling.

Primary lesions of the lungs also occur in various domesticated mammals, though not so frequently as in birds. Cattle, sheep, and especially horses are known to develop aspergillosis. As with the birds, infection comes from contaminated hay or grain, the spores being inhaled. In some cases particles of inhaled vegetable matter have

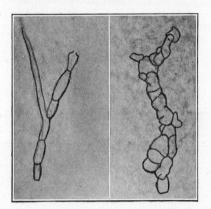

been found in the lesions. The pulmonary lesions may be either nodular or pneumonic as in birds.

A. fumigatus is also pathogenic to man. Some of the cases described are infections of the external ear. The extent of the disease may vary from a mere plugging of the ear canal with mycelium, leading to impaired hearing, to ulceration and suppuration of the walls of the canal, or even to penetration of the

Fig. 106. Aspergillosis. Hyphal fragments of *Aspergillus fumigatus* in human sputum.

drum and invasion of the middle ear. The milder cases are the more numerous. Other species of Aspergillus may also produce this condition, particularly *A. niger, A. nidulans,* and *A. flavus.* According to Siebenmann [6] in Germany about 1 per cent of all ear cases are Aspergillus infections. Aspergillosis of the ear is said to be particularly frequent in India.

Aspergillosis of the lung also occurs in man, but it is rare.[3, 4, 5] The majority of cases have been reported in France, though the disease is also well known in Germany. The disease may be primary, or secondary to some other condition, particularly tuberculosis. Lang and Grubauer reported a case in which bronchiectasis was apparently a predisposing cause. Secondary cases are more common than primary ones. It is quite possible that some of the cases reported as primary were actually secondary to some other disease whose traces were obliterated by the aspergillosis. On the other hand, it is quite probable that some cases of primary pulmonary aspergillosis are overlooked, being mistakenly diagnosed tuberculosis. Clinically the disease resembles tuberculosis very closely, perhaps advancing somewhat more rapidly. According to Lapham [3] cases of primary aspergillosis give positive tuberculin reactions; conversely Nicaud found that an advanced case of tuberculosis gave positive cutaneous reactions with an extract of *A. fumigatus*. Extensive cavity formation occurs in the lungs. The diagnosis is made by finding the mycelium in the sputum, where it occurs as short hyphal fragments, often encrusted, and by isolating the fungus in culture. See Fig. 106. The latter procedure is easy when sputum is planted on Sabouraud agar slants because the fungus grows fairly rapidly and is not inhibited by bacterial growth. The prognosis is not good. Internal administration of iodides is said to be of value, even curative, in some cases, but this treatment must be followed with caution since it may result in the rapid spread of the disease as in the case of blastomycosis.

A considerable number of cases of primary pulmonary aspergillosis were reported in France some years ago, especially by Renon.[4] In these cases the infection was an occupational disease occurring in individuals engaged at that time in occupations which peculiarly subjected them to the possibility of inhaling large numbers of spores. These were the "gaveurs des pigeons" who fattened squabs for the market by filling their mouths with grain, chewing it fine, and then with their tongues forcing the mass into the esophagus of the birds. The second group was the "peigneurs des cheveux" who prepared hair for the manufacture of wigs by mixing it with corn meal to remove oil and then combing it out. In both cases the source of the infection is obvious enough, though in the first it is possible that the infection may have come from the bird rather than the grain, for some of the pigeons were found to have aspergillosis infections of the mouth.

Experimentally inoculated into laboratory animals, *A. fumigatus* produces lesions which vary according to the virulence of the strain and the dosage. Many strains isolated from air or vegetable matter show no pathogenicity. Strains freshly isolated from spontaneous infections may exhibit a surprising degree of virulence, a small dose of spores suspended in salt solution killing a pigeon overnight when inoculated intravenously. No lesions are apparent in such acute infections. With smaller doses or less virulent strain, multiple miliary abscesses occur in various viscera, especially the lungs. Intravenous inoculations into rabbits usually causes death within 3 to 5 days. Multiple minute abscesses in the cortex of the kidneys are the most striking lesions in these rabbits. Subcutaneous or intraperitoneal inoculations produce localized lesions which may not be fatal.

Experimental infections may also be produced by causing the spores to be inhaled. If one dusts spores into a tumbler and holds this over a pigeon's head for a minute or two, rapidly fatal hemorrhagic pneumonia develops. Henrici [2] succeeded in producing only very acute infections in this way. On the other hand, by feeding wheat which had been overgrown with the mold, he succeeded in two out of four pigeons in obtaining an infection of the air sacs very similar to the natural disease, death occurring in about 6 weeks. Microscopically both the natural and experimental lesions may vary considerably according to the virulence of the strain. Usually there is extensive necrosis in the vicinity of the organisms, with some suppuration. In the nodular lesions of the lungs there may be some production of fibrous tissue. In the lesions branched segmented hyphal fragments may be found (Fig. 106), with conidiophores in various degrees of development where the fungus reaches a surface exposed to the air. In the miliary abscesses produced by intravenous inoculation one finds small masses composed of radiating filaments somewhat resembling a granule of *Actinomyces bovis*, save that the filaments are fewer and coarser.

LITERATURE

1. Fox, H., *Disease in Captive Wild Mammals and Birds*, Lippincott, Philadelphia, 1923.
2. Henrici, A. T., An endotoxin from *Aspergillus fumigatus*, *J. Immunol.*, **36**, 319 (1939).
3. Lapham, M. E., Aspergillosis of the lungs and its association with tuberculosis, *J. Am. Med. Assoc.*, **87**, 1031 (1926).
4. Renon, L., *Étude sur l'Aspergillose chez les animaux et chez l'homme*, Masson et Cie., Paris, 1897.
5. Schneider, L. V., Primary aspergillosis of the lungs, *Am. Rev. Tuberc.*, **22**, 267 (1930).
6. Siebenmann, F., *Die Fadenpilze und ihre Beziehungen zur otomycosis aspergillina*, Bergmann, Wiesbaden, 1883.

MYCETOMA

Carter [2] [*] proposed the term mycetoma to designate a type of fungus infection usually localized to the foot and characterized by a conspicuous deformity in which the foot is greatly enlarged. It was frequently seen in India and, according to Carter, Colebrook introduced into medical literature the name Madura foot by which the condition was popularly known near Madura, India. Carter showed that the condition was not an etiological entity and he de-

* Literature citations for this section will be found on page 214.

scribed the appearance of the fungi he found in two different types of cases, so far as the techniques of that day permitted.

Further studies showed that not two but many fungi were capable of causing mycetoma, and Brumpt [1] described several of these and related them to certain clinical types. Pinoy [8] observed that the mycetomas could be separated into two groups on the basis of the size of the fungi, and he proposed a division between the actinomycoses caused by Actinomyces and Nocardia, and the true mycetomas caused by fungi having larger hyphae than those of the actinomycetes. Chalmers and Archibald [4] accepted this division but proposed the name maduromycosis as a substitute for true mycetomas. Their name has been widely used, sometimes in the sense in which it was proposed but more often as a synonym for mycetoma.

We prefer the original name, mycetoma, because (1) the name maduromycosis is not specific but designates infections caused by several unrelated species belonging in some eight or ten genera of Hyphomycetes and Ascomycetes, and (2) the name is a source of confusion because of its derivation from a geographical place to which the disease is not limited, and by derivation it suggests both Madurella (a genus of Hyphomycete causing mycetoma) and Nocardia madurae (an actinomycete causing mycetoma of the type not included under maduromycosis). The name mycetoma properly refers to both types of infection discussed by Pinoy.

Clinical. Mycetoma is a fungus infection of the skin and subcutaneous tissues characterized by swelling, destruction of tissues (including bone in some cases), formation of fistulae, and production of pus in which there are well-organized mycotic granules. The character of these granules varies according to the species of fungus producing them. They may be hard or soft; white, yellow, red or black; pin-point or up to 3 or 4 mm. in size; and the fungus hyphae may be the 0.5μ to 1μ hyphae of actinomycetes or the larger hyphae and chlamydospores of Hyphomycetes or Ascomycetes.

When the lesion is on the foot the latter is enlarged and there is usually a characteristic convex swelling of the plantar surface. The infection usually follows a wound such as that caused by penetration of a splinter or thorn and this probably accounts for the frequent occurrence on the foot. Lesions may be on the hand, however, and rarely on other parts of the body.

Diagnosis. The clinical appearance of a typical case of mycetoma is distinctive, but the diagnosis rests finally upon the laboratory demonstration of the fungus granules. Because of the many fungi capable of causing mycetoma [3, 7] the diagnosis is not complete until the fungus is isolated in culture and identified.

Pus should be collected and examined for granules. The shape, size, consistency, and color of these should be noted. A drop of pus containing granules should be placed on a slide under a cover slip. If the pus is thick it can be mixed with a drop of 10 per cent sodium hydroxide. Most of the fungi causing mycetoma grow on Sabouraud agar, although some of them grow very slowly at first. The optimum temperature for most species is near 30° C.

Treatment and Diagnosis. Although mycetoma usually remains localized and does not endanger life, a few cases have been observed in which systemic infection has been caused by fungi similar to those found in some rare types of mycetoma. (Actinomycosis caused by *Actinomyces bovis* is excluded from this discussion.) In the great majority of cases the infection does not extend above the foot even in cases of many years' duration. The prognosis from the viewpoint of life is therefore good, but no treatment of the infection, except radical surgery, is effective.

Appearance of the Fungi in Tissues. In all cases of mycetoma the fungus forms granules or microcolonies in the tissues, but these differ, as noted above. When *Nocardia madurae* and *N. mexicana* are involved the granules are composed of densely packed, radiating, delicate hyphae 0.5μ to 1μ in diameter. The color is white or yellow. *N. somaliensis* and *N. Pelletieri* also form granules with small hyphae but the color is reddish yellow or red.

The granules as well as the hyphae formed by Hyphomycetes and Ascomycetes are somewhat larger than those formed by Nocardia. In some cases chlamydospores are conspicuous elements of the granule. *Phialophora Jeanselmei* [9] and species of Madurella form black granules. The granules formed by *Allescheria Boydii* (*Monosporium apiospermum*), Indiella spp., and Aspergillus spp. are white to yellowish. The granule may be composed largely of chlamydospores, but usually there is some degree of radial orientation of hyphae. There is sometimes an acidiphilic zone at the periphery of sectioned granules and this staining reaction and the enlarged hyphal tips at the periphery bear a superficial resemblance to the "clubs" which surround the granule of *Actinomyces bovis*. See Chapter XIII.

Appearance in Culture. The large number of species of fungi associated with mycetoma make it impossible to generalize about their characteristics in culture. A few representative fungi will be described briefly.

Species of Nocardia retain in culture the small size which characterizes their hyphae in granules in pus. *Nocardia madurae* grows on agar as a glabrous, wrinkled, grey colony which is in some instances covered with short, white, aerial hyphae. No conidia are formed but in old cultures the cells formed by fragmentation of the hyphae serve as reproductive structures. *N. mexicana* grows slowly and forms heaped, folded colonies rather than spreading widely over the agar surface. The color varies from white (in strains or cultures with aerial hyphae) to yellow or orange. Most strains have a strong musty odor. See page 379 for further discussion of mycetomas caused by Nocardia spp.

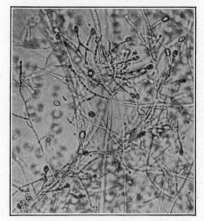

Phialophora Jeanselmei grows on Sabouraud agar as a mouse-grey to olive-colored colony closely resembling that of *P. verrucosa* which causes chromoblastomycosis.[6] There is also a close microscopical resemblance between the two fungi. Species of Madurella are grey to black and most of them grow slowly, forming dome-shaped colonies in which conidia are very few or entirely lacking.

Perhaps the most frequent cause of mycetoma in the United States

Fig. 107. *Allescheria Boydii.* Conidial stage (*Monosporium apiospermum*) on Sabouraud agar. From Conant *et al., Manual of Clinical Mycology*, Saunders, 1944.

is *Monosporium apiospermum*. It has been shown recently that this fungus is the imperfect form of *Allescheria Boydii*.[5] The fungus produces on Sabouraud agar a rapidly spreading, floccose, mouse-grey colony. The conidia are borne singly or in small groups at the tips and sides of simple or branched conidiophores. They are elliptical, egg-shaped, or clavate, with a truncate base, and, under the microscope, they are brown. They are 3.5 to 7.5 by 5 to 15μ.

The ascocarp of *A. Boydii* is globose, 50 to 200μ in diameter, without ostiole (cleistocarpous) and the wall is thin and dark brown. The asci are subglobose, 8 to 20μ in diameter, evanescent, and each contains eight ovoid ascospores 4 to 4.5 by 6 to 7.5μ in size with slightly thickened brown walls.

Geographical Distribution. Mycetoma occurs throughout the world but is more common in tropical and subtropical countries in persons who do not wear shoes and so are more often exposed to injury. The specific agents of mycetoma are to some extent geographically limited. Thus, *Nocardia madurae* is more common in southeastern Asia and the Pacific islands. *N. mexicana* is seen in southern United States and Mexico. The other etiological fungi, except for a few rare or poorly known species, seem to have a wider distribution.

Habitat. The fungi of mycetoma are not transmitted from person to person but are obviously related to trauma in most cases. It is assumed that the fungi ordinarily grow in soil or on dead vegetation and become pathogenic only when introduced by accident into the subcutaneous tissues.

LITERATURE

1. BRUMPT, E., Les mycétomes, *Arch. Parasitol.*, **10**, 489 (1906).
2. CARTER, H. V., On "Mycetoma" or the fungus-like disease of India, *Trans. Med. Phys. Soc. Bombay*, **7**, 206 (1862).
3. CARRIÓN, A. L., and J. KNOTT, Mycetoma by *Monosporium apiospermum* in St. Croix, Virgin Islands, *Puerto Rico J. Pub. Health Trop. Med.*, **20**, 84 (1944).
4. CHALMERS, A. J., and R. G. ARCHIBALD, A Sudanese maduromycosis, *Ann. Trop. Med. Paras.*, **10**, 169 (1916).
5. EMMONS, C. W., *Allescheria Boydii* and *Monosporium apiospermum,* *Mycologia*, **36**, 188 (1944).
6. ———, *Phialophora Jeanselmei* comb. n. from mycetoma of the hand, *Arch. Path.*, **39**, 364 (1945).
7. GAMMEL, J. A., The etiology of maduromycosis, *Arch. Dermatol. Syphilol. (Chicago)*, **15**, 241 (1927).
8. PINOY, E., Actinomycoses et mycétomes, *Bull. inst. Pasteur*, **11**, 929, 977 (1913).
9. SYMMERS, D., and A. SPORER, Maduromycosis of the hand, *Arch. Path.*, **37**, 309 (1944).

CHAPTER VIII

BIOLOGICAL ACTIVITIES OF MOLDS

ECOLOGY OF MOLDS

The molds in many habitats grow more slowly than do the bacteria. Consequently we do not generally find them growing to any great extent in environments where they have to compete with the latter. However, where conditions are unfavorable for bacteria, there will nearly always be found one or more species of mold capable of developing. Thus we find them growing abundantly on starchy foods which are not favorable to most bacteria, in foods containing a high percentage of sugar which inhibit bacteria because of their high osmotic pressure, in habitats too dry for bacterial development, and in acid materials, as fruit juices or sour milk.

Although they grow slowly, they may develop on materials which we would ordinarily consider as supplying but very small amounts of nutrients, like tanned leather, linen, or cotton cloth, if these are damp enough. In fact, molds may develop in the most surprising situations, and may grow on very unusual substrates. They not infrequently appear in laboratory reagents of various kinds, where small traces of organic matter may be present, sometimes in solutions in which one would think life would be impossible. Thus molds are quite versatile in their ability to adapt themselves to particular environments, and it is difficult to make generalized statements without noting numerous exceptions.

Moisture is of course requisite for growth, since molds like all other biological forms must absorb food in solution. They can get along, however, with much smaller amounts of water than are required by bacteria, and in particular can grow in solutions of much higher osmotic pressure. Thus they may be found forming scums on the brine solutions of pickling vats, or on the surfaces of hams or other salt meats; it is well known that they will grow on syrups and jellies' which will not permit the growth of bacteria.

Relative humidity of the atmosphere was found by Thom and Shaw [66] to be a critical factor for the growth of molds on butter, very little growth taking place if the humidity was below 70 per cent.

On the other hand, Lewis and Yesair [32] found humidity had little effect on the growth of mold on Frankfurter sausages, probably because the substrate contained sufficient moisture.

There are probably very few, if any, strictly anaerobic molds, and the great majority are strictly aerobic. However, a few species, notably some of the Mucors and certain strains of the Penicillia may grow to some extent under reduced oxygen tension. The organism used in ripening Roquefort cheese, *Penicillium roqueforti*, can develop with less oxygen than is required by most molds. Williams, Cameron, and Williams [73] have reported the isolation of two strains of "facultatively anaerobic mold of unusual heat resistance." These organisms were identified as strains of an undescribed species of Penicillium by Thom. They proved to be capable of growing in high vacuum.

The different species of molds vary markedly in their temperature requirements. See Chapter III. In general it may be stated that the optimum temperature for most species lies somewhere near 30° C. Some growth will take place at temperatures considerably below this, and most forms may grow somewhat at temperatures up to 37° C. or even higher. Most species of Penicillium have their optimum temperature between 20° and 25° C. and may fail to grow at temperatures above 30° C. On the other hand, with many species of Aspergillus the optimum temperature will be around 35° C. One species pathogenic for birds (*Aspergillus fumigatus*) finds its optimum at 40° C. The thermal death points also vary markedly with the species. Some types of spores are of course much more resistant than vegetative mycelium but not nearly so resistant as the spores of bacteria. Thom and Ayres [64] have studied the heat resistance of mold spores with regard to pasteurization of milk. A temperature of 62.8° C. for 30 minutes was sufficient to destroy practically all. Macy, Coulter, and Combs [35] likewise found molds easily destroyed by pasteurization processes. Flashing for 30 seconds at a temperature of 73.9° to 79.4° C. was necessary to obtain an equal degree of sterilization. Lewis and Yesair found that 60° C. for 5 minutes was sufficient to kill all the molds from meat products which they studied. With dry heat, of course, higher temperatures are required. One of the strains of the facultatively anaerobic penicillia referred to previously, described by Williams and coworkers, produces sclerotia of unusually high resistance to heat.

NUTRITIONAL REQUIREMENTS OF MOLDS

Adequate supplies of elements such as carbon, nitrogen, hydrogen, oxygen, phosphorus, sulphur, and magnesium must be furnished the molds.

The sugars, sucrose, glucose, or fructose, serve as excellent sources of carbon for most fungi. Other sugars including pentoses, alcohols, organic acids, oils, higher paraffins, and polysaccharides have also proved capable of satisfying, at least partially, the carbon requirements of certain molds. Tamiya,[61] who has carried out one of the more elaborate studies on the relation between chemical structure and assimilability, has made the interesting observation that some compounds can serve satisfactorily for respiration but not for growth. He further noted that no constant relation exists between respiration and growth since the former was found to vary with the source of carbon. Steinberg[60] has noted that practically all tests of assimilability of a carbon source are based on experiments with pure compounds. Since fungi under normal conditions grow on mixtures of carbon compounds, he has suggested that the results of tests with single carbon sources cannot serve as final tests of assimilability.

In general, the molds are capable of utilizing a large number of nitrogen compounds. Robbins[51] has suggested that fungi fall into four groups when classified on the basis of their nitrogen requirements. The groups may be referred to as the nitrogen-fixing, the nitrate, the ammonium, or the organic nitrogen compound users. The first group, according to Robbins, is capable of utilizing nitrate, ammonium, or organic nitrogen in addition to being able to use atmospheric nitrogen. Those organisms in the second group, incapable of using gaseous nitrogen but able to use nitrate nitrogen, can grow also with ammonium or organic nitrogen sources. The organisms of the third group are capable of developing only in the presence of ammonium or organic nitrogen compounds. The last group consists of those organisms which can satisfy their nitrogen requirements only with organic nitrogen sources. However, it should be noted and emphasized here in connection with the first group of molds that the belief in the general ability of the fungi to fix gaseous nitrogen is no longer held. Therefore, there would be very few, if any, molds which would be placed in the first group. It should also be pointed out that the nitrogen requirements of an organism are not fixed but vary with the source of carbon. Robbins' scheme of classification need not be altogether discarded, however, because the nitrogen requirements of the fungi could be based on comparative responses with an identical carbon source.

That heavy metals play an essential role in the nutrition of molds has been recognized since the earliest investigations dealing with the cultivation of these fungi in synthetic media. In addition to phosphorus, sulphur, magnesium, and potassium, certain other elements are not only desirable but also often necessary to obtain the maximum yield of fungi from synthetic media. Originally it was held that elements added to the media in minute quantities were beneficial because these substances acted as chemical stimulants. It was postulated that the accelerated and increased growth of fungi in media containing these elements was due to the physiological response of the organism to the toxic properties of these elements, now known to be essential. This concept was based on the notion that poisons when added in minute quantities act as stimulants. It was assumed, of course, that the control media were free of trace elements. Hence growths on such media were considered normal and increases in growth were thought to be due to the "stimulating effect" of the added heavy metals. Steinberg [59] has presented evidence to disprove this chemical stimulation theory. By using extremely efficient methods of purification, this investigator was able to prepare media free of traces of heavy metals. The growth of *Aspergillus niger* was so scanty in such media and such large increases in yield were obtained when zinc and iron were added that he regarded the chemical stimulation theory as untenable. He considered these two elements just as essential to the nutrition of the mold as carbon and nitrogen. In addition to zinc and iron, elements such as copper, manganese, molybdenum, and gallium are now considered not only requisite for maximum growth but also absolutely essential for growth in general of the filamentous fungi. It is generally safe to assume that these elements, which are required only in very minute quantities, are normally present as impurities in sufficiently large amounts (in the chemicals, in most samples of distilled water prepared by the usual methods and glassware used for cultural purposes) despite the fact that these elements are not purposely included in most media used for culturing these organisms.

In addition to the above-mentioned elements which must be furnished the molds, some fungi require certain organic substances for growth. Thus thiamin has been found essential or beneficial for the growth of most molds. Robbins and Kavanagh [52, 53] have shown that some fungi require the intact thiamin molecule; others may require only the pyrimidine and thiazole portions; and still others may require only the pyrimidine or thiazole fractions, capable of synthesizing whichever portion is lacking. Biotin, pyridoxine, p-aminobenzoic acid, choline, and inositol are also required by some fungi. Advantage has been taken of the essentiality of these substances for the growth of certain fungi by various investigators to devise assay methods because the growth is often proportional to the amount of these substances in the culture medium. To a set of cultural vessels containing a medium nutritionally complete in every respect, except for the test substance for which the assay is being made, are added varying quantities of a material with an unknown content of the test substance. The degree of growth, being dependent on the amount of the test substance, indicates the amount of the test substance in the material. Similar assay methods have also been devised for certain amino acids using molds as test organisms. The principle of using molds for such assays has been employed to measure the available phosphorus and potassium in soil samples.

. Some very interesting and fundamental studies have been carried out using mutants of Neurospora. Horowitz and Srb [28] obtained seven mutants of *Neurospora crassa* incapable of synthesizing arginine, i.e., arginine had to be furnished these mutants for them to grow. These mutants were obtained by exposing the parent organism to ultraviolet and x-radiations; presumably a certain gene or set of genes was thus destroyed. Each of these mutants differed from the normal by a different gene. One strain grew only when arginine was added. Others grew on either arginine or citrulline, thus showing that the latter could be converted to arginine. Others proved capable of using arginine, citrulline, or ornithine. Thus it was deduced that ornithine, too, could be converted to arginine. Each of the mutants capable of utilizing ornothine was also able to use citrulline, whereas the reverse was not always true. Because no strain was found capable of utilizing ornithine and arginine but not citrulline, it was concluded that citrulline was an essential intermediate in the synthesis of arginine from ornithine. The importance of this type of investigation with molds should not be underestimated. By such studies, metabolic cycles as the above-described ornithine cycle of Krebs and Hensleit occurring in higher biological forms can be readily studied with the lower biological forms such as molds. The applications of such types of investigations are not limited to the fungi themselves but are of use in studying the nutritional and metabolic activities of higher biological forms.

MOLD FERMENTATION

Citric Acid Fermentation. Various molds produce citric acid from sugars but strains of *Aspergillus niger* are apparently more active than other species, and have been used more extensively for both experimental and commercial purposes. Wehmer,[71] who was studying the fermentations of molds, first noted that some produce citric acid. He named these molds Citromyces, but they were later classified with the monoverticillate Penicillia.

Currie and Thom [15] found that with some strains there was a lag between the curves for total acidity and oxalic acid, an acid then known to be produced by some molds, during the fermentation. This led to a search for another acid, which was subsequently identified by Currie [14] as citric acid. This was considered an intermediary product in the fermentation. According to this worker, the oxidation of sugar by *A. niger* proceeded as follows.

$$\text{Carbohydrate} \rightarrow \text{Citric acid} \rightarrow \text{Oxalic acid} \rightarrow CO_2$$

Although this view is no longer held, Currie made other contributions to our knowledge of the citric acid fermentation. He showed that the proportion of oxalic and citric acids could be controlled by pH and the addition of inorganic salts. Low pH was found to favor the production of citric acid and suppress the formation of oxalic acid. Furthermore, it minimized the danger of contamination.

A large number of fungi have since been found capable of producing citric acid. Strains of Aspergillus, Penicillium, Mucor have been found to produce this acid, but strains of the *A. niger* group have proved the most satisfactory in the production of citric acid. The most desirable strains are those which efficiently convert sugar to the acid, are easily cultivated, retain their biochemical characteristics, and produce the least amount of other metabolic products.

Doelger and Prescott,[16] among others, corroborated the findings of Currie and carried out further extensive studies on the techniques of this fermentation. They found that the successive transfer of spores in the same medium stimulates the mold to give high yields of citric acid. They also observed that it was best to seed only one fourth to one half of the surface area of the medium. Where high yields were obtained, the molds produced very little if any spores. Thus sporulation, or lack of it, could be used as an index of the efficiency of a fermentation, according to these men.

Although many organic substances may be fermented to citric acid, sucrose and fructose have generally given the best results. Doelger and Prescott found that in batches which were allowed to ferment for 9 to 12 days, mashes containing 14 per cent sucrose were found to give the highest yields. They recommended the use of sucrose or technical glucose for industrial fermentations. These sugars were preferable to maltose or molasses. Fructose was also found to give high yields but its use would not be commercially feasible. Increasing the sugar content, or replacing part of the sucrose with glucose or fructose, or partially hydrolyzing sucrose during the sterilization process lowered the yields. However, molasses is used in present-day commercial practice.

Currie and Doelger and Prescott have shown that the molds generally produce more citric acid when inorganic salts containing potassium, phosphorus, magnesium, sulphur, and nitrogen are added to the fermentation liquor. Conflicting reports are found in the literature concerning the addition of iron and zinc. There is a distinct possibility that the strains of molds used react differently to the additions of these metals. Doelger and Prescott noted that the source of water used made a difference in the yields obtained. This observation may be linked with the mineral requirements of the molds. Where the water is deficient in trace amounts of these elements the addition of metals may help, and where there is already an abundance they may exert a toxic effect.

These men also found that the pH range of 1.6 to 2.2 was the most suitable for carrying out the fermentation with their organism. They recommend the use of hydrochloric acid in adjusting the pH to this range. Sulphuric, nitric, acetic, and formic acids were found to be inferior to this mineral acid. Whereas Wehmer and others have advocated the use of calcium carbonate to neutralize the acid formed during the fermentation, Prescott and Dunn [44] advise against its use. They maintain that its absence favors higher yields, shortens the fermentation periods, and decreases the possibilities of contamination.

Doelger and Prescott also studied the influence of the ratio of the surface area to the volume of the fermentation mash. They advocated the use of shallow pans of aluminum of high grade of purity for growing the mold and carrying out the fermentation. In such pans, there would be large surface areas of mycelium exposed to relatively shallow layers of medium. Agitation of the medium was found to be undesirable.

The optimum temperature range was found to be from 26° to 28° C. and the fermentation was generally completed in 7 to 10 days. The optimum amount of air passed over the mold mycelial mats varies with each installation of equipment, too low or too high supplies decreasing the yields of citric acid. While 60 per cent of the sugar may usually be recovered as citric acid, yields as high as 87, 90.7, and even 100 per cent have been reported.

After the fermentation is completed, the liquor is drained off and the mat pressed to remove any residual citric acid. Calcium carbonate may be used to adjust the pH of the liquor to approximate neutrality and calcium citrate is precipitated from a hot solution. The addition of sulphuric acid removes the calcium, which settles out as calcium sulphate, and citric acid is then recovered.

Cahn [7] has recommended that cane or beet pulp impregnated with molasses or sucrose be fermented at 20° to 35° C. He claims that the production of citric acid with the use of solid material shortens the fermentation period to 3 or 4 days and, because the fermentation proceeds so rapidly, the deleterious effects of bacterial contamination are obviated. Yields of 45 per cent on the basis of sugar in the molasses or 55 per cent on the basis of sucrose were claimed.

The exact details employed in the commercial production of citric acid have not been made available to the public as yet. The reader is referred to the publications of Currie, Doelger and Prescott, and to *Industrial Microbiology* by Prescott and Dunn for further generally known details on the techniques employed in this tricarboxylic acid fermentation.

Various theories have been suggested for the mechanism of the production of citric acid. Because the theory must be such as to explain its formation from two up to seven and even twelve carbon compounds, and because it must account for the high yields mentioned above, those which have been proposed up to now have been considered untenable.

In general there seem to be two schools of thought. One school maintains that the hexose chain is not broken but becomes transformed to citric acid with its forked chain. The other proposes that the hexose is initially split to shorter carbon chain compounds and subsequently built up to citric acid.

Challenger and his associates [10] and Franzen and Schmitt [19] present evidence in support of the hypothesis that glucose is not broken down but is converted to the forked tricarboxylic acid. They suggest the following series of reactions.

$C_6H_{12}O_6 \rightarrow$ Glucose

$$
\begin{array}{llll}
\text{COOH} \rightarrow & \text{COOH} \rightarrow & \text{COOH} \rightarrow & \text{COOH} \\
\cdot & \cdot & \cdot & \cdot \\
\text{CHOH} & \text{CHOH} & \text{CH}_2 & \text{CH}_2 \\
\cdot & \cdot & \cdot & \cdot \\
\text{CHOH} & \text{CHOH} & \text{C:O} & \text{HOC} \cdot \text{COOH} \\
\cdot & \cdot & \cdot & \cdot \\
\text{CHOH} & \text{CHOH} & \text{C:O} & \text{CH}_2 \\
\cdot & \cdot & \cdot & \cdot \\
\text{CHOH} & \text{CHOH} & \text{CH}_2 & \text{COOH} \\
\cdot & \cdot & \cdot & \text{Citric} \\
\text{CH}_2\text{OH} & \text{COOH} & \text{COOH} & \text{acid} \\
\text{Gluconic} & \text{Saccharic} & \beta,\gamma\text{-Diketo-} & \\
\text{acid} & \text{acid} & \text{adipic} & \\
& & \text{acid} &
\end{array}
$$

Bernhauer,[1] however, feels that the gluconic and saccharic acids found in the mold cultures (the presence of which is advanced as supporting evidence by the proponents of the first school of thought) originate from a side reaction. Various hypotheses have been advanced by the advocates of the second group of workers who maintain that sugar is first broken down and the intermediary substances subsequently condensed to form citric acid. The mechanism proposed by Bernhauer and Böckl [2] is typical of the various ones which have been suggested in that all or most believe that a condensation of a dicarboxylic acid and acetic acid occurs. (See reactions on the following page.)

As yet, even among the workers who claim that there is a condensation of intermediate carbon compounds, there seems to be a divergence of opinions. For greater details, consult the publications of Bernhauer and Iglauer,[3] Ciusa and Brüll,[12] Chrzaszcz and Janicki,[11] and Wells and his associates.[72]

The latter group of workers has carried out careful carbon balance experiments which demonstrated that some of the theories which have been advanced are quite untenable. They obtained yields of citric acid which could not be explained by many of the fermentation mechanisms which have been proposed, i.e., the actual yields proved to be higher than the theoretical. Furthermore the citric acid-carbon dioxide ratios found by them experimentally were higher than the theoretical.

Gluconic Acid Fermentation. That bacteria and molds are capable of transforming glucose to gluconic acid by a simple oxidation has been known for some time. As early as 1878, Boutroux noted that a bacterium, *"Mycoderma aceti" (Acetobacter aceti)*, could produce this acid. In 1922, Molliard [40] observed that *"Sterigmatocystis nigra" (Aspergillus niger)* grown on sucrose mashes produced gluconic acid

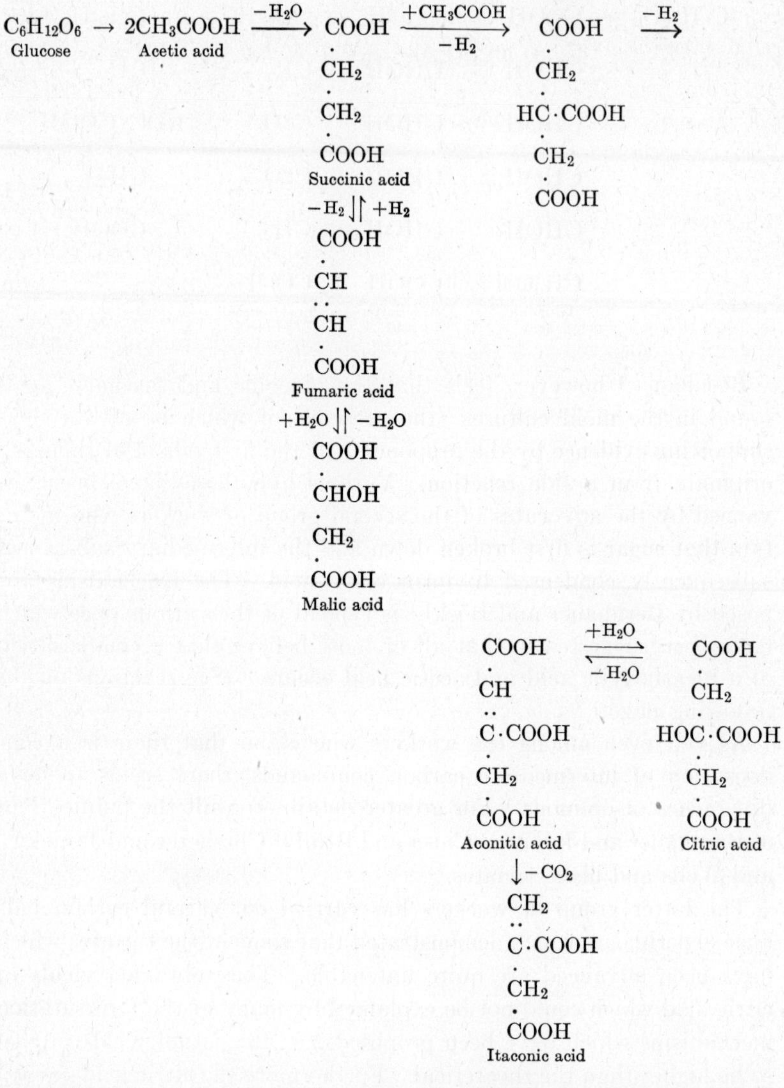

$$C_6H_{12}O_6 \rightarrow 2CH_3COOH \xrightarrow{-H_2O} \begin{array}{c} COOH \\ \cdot \\ CH_2 \\ \cdot \\ CH_2 \\ \cdot \\ COOH \end{array} \xrightarrow[-H_2]{+CH_3COOH} \begin{array}{c} COOH \\ \cdot \\ CH_2 \\ \cdot \\ HC \cdot COOH \\ \cdot \\ CH_2 \\ \cdot \\ COOH \end{array} \xrightarrow{-H_2}$$

Glucose   Acetic acid

Succinic acid

$$-H_2 \updownarrow +H_2$$

$$\begin{array}{c} COOH \\ \cdot \\ CH \\ \cdot\cdot \\ CH \\ \cdot \\ COOH \end{array}$$

Fumaric acid

$$+H_2O \updownarrow -H_2O$$

$$\begin{array}{c} COOH \\ \cdot \\ CHOH \\ \cdot \\ CH_2 \\ \cdot \\ COOH \end{array}$$

Malic acid

$$\begin{array}{c} COOH \\ \cdot \\ CH \\ \cdot\cdot \\ C \cdot COOH \\ \cdot \\ CH_2 \\ \cdot \\ COOH \end{array} \xrightleftharpoons[-H_2O]{+H_2O} \begin{array}{c} COOH \\ \cdot \\ CH_2 \\ \cdot \\ HOC \cdot COOH \\ \cdot \\ CH_2 \\ \cdot \\ COOH \end{array}$$

Aconitic acid   Citric acid

$$\downarrow -CO_2$$

$$\begin{array}{c} CH_2 \\ \cdot\cdot \\ C \cdot COOH \\ \cdot \\ CH_2 \\ \cdot \\ COOH \end{array}$$

Itaconic acid

in addition to citric and oxalic acids. Bernhauer [1] in 1924 noted that a strain of *A. niger* produced gluconic acid in the presence of calcium carbonate. He found that contrary to what was found in the citric acid fermentation (where relatively high temperatures, abundant supplies of nitrogen, and heavy mats are desirable) gluconic acid fermentation was favored by low temperatures, low supplies of nitrogen, and thin mat productions. Men of the Northern Regional Research Laboratory of the U. S. Department of Agriculture, May, Herrick, Wells, Moyer, and their associates, have carried out extensive studies on the methods and apparatus which are best suited for the production of this acid.

In the original shallow-pan method investigated by Herrick and May,[27] the organism used was *Penicillium purpurogenum* var. *rubrisclerotium* (Thom No. 2670). With this method of production, the gluconic acid yield was the best with a high concentration of sugar, 20 to 25 per cent solution of glucose, and a temperature of 25° C. The efficiency in the conversion of sugar to gluconic acid was found to be affected by the ratio of surface to volume of liquid, a ratio between 0.25 and 0.30 being the most feasible. Although agitation of the nutrient solution proved favorable when the concentration of the sugar was low, it did not affect the production of the acid when the sugar concentration was high. The fermentation could be carried out successfully over a wide *p*H range, 3 to 6.4. Yields of 55 to 65 per cent were obtained in about 11 days. The mold was grown on a glucose-salt solution in aluminum pans placed in a sterilizable chamber.

Since Schreyer,[57] working with *A. fumaricus*, first demonstrated in 1928 that the yield of this acid could be increased by agitation, aeration, and the use of calcium carbonate, a number of investigators have studied this technique of fermentation. With submerged growths of *P. chrysogenum*, aerated with filtered and humidified air, May, Herrick, Moyer and Wells [36] were able to obtain 80 to 87 per cent yields in about 8 days. The temperature used was 30° C. and calcium carbonate was added at the rate of 1 gram for every 4 grams of glucose. In addition to glucose, salts were added to the medium and nitrogen was supplied in the form of ammonium nitrate.

Herrick, Hellbach, and May [26] have also developed a rotary drum, submerged growth method using a strain of *A. niger*. The advantage of the rotating drum, submerged growth method (which they have developed to a pilot plant scale) over the aerated and agitated, submerged growth method was that the fermentation time could thus be cut down considerably, 80 per cent yields being obtained in a little over 2 days. The rotary drum apparatus is essentially a horizontally mounted, hollow, aluminum cylinder closed at both ends and equipped with buckets and baffles placed on the inside walls. The drum is slowly rotated to keep the fermenting culture aerated and mixed. A semi-continuous process has also been developed.[42] For specific details of the processes, the reader is referred to the publications of the Northern Regional Research Laboratory investigators.

Miscellaneous Minor Fermentations. GALLIC ACID. The production of citric and gluconic acids depends on fermentative changes brought about by molds. However, the production of gallic acid depends on a hydrolytic change, the hydrolysis of tannin. Scheele in 1787 first discovered gallic acid in an infusion of gallnuts which had been acted upon by a mold, but Van Tieghem [67] carried out the first real investigation of this hydrolysis. He demonstrated that gallnut extract made and kept sterile would not form gallic acid. However, on growth of the *Aspergillis niger* and *Penicillium glaucum* groups of molds, the acid was produced. Later workers showed that molds of *A. niger* group produced an extracellular enzyme, tannase, which was capable of hydrolyzing tannin to gallic acid.

Calmette [8] has patented a method whereby the clear tannin extract is placed in vats and sterilized, inoculated with "*A. gallomyces*," and the fermentation allowed to proceed. Agitation and introduction of large volumes of sterile air keep the organism submerged.

FUMARIC ACID. This unsaturated dicarboxylic acid was first reported to be produced by molds by Ehrlich [17] in 1911. Whereas certain species of the genera Mucor, Circinella, Cunninghamella, Penicillium, and Aspergillus produce small amounts of fumaric acid, strains of *Rhizopus nigricans* form large amounts of this acid. The nutrient solution used is a salt-glucose medium in which the carbohydrate-nitrogen ratio is, for highest yields, kept at a range between 25:1 and 300:1. Waksman,[69] who has patented a commercial process for the production of fumaric acid, found that the addition of zinc may modify these conditions. Thus the zinc and also the iron (which displays an antagonistic effect to zinc) contents must be rigidly controlled. The zinc seems to stimulate the mycelial growth of the mold at the expense of fumaric acid production whereas the latter has the reverse effect. He also found that the most favorable sources of nitrogen were salts of ammonia. The optimum temperature for the development of mycelium is 35° C. and the fermentation is best carried out at about 28°. Once the desired level of mycelial growth has been attained, the nutrient solution may be drained off and fresh liquor added in which the fermentation proceeds. This fresh liquor may be a 20 per cent pure sugar solution devoid of salts and other nutrients.

KOJIC ACID. This acid is of academic interest only, at the present time. It was isolated by Saito [56] in 1907 and studied and its constitution established by Yabuta [74] in 1924. Its chemical structure is

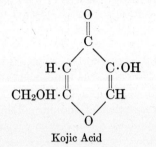

Kojic Acid

Since the initial reports of these Japanese workers, numerous papers have appeared on various aspects of the fermentation. Originally isolated as a by-product of the fermentation of steamed rice by an organism of the *Aspergillus flavus-Oryzae* group, it has since been found that several species of Aspergillus, *Penicillium Daleae,* and certain bacteria (species of Acetobacter) form it.

A large number of compounds can serve as the source of carbon, but the highest yields have been obtained by fermentation of glucose or xylose. Ammonium salts, especially ammonium nitrate, serve as good sources of nitrogen. Fermentations have been carried out over the pH range of 2.0 to 5.0 depending upon the organisms with which the individual investigators were working. Most of the studies have been carried out at temperatures ranging from 20° to 35° C., but May and his associates [37] recommend a range from 30° to 35° C. Depending on a number of factors, i.e., the mold species, incubation temperature, pH, salts, the fermentation generally requires from 7 to 20 days for completion. Yields of over 50 per cent have been reported by several investigators. May and his associates [38] observed that ethylene chlorohydrin when added in fairly low concentrations (0.01 per cent) markedly increases the yield of kojic acid in a fermentation period of 10 days.

Numerous mechanisms for the formation of kojic acid have been proposed. Yabuta and others have suggested that glucose is oxidized and dehydrated to kojic acid in the following manner.

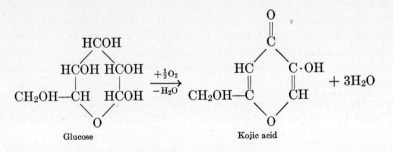

Glucose   Kojic acid

However, kojic acid can be formed from carbon compounds simpler than glucose so this reaction would necessitate the assumption that these compounds are first converted to glucose. Condensation of acetaldehyde normally occurring in a true alcoholic fermentation has been suggested. However, the experimental findings of Katagiri and Kitahara [31] and Gould [22] do not fit in very well with this theory. They found that the addition of sodium sulphite (an acetaldehyde binding or fixing compound) did not prevent the formation of kojic acid from glucose. However, dihydroxyacetone can be converted to kojic acid. Challenger and coworkers [9] and May and associates [37] suggest the possibility of a three carbon intermediate precursor. Challenger and his associates suggest the following reactions.

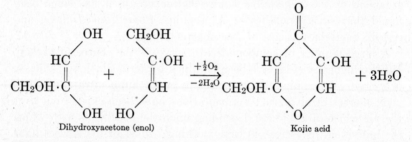

Dihydroxyacetone (enol)   Kojic acid

More research must be carried out before the problem can be considered settled.

Kojic acid is bacteriostatic in action, apparently more so against the Gram-negative than the Gram-positive groups of organisms, but it is toxic to laboratory animals. A few dyes and resins have been prepared experimentally from this acid.

Miscellaneous Acids, Metabolic Products, and Pigments. In addition to the acids formed by molds mentioned in the foregoing passages, various forms of the filamentous fungi produce a great variety of organic acids and other metabolic products when grown on glucose-salt media. Particularly active in investigating the chemistry of the filamentous fungi have been Raistrick,[49] Clutterbuck,[13] and their associates. Some of the compounds produced by the molds are listed in Tables 1 and 2. These tables are adapted from those compiled by Porter [43] in his excellent *Bacterial Chemistry and Physiology*. The nomenclature of the molds is that given by Porter which in general is that of the original writers. An idea of the enormously varied synthetic abilities of the molds can be obtained by an examination of these tables. As yet, most of these substances are of academic interest only, but the future may find useful functions for some of them.

That filamentous fungi growing in synthetic media with sugar synthesize amino acids is self-evident since the cell material must contain proteins. Contrary to the much quoted opinion of Abderhalden, cyclic amino acids are among those synthesized, and proline, phenylalanine, tryptophan, and tyrosine have been definitely identified. Indeed all the proteins essential for animal growth are present in a number of molds. Skinner and Muller [58] have grown molds on media consisting of inorganic salts and sugar and fed the mold as the sole source of protein to weanling rats. Although the rate of growth was slow it was definite. The limiting amino acid in all cases was methionine (or cystine). With the addition of one or the other of these amino acids the rate of growth of the animals was very much enhanced. The female animals were raised to maturity and they produced litters of young with no other protein food than mold mycelium plus cystine. This synthetic ability of molds was utilized in World War I according to Pringsheim and Lichtenstein.[48] Straw was inoculated with a species of Aspergillus and ammonium salts were added. This material was fed to cattle after the inorganic nitrogen was transformed to mold proteins.

Because of the high fat content of the mold mycelium, studies have been carried out to investigate the production of fats by molds. As much as 41.5 per cent of the mold mycelium may consist of fat according to Ward, Lockwood, May, and Herrick.[70] Most of the investigations have been carried out by cultivating the fungi on salt-glucose media. See Prescott and Dunn [44] for a discussion of the production of fats by molds.

The mycelium and spores of the various fungi are often brightly colored. Some of the pigments have been isolated and studied. Prescott and Dunn suggest the possibility that molds may be used commercially in the production of dyestuffs. The Chinese have long used *Monascus purpureus*, which produces a red pigment, in coloring rice, "Ang-quac," "wines," and sauces. The mold mycelium develops through the rice, giving it a friable texture and coloring the entire mass red or purple, or shades in between, depending upon the pH. This mold is also the cause of red silage, forming red masses up to one-third meter in diameter. Table 3 (pages 240 to 247) is an adaptation of a compilation by Porter [43] of some of the pigments produced by molds. Here also the nomenclature is that of Porter.

TABLE 1
MISCELLANEOUS ACIDS PRODUCED BY FUNGI

Acid	Formula	Produced by	Reference
Aconitic M.P. 191°C.	$HOOC \cdot CH_2C = CH \cdot COOH$ $\qquad\qquad\quad COOH$	*Aspergillus niger*	Bernhauer and Böckl (1932)
Aspergillic M.P. 84°–96°C.	$C_{12}H_{20}N_2O_2$	*Aspergillus flavus*	White and Hill (1943)
Byssochlamic M.P. 163.5°C.	$C_{18}H_{20}O_6$	*Byssochlamys fulva*	Raistrick and Smith (1933)
Carlic (*l*-α[γ-hydroxybutyryl]-γ-carboxymethyltetronic acid) M.P. 176°C.		*Penicillium charlesii*	Clutterbuck, Raistrick, and Reuter (1935)
Carlosic (*l*-α-butyryl-γ-carboxy-methyltetronic acid) M.P. 181°C.		*Penicillium charlesii*	Clutterbuck, Raistrick, and Reuter (1935)
Carolinic (α[β-carboxypropionyl]-γ-methyltetronic acid) M.P. 129°C.		*Penicillium charlesii*	Clutterbuck, Raistrick, and Reuter (1935)

Acid	Structure	Organism	Reference
3:5-Dihydroxyphthalic M.P. 188°–190°C.	COOH, COOH, OH, HO	Penicillium brevi-compactum	Oxford and Raistrick (1932)
Dimethylpyruvic	H_3C H / C·CO·COOH / H_3C	Aspergillus niger	Hida (1935) [cited by Birkinshaw (1937)]
Emodic (4:5:7-trihydroxyanthraquinone-2-carboxylic acid) M.P. 363°–365°C.	O, COOH, HO, OH, O, OH	Penicillium cyclopium	Anslow, Breen, and Raistrick (1940)
l-Ethylene oxide-α-β-dicarboxylic acid M.P. 179°–180°C.	HOOC·CH / O / HC·COOH	Penicillium viniferum, Monilia formosa	Sakaguchi, Inoue, and Tada (1939)
Formic	HCOOH	Aspergillus oryzae	Takodoro (1935)
Fulvic M.P. 246°C.	$C_{14}H_{12}O_8$	Penicillium griseo-fulvum, etc.	Oxford, Raistrick, and Simonart (1935)
Gentisic (2:5-dihydroxybenzoic acid) M.P. 197°–198°C.	COOH, OH, HO	Penicillium griseo-fulvum, etc.	Raistrick and Simonart (1933)
Glaucanic (very similar to byssochlamic acid)	$C_{18}H_{20}O_6$	Certain strains of Penicillium glaucum	Birkinshaw (1937)

TABLE 1 (*Continued*)

MISCELLANEOUS ACIDS PRODUCED BY FUNGI

Acid	Formula	Produced by	Reference
Glaucic M.P. 237°–238°C.	$C_{17}H_{22}O_5$	*Aspergillus glaucus*	Sumiki (1933)
Glauconic	$C_{18}H_{20}O_7$	Strains of *Penicillium glaucum*	Birkinshaw (1937)
Glucuronic	CHO $\\ $ (CHOH)$_4$ $\\ $ COOH	*Ustulina vulgaris*	Winschendorff and Killian (1928)
Glycolic and glyoxylic	H$_2$COH—COOH $\\ $ CHO—COOH	*Aspergillus niger*	Bernhauer and Scheuer (1932) [cited by Birkinshaw (1937)]
Helvolic M.P. 204.5°–205.5°C.	$C_{32}H_{44}O_8$	*Aspergillus fumigatus*	Chain, Florey, Jennings, and Williams (1943)
2-Hydroxymethylfurane-5-carboxylic (Sumiki's acid)	HC——CH $\\ $ HOOC·C C·CH$_2$OH $\\ $ O	*Aspergillus glaucus, Aspergillus clavatus, Aspergillus oryzae,* etc.	Sumiki (1929) [cited by Birkinshaw (1937)]

Acid	Structure	Organism	Reference
γ-Ketopentadecoic M.P. 92.6°C.	$H_3C \cdot (CH_2)_{10} \cdot CO \cdot (CH_2)_2 \cdot COOH$	Penicillium spiculisporum	Raistrick (1938)
Lactic	$CH_3 \cdot CHOH \cdot COOH$	Mucor and Rhizopus species	Raistrick (1938)
Luteic	Glucose and malonic acid formed on hydrolysis	Penicillium luteum	Birkinshaw and Raistrick (1933)
Malic	$HOOC \cdot CH_2 \cdot CHOH \cdot COOH$	Aspergillus and Clasterosporium, species	Birkinshaw (1937)
l-γ-Methyltetronic M.P. 115°C.		Penicillium charlesii	Clutterbuck, Raistrick, and Reuter (1935)
Methylsalicylic (6-hydroxy-2-methylbenzoic acid)		Penicillium griseo-fulvum, Penicillium flexuosum	Oxford, Raistrick, and Simonart (1935)
Minioluteic (γ-lactone of α-β-dihydroxy-n-tetradecanoic acid) M.P. 171°C.		Penicillium minio-luteum	Birkinshaw and Raistrick (1934)

TABLE 1 (*Continued*)

MISCELLANEOUS ACIDS PRODUCED BY FUNGI

Acid	Formula	Produced by	Reference
Mycophenolic M.P. 141°C.		*Penicillium brevi-compactum*	Clutterbuck and Raistrick (1933)
Penicillic (γ-keto-β-methoxy-δ-methylene-Δ^{α}-hexenoic acid or the corresponding γ-hydroxylactone) M.P. 83°–84°C.		*Penicillium puberulum, Penicillium cyclopium*	Birkinshaw, Oxford, and Raistrick (1936)
Puberulic M.P. 296°C.		*Penicillium puberulum, Penicillium aurantio-virens*	Birkinshaw and Raistrick (1932)

		$Aspergillus\ niger$	
Pyruvic	$CH_3 \cdot CO \cdot COOH$		Hida (1935) [cited by Birkinshaw (1937)]
Spiculisporic (γ-lactone of γ-hydroxy-β-δ-dicarboxy-pentadecoic acid)	CH_3 $(CH_2)_9$ $HC \cdot COOH$ HC —— O $HC \cdot COOH$ — CH_2 CO	$Penicillium\ spiculisporum$	Clutterbuck, Raistrick, and Rintoul (1931) Birkinshaw and Raistrick (1934)
Succinic	$CH_2 \cdot COOH$ $CH_2 \cdot COOH$	$Mucor$ species, $Aspergillus$ $terreus$, $Penicillium$ $aurantio$-$virens$	Birkinshaw (1937)
Stipitatic M.P. 302°–304°C.	$C_8H_6O_5$	$Penicillium\ stipitatum$	Birkinshaw, Chambers, and Raistrick (1942)
Terrestric (hydrate) (α-[L-γ-hydroxy-n-hexanoyl]-L-γ-methyltetronic acid) M.P. 89°C.	$HO \cdot C \!=\!\!=\! C \cdot CO \cdot (CH_2)_2 \cdot CHOH \cdot C_2H_5$ $H_3C \cdot CH$ —— CO O	$Penicillium\ terrestre$	Birkinshaw and Raistrick (1936)

Reprinted by permission from *Bacterial Chemistry and Physiology*, by J. R. Porter, published by John Wiley and Sons, Inc.

TABLE 2

MISCELLANEOUS METABOLIC PRODUCTS OF FUNGI

[From Iwanoff and Zwetkoff (1936), Birkinshaw (1937), Lockwood and Moyer (1938), Raistrick (1938, 1940), and Others]

Product	Formula	Produced By
Aldehydes		
Acetaldehyde	$CH_3 \cdot CHO$	*Aspergillus, Mucor,* and *Penicillium* species
Anisaldehyde [1] (p-methoxybenzaldehyde)	$CH_3O \cdot C_6H_4 \cdot CHO$	*Trametes suaveolens*
Palitantin [2] (unsaturated dihydroxyaldehyde) M.P. 135°–163°C.	$C_{14}H_{22}O_4$	*Penicillium palitans*
Alcohols		
Ethyl [3]	C_2H_5OH	*Fusarium lini* and related species: certain *Aspergillus* and *Penicillium* species
Gentisyl [4] (2:5-dihydroxybenzyl alcohol) M.P. 100°C.	OH $\bigcirc CH_2OH$ OH	*Penicillium patulum*
Glycerol	$CH_2OH \cdot CHOH \cdot CH_2OH$	Certain *Aspergillus, Helminthosporium,* and *Clasterosporium* species
i-Erythritol	$HOCH_2 \cdot (CHOH)_2 \cdot CH_2OH$	*Penicillium* species
Mannitol	$HOCH_2 \cdot (CHOH)_4 \cdot CH_2OH$	*Byssochlamys fulva, Aspergillus, Penicillium, Helminthosporium,* and *Clasterosporium* species
Esters		
Ethyl acetate	$CH_3 \cdot COOC_2H_5$	*Penicillium digitatum*
Methyl anisate [1]	$CH_3O \cdot C_6H_4 \cdot COO \cdot CH_3$	*Trametes suaveolens*
Nitrogenous substances		
Alkaloids	$C_{16}H_{16}O_2N_2,$ $C_{19}H_{23}O_2N_3,$ $C_{21}H_{27}O_3N_3,$ etc.	Ergot
Choline	$(CH_3)_3NOH \cdot CH_2 \cdot CH_2OH$	*Boletus elegans*
Hydroxylamine	NH_2OH	*Aspergillus niger*
Nitrogenous acid [5]	$C_{22}H_{28}O_5N$	*Penicillium griseo-fulvum*
Nitrogenous acid [5]	$C_{40}H_{79}O_5N$	*Penicillium brefeldianum*
Phenylethylamine	$(C_6H_5) \cdot (C_2H_5)NH$	*Boletus luteus*
Urea	$H_2N \cdot CO \cdot NH_2$	*Aspergillus niger*
Proteins, amino acids, etc.		

[1] Birkinshaw, Bracken, and Findlay (1944).
[2] Birkinshaw and Raistrick (1936).
[3] Nord (1939), Gould and Tytell (1941), Tytell and Gould (1941).
[4] Birkinshaw, Bracken, and Raistrick (1944).
[5] Oxford, Raistrick, and Simonart (1935).

TABLE 2 (*Continued*)

MISCELLANEOUS METABOLIC PRODUCTS OF FUNGI

[From Iwanoff and Zwetkoff (1936), Birkinshaw (1937), Lockwood and Moyer (1938), Raistrick (1938, 1940), and Others]

Product	Formula	Produced By
Sulfur substances Thiourea Cyclic choline [6]	$H_2N \cdot CS \cdot NH_2$ $(CH_3)_3N \cdot CH_2 \cdot CH_2O \cdot SO_2$ $\rule{1cm}{0.4pt} O \rule{1cm}{0.4pt}$	*Verticillium albo-atrum,* *Botrytis cinerea* *Aspergillus sydowi*
Chlorine substances Caldariomycin [7] (2:2-dich- lorocyclopentane-1:3- diol) M.P. 121°C.	Cl_2 C HCOH HCOH $H_2C \rule{1cm}{0.4pt} CH_2$	*Caldariomyces (Fumago)*
Erdin [8] M.P. 211°C. Geodin [8] M.P. 235°C. Griseofulvin [9] M.P. 218°–219°C.	$C_{15}H_7O_6(OCH_3)Cl_2$ $C_{15}H_6O_5(OCH_3)_2Cl_2$ OCH_3 H_3CO $Cl \quad O \quad CH_3$ $COOCH_3$	*Aspergillus terreus* *Aspergillus terreus* *Penicillium griseo-fulvum*
Arsenic and selenium sub- stances [10] Dimethyl-*n*-propylarsine Dimethyl selenide Trimethylarsine	$(CH_3)_2 \cdot As \cdot (C_3H_7)$ $Se \cdot (CH_3)_2$ $As \cdot (CH_3)_3$	*Penicillium brevicaule*
Miscellaneous substances Mellein or ochracin M.P. 58°C.	O $OH \quad C$ O $CH \cdot C_2H_5$	*Penicillium griseo-* *fulvum, Aspergillus* *melleus, Aspergillus* *ochraceus*

[6] Woolley and Peterson (1937).
[7] Clutterbuck, Mukhopadhyay, Oxford, and Raistrick (1940).
[8] Calam, Clutterbuck, Oxford, and Raistrick (1939).
[9] Oxford, Raistrick, and Simonart (1939).
[10] Thom and Raper (1932), Challenger and Rawlings (1936).

TABLE 2 *(Continued)*

MISCELLANEOUS METABOLIC PRODUCTS OF FUNGI

[From Iwanoff and Zwetkoff (1936), Birkinshaw (1937), Lockwood and Moyer (1938), Raistrick (1938, 1940), and Others]

Product	Formula	Produced By
Miscellaneous substances (*cont.*) Sulochrin [11] (methyl ester of 2:6:4'-trihydroxy-4-methyl-6'-methoxybenzo-phenone-2'-carboxylic acid) M.P. 262°C.		*Oöspora sulfurea-ochracea*
Terrein [12] (4-propenyl-2-hy-droxy-3:5-oxidcyclopen-tane-1-one) M.P. 127°C.		*Aspergillus terreus*

[11] Nisikawa (1940).

[12] Clutterbuck, Raistrick, and Reuter (1937).

Reprinted by permission from *Bacterial Chemistry and Physiology*, by J. R. Porter, published by John Wiley and Sons, Inc.

MOLD ENZYME PREPARATIONS

From the foregoing sections it can be seen that molds must possess a wide variety of enzymes to carry out the various changes. Some enzymes catalyze certain useful reactions and can be utilized by man. Hence, some molds have been grown for their enzyme content.

An extremely useful enzyme which can be prepared from certain strains of the *Aspergillus flavus-Oryzae* group of organism is amylase (diastase). This enzyme hydrolyzes starch to dextrins and sugars. A number of methods have been used to prepare amylase industrially. In the oldest method, rice or wheat bran is moistened to about 60 per cent water content. It is then steamed for 1 to 2 hours to solubilize the starch and destroy some of the undesirable contaminating organisms present. The solid medium is allowed to cool to about 30° C. and is then inoculated with spores of a selected strain of Aspergillus. The inoculated and well-mixed bran is then placed in shallow layers on trays, provided with false bottom wire nets, the trays being stacked on racks. At first, it may be necessary to apply external heat to keep the temperature at 30° C. However, as the mold develops, heat is generated and the molding bran must be cooled. Ample amounts of moist (to prevent the drying of bran) air to furnish oxygen for the mold and to cool the bran are essential. In about 48 hours the development of the mold, and of the enzyme, is at a maximum. The molding material may now be dried or the crude amylase preparation extracted with water. A precipitate of the crude enzyme may be obtained by the addition of aqueous extract to alcohol to produce a 70 per cent alcohol concentration. The alcohol precipitate, dried *in vacuo* at 30° C. and powdered, presents a white to a whitish yellow appearance. Aqueous solutions of amylase, if not to be used for medicinal purposes, should be preserved with chemical antiseptics such as chloroform, toluene, thymol, phenol. Addition of sodium chloride to produce a 20 per cent concentration has also been recommended. In the Orient, amylase preparations of strains of *A. flavus-Oryzae* group have been used in much the way we use malt in the occidental countries. The use of this mold enzyme preparation was introduced in the United States by Takamine. At present commercial mold amylase preparations may be obtained under various trade names. It should be noted that most of these preparations are not pure amylase but actually mixtures of various enzymes and thus may display proteolytic activity in addition to their amylolytic property.

A more recent development has been the growing of the desired mold on bran placed in rotating drums, much like those used in drying germinated barley (in the preparation of malt). The moistened bran, after inoculation, is tumbled in the rotating drums until the mycelial growth and amylase contents are at a maximum.

The most recent method advocated for the production of fungus amylases is that described by Fulmer and his associates.[33] They employ aluminum pots or pans with holes drilled in the bottoms. The pots are filled with wheat bran moistened with $0.3 N$ hydrochloric acid and inoculated with sporulated cultures of the mold. The initial temperature of the mash is 30° C., but with the rapid growth of the mold it rises to 37° to 40° C. in about 8 hours. Air is then passed through the mash to maintain a temperature below 45° C. After 12 to 24 hours of aeration the contents of the pots are removed and dried. These investigators found that while certain strains of Rhizopus gave good yields, strains of *A. flavus-Oryzae* group gave not only good yields but also the most consistent results.

Amylase is used in the preparation of sizes and adhesives, textile desizing, clarification of certain fruit juices, and the like.

Invertase, an enzyme which hydrolyzes sucrose to invert sugar, i.e., glucose and levulose, can also be prepared from certain molds. It is used in the confectionery and syrup industry. Protease, a mix-

TABLE 3

PIGMENTS PRODUCED BY CERTAIN FUNGI

Pigment	Structural Formula	Fungus	Reference
Aspergillin (brown)	Similar to humic acids from peats	Aspergillus niger, spores	Quilico (1933)
Atromentin (brown) ($C_{18}H_{12}O_6$)		Paxillus atromentosus	Kögl and Becker (1928)
Aurantin (yellow) ($C_{16}H_{22}O_3$)		Oöspora aurantia	Birkinshaw (1937)
Aurofusarin (orange-yellow) ($C_{30}H_{20}O_{12}$) M.P. above 360°C.		Fusarium culmorum	Ashley, Hobbs, and Raistrick (1937)
Auroglaucin (golden-orange) ($C_{19}H_{22}O_3$) M.P. 146°–152°C.		Aspergillus glaucus, species	Gould and Raistrick (1934) Cruickshank, Raistrick, and Robinson (1938)

Boletol (blue) ($C_{15}H_8O_7$) M.P. 253°C.		*Boletus luridus Boletus satanas*	Kögl and Deijs (1934)
β-Carotene (yellow)		*Mucor hiemalis Phycomyces blakesleeanus*	Birkinshaw (1937)
Carviolacin (red to orange) ($C_{20}H_{16}O_7$) Carviolin (red to orange) ($C_{16}H_{12}O_6$)		*Penicillium carmin-oviolaceum*	Hind (1940)
Catenarin [β-(hydroxymethyl)-1:5:8-trihydroxyanthra-quinone] (red) ($C_{15}H_{10}O_6$) M.P. 246°C.		*Helminthosporium catenarium Helminthosporium gramineum Helminthosporium tritici-vulgaris Helminthosporium velutinum*	Raistrick, Robinson, and Todd (1934)

TABLE 3 (Continued)

PIGMENTS PRODUCED BY CERTAIN FUNGI

Pigment	Structural Formula	Fungus	Reference
Chrysogenin (yellow) ($C_{18}H_{22}O_6$)		*Penicillium chrysogenum* *Penicillium notatum*	Clutterbuck, Lovell, and Raistrick (1932)
Citrinin (yellow) ($C_{13}H_{14}O_5$) M.P. 166°–170°C.		*Penicillium citrinum*	Hetherington and Raistrick (1931)
Citromycetin (lemon-yellow) ($C_{14}H_{10}O_7 \cdot 2H_2O$) M.P. 283°–285°C.		*Citromyces glaber* *Citromyces pfefferianus*	Hetherington and Raistrick (1931)

Cynodontin (probably 1:4:5:8-tetrahydroxy-2-methylanthraquinone) (bronze-like) ($C_{15}H_{10}O_6$) M.P. 260°C.		*Helminthosporium cynodontis* *Helminthosporium euchlenae*	Raistrick, Robinson, and Todd (1933)
Emodic acid (4:5:7-trihydroxyanthraquinone-2-carboxylic acid) (orange) ($C_{15}H_8O_7$) M.P. 363°–365°C.		*Penicillium cyclopium*	Anslow, Breen, and Raistrick (1940)
Ergochrysin (yellow) ($C_{28}H_{28}O_{12}$) M.P. 266°C.		*Ergot*	Bergmann (1932)
Erythroglaucin (ruby-red) ($C_{16}H_{12}O_6$) M.P. 205°–206°C.		*Aspergillus ruber* *Aspergillus glaucus,* species	Ashley, Raistrick, and Richards (1939) Gould and Raistrick (1934)
Flavoglaucin (lemon-yellow) ($C_{19}H_{28}O_3$) M.P. 97°–105°C.		*Aspergillus glaucus,* species	Gould and Raistrick (1934)
Fulvic acid (yellow) ($C_{14}H_{12}O_8$) M.P. 246°C.		*Penicillium Brefeldianum Penicillium flexuosum Penicillium griseo-fulvum*	Oxford, Raistrick, and Simonart (1935)

TABLE 3 (Continued)

PIGMENTS PRODUCED BY CERTAIN FUNGI

Pigment	Structural Formula	Fungus	Reference
Fumigatin (3-hydroxy-4-methoxy-2:5-toluquinone) (maroon) ($C_8H_8O_4$) M.P. 116°C.		Aspergillus fumigatus	Anslow and Raistrick (1938)
Helminthosporin (2-methyl-4:5:8-trihydroxyanthraquinone) (dark-maroon crystals) ($C_{15}H_{10}O_5$) M.P. 226°–227°C.		Helminthosporium gramineum	Charles, Raistrick, Robinson, and Todd (1933)
Lactarazulene (blue) ($C_{15}H_{18}$) Lactaroviolin (red-violet) ($C_{15}H_{14}O$)		Lactarius deliciosus	Willstaedt (1935, 1936, 1939)
Monascoflavin (yellow) ($C_{17}H_{22}O_4$)		Monascus purpureus	Birkinshaw (1937)
Monascorubrin (red) ($C_{22}H_{24}O_5$)		Monascus purpureus	Birkinshaw (1937)

Pigment	Structure	Organism	Reference
Muscarufin (orange-red) ($C_{25}H_{16}O_9$) M.P. 275.5°C.		*Amanita muscaria*	Kögl and Erxleben (1930)
Oösporin (purple-brown with $FeCl_3$) ($C_{10}H_{14}O_2$)		*Oöspora aurantia*	Birkinshaw (1937)
Penicilliopsin (orange) ($C_{30}H_{24}O_8$) M.P. 330°C.		*Penicilliopsis clavariae-formis*	Oxford and Raistrick (1940)
Phenicin (yellow, red, or violet, depending on pH) ($C_{14}H_{10}O_6$) M.P. 230°–231°C.		*Penicillium pheiceum*	Posternak (1938)
Physcion (red-orange) ($C_{16}H_{12}O_5$) M.P. 203°–204°C.		*Aspergillus glaucus,* species	Ashley, Raistrick, and Richards (1939)

TABLE 3 (*Continued*)

PIGMENTS PRODUCED BY CERTAIN FUNGI

Pigment	Structural Formula	Fungus	Reference
Polyporic acid (2:5-diphenyl-3:6-dihydroxybenzoquinone) (yellow) ($C_{18}H_{12}O_4$) M.P.206°–207°C.		*Polyporus rutilans*	Kögl (1925)
Ravenelin (3-methyl-1:4:8-trihydroxyxanthone) ($C_{14}H_{10}O_5$) M.P. 267°–268°C.		*Helminthosporium ravenelii* *Helminthosporium turcicum*	Raistrick, Robinson, and White (1936)
Rubrofusarin (red) ($C_{15}H_{12}O_5$) M.P. 210°–211°C.		*Fusarium culmorum*	Ashley, Hobbs, and Raistrick (1937)
Sclerotiorine (yellow-brown in alkali) ($C_{20}H_{20}O_5Cl$) M.P. 206°–207°C.		*Penicillium sclerotiorum*	Curtin and Reilly (1940)

Spinulosin (6-hydroxyfumigatin (blue-purple) $(C_8H_8O_5)$ M.P. 200 °C.	H_3C ... OH ... O ... OCH_3 ... HO ... O	*Penicillium spinulosum*	Anslow and Raistrick (1938)
Telephoric acid (indigo-blue) $(C_{20}H_{12}O_9)$	OH ... $(CH{=}CH)_2COOH$ ... OH ... O ... O ... OH ... $COOH$ ... HO	*Telephora*, species	Kögl, Erxleben, and Jänecke (1930)
Tritisporin [1:3:5:8-tetrahydroxy-6-(or 7)-(hydroxymethyl) anthraquinone] (red-brown) $(C_{15}H_{10}O_7)$ M.P. 260°–262°C.	OH O OH ... $HOCH_2$ ... OH ... OH O	*Helminthosporium tritici-vulgaris*	Raistrick, Robinson, and Todd (1934)
Verdazulene (green) $(C_{15}H_{16})$		*Lactarius deliciosus*	Willstaedt (1939)
Xylindein (malachite-green) $(C_{34}H_{26}O_{11})$		*Peziza aeruginosa* (wood-rotting fungus)	Rommier (1868) White (1939)

Reprinted by permission from *Bacterial Chemistry and Physiology*, by J. R. Porter, published by John Wiley and Sons, Inc.

ture of proteolytic enzymes (proteinases, polypeptidases, dipeptidases), may be obtained from certain strains of the *A. flavus-Oryzae* group. They are used in the manufacture of glue, degumming silk, in dehairing and bating of hides, in making chill-proof beer, and so on. Pectinase, an enzyme hydrolyzing pectin, may be obtained from certain strains of Penicillium and is used in clarifying certain fruit juices.

USE OF MOLDS IN FOOD PRODUCTS

The ripening processes used for certain cheeses such as the Roquefort type (Roquefort, Gorgonzola, Stilton, American Blue-veined), Camembert, and Brie are dependent largely on the metabolic activities of certain molds.

In the preparation of Roquefort cheese, a friable, hard curd cheese, the proteins of the milk are coagulated by a preliminary lactic acid fermentation (carried out by *Streptococcus lactis*) and the addition of rennet. After the curd has set, it is cut into small sections to allow the whey to drain. *Penicillium roqueforti* is grown on rye bread and the entire moldy mass dried and powdered. This powder is then sprinkled in with the curd as the latter is placed in sterilized hoops. The curd is mechanically perforated to allow sufficient aeration for the growth of the mold. The ripening process which requires from 5 to 6 months takes place under carefully controlled conditions of temperature and humidity. Salt is periodically applied to the surface of the ripening cheese to cut down the population of undesirable microorganisms. *P. roqueforti* develops through the cheese, particularly around the holes that have been punched in the curd. It is believed that its lipolytic activities in forming caproic, caprylic, and capric acids or their derivatives are responsible for the development of the desirable aroma and flavor. In the original Roquefort method ewe's milk was used but the Roquefort-type cheese on the American market, at least, is prepared from cow's milk.

Camembert cheese, a soft curd-type cheese, is ripened by the use of *P. camemberti*. The curd is first produced by the action of rennet, not as much whey being allowed to drain out as with the Roquefort-type cheese. The curd is placed in rather small forms because the ripening process depends very largely on the diffusion of enzymes from the surface (where the mold develops) to the interior, and the ripening period would be prolonged with larger cheeses. The mold is, as with the Roquefort-type cheese, grown on bread which is then dried and powdered. The mold product is dusted upon the surface of the curd which is then allowed to ripen under controlled conditions of temperature and humidity. The Penicillium grows over the surface of the curd, producing an abundant snow-white mycelium. After a time, it may form a light green coat of conidia. The ripening process depends upon the proteolytic activities of the organism; when mature, about 80 per cent of the nitrogenous matter has been made water soluble.[5] The ripening begins on the surface and gradually proceeds toward the interior. After the cheese has been properly ripened by *P. camemberti*, it may undergo rapid spoilage by a secondary growth of other organisms and so it must be marketed shortly after ripening. The cheese is often packed before it is fully matured, the ripening process being allowed to continue in the container. Cheese of the Brie type is also produced in a manner similar to that used for the manufacture of Camembert cheese. A special mold is allowed to develop on the surface of the curd.

Strains of organisms of the *Aspergillus flavus-Oryzae* group play important roles in the national economy of the Far Eastern countries, the mold being used in the preparation of many foods. The mold serves the same function in their economy that malt does in the occidental countries. A large number of food preparations used in Japan and China are fermented foods. The conversion of starch to sugars is brought about by the amylolytic enzymes and the proteins hydrolyzed by the proteolytic enzymes of strains of *A. flavus-Oryzae*.

The term koji has been applied by the Japanese to starter. This preparation, generally grown in rice or rice and wheat bran or meal, is a rather mixed culture from which a number of organisms can be obtained. There are several types of koji. Each type is used for a specific product as: sake koji for making rice beer or "wine"; shoyu koji for making shoyu (soy sauce); miso koji for making miso, a thick brown paste or porridge; and shochu koji for making shochu (distilled alcoholic drink). Koji is thus applied to a variety of products, made in a number of ways, depending upon its ultimate usage, and from a number of substances. The predominating organism in the mixed cultures may also vary. It may be prepared by inoculating the steamed rice or wheat bran after cooling with spores of a strain of the *A. flavus-Oryzae* group. The moist, inoculated mass is incubated at 25° to 30° C. for a few hours in a heap until the hyphae of the mold develop. Then it is spread out in shallow layers until the enzymatic (amylolytic and proteolytic) contents are at their maxima. During the growth and development of mycelium the moist mass heats considerably so it is occasionally stirred. If the product is not used immediately, it may be dried.

Shoyu (soy sauce) is a sauce prepared from soybean. The beans are cooked, mixed with ground, roasted wheat and koji, and allowed to ferment. The mash is allowed to incubate until the sporulating mycelium develops, this process taking about 3 days. The molding mass is then placed in a concentrated salt brine where the aging takes place. The liquor may be agitated occasionally to advantage. During this aging process, an enzymatic digestion occurs; the cell structure of the bean is broken down, the small amount of starch is converted to sugar by the diastase and the proteins of the bean are hydrolyzed by the proteolytic enzymes of the mold. The fermenting liquor acquires a dark brown color during the aging process which may extend over a period of a few months to a few years. The salt concentration is very high (about 15 per cent), and though various yeasts and bacteria are present they play only a minor role in the process. The final product, after pressing, boiling, and filtration, bears a striking resemblance to meat extract, in both flavor and composition. The resemblance in flavor to meat extract is due to the presence of the sodium salt of glutamic acid, an amino acid formed from the hydrolysis of soybean proteins during the aging. Soy sauce reaches occidental tables in condiments such as Worcestershire sauce of which it forms the base.

Miso (soybean paste or porridge) is prepared by mixing mashed, steamed soybeans, salt, and koji and allowing the whole to undergo a brief fermentation. The bean is partially digested, the starch and proteins are hydrolyzed to produce the characteristic flavor, and the high salt concentration prevents the development of putrefactive organisms. Miso may be used for broths or it may be used for "curing" vegetables, fish, and other foods.

Tamari is a soybean sauce differing from shoyu in that rice is often added and the dominant organism involved in bringing about the changes is *A. tamarii*. The ripening process is generally shorter.

Mucor Rouxii has been used industrially for the production of alcohol. It secretes both amylase and the zymase complex of enzymes, and can therefore produce alcohol directly from starch without any malting process. It is used in the Orient for preparing alcoholic beverages from rice. It is marketed under the name Chinese yeast, in little balls of rice meal, much as we in the Occident sell yeast cakes. It has also been used commercially for alcohol production in Europe.

A number of species of Rhizopus closely resembling *Rhizopus nigricans* have been obtained from ferments used in oriental countries. They are all very active in changing starch to sugar. *R. japonicus* occurs as a contaminant or accompanying ferment, along with strains of the *A. flavus-Oryzae* group, in koji. It is actively diastatic, and has been used commercially in Europe in malting corn meal preparatory to alcoholic fermentation. It also produces a little alcohol itself. *R. Oryzae* is a similar mold obtained from Javanese raji, a ferment used in the preparation of the alcoholic beverage arrak from rice. *R. Tritici* is obtained from a preparation grown on wheat meal.

The use of *Neurospora sitophila* in Java to produce a fermented food product has been described. Ground peanuts are inoculated with spores of this mold and pressed into cakes, which on incubation develop the bright orange color of the fungus. A number of proteolytic, saccharolytic, and lipolytic enzymes have been studied in *N. sitophila* and probably many of these take part in the ripening of the product.

MOLD SPOILAGE IN FOOD PRODUCTS

The ability of molds to grow (though slowly) at relatively low temperatures, and their ability to multiply in media of high osmotic pressure or high acidity, fit them for growth in a number of food products which have been treated in various ways to prevent bacterial decomposition. Thus we find them as important causes of spoilage in preserved fruits and jellies, pickles, butter and cheese, salted, dried, and smoked meats, and stored fruits and vegetables. Storage for a sufficient length of time in a sufficiently humid atmosphere is the condition which may lead to mold development.

The absence of air and the temperatures of processing are sufficient to eliminate molds as an important problem in commercially canned foods. However, the imperfect sealing of mason jars used in home canning frequently allows mold development on home-packed fruits, jellies, and vegetables. Species of Aspergillus and Penicillium are most frequently found. Of commercial products packed in sealed containers, tomato catsup seems to be most commonly contaminated with molds. This is apparently due to the use of overripe tomatoes which have not been properly processed. Methods of enumerating mold mycelia and spores, as well as yeasts and bacteria, in catsup have been described by Howard.[29] Molds may also develop in cans of sweetened and condensed milk, forming small masses known as buttons. According to Rogers, Dahlberg, and Evans [54] this condition is due mainly to *Aspergillus repens,* though other molds may also be responsible. They grow until the residuum of air in the product has been used up, and may be prevented by low storage temperatures or by sealing the cans under vacuum.

Molds cause considerable trouble in the meat-packing industry, particularly with the various kinds of preserved meats. The growth of molds on hams, sausages, and bacon is very superficial and causes no pronounced decomposition of the product, but does cause marked economic loss through the expense of "reconditioning" the product and the reduced value due to its altered appearance. Molds and yeasts usually multiply extensively in the pickling vats. They are considered desirable by some packers, as they are supposed to take part in the chemistry of the pickling process and produce desirable flavors. However, others consider them undesirable.

The occurrence of molds on meat products appears to be largely determined by the degree of handling and the humidity of the storage rooms. Lewis and Yesair [32] isolated the following species from various meats, pickling solutions, and the walls or containers of the packing plants: *Mucor racemosus, Rhizopus nigricans,* a species of Mortierella, *"Oidium lactis," Neurospora sitophila, Monascus purpureus, "Aspergillus glaucus," A. niger, A. clavatus, Penicillium expansum, Alternaria tenuis,* and a species of Fusarium. These were studied with regard to their temperature relations, their ability to adhere to and stain sausages, and the effects of various humidities, as well as their resistance to sodium hypochlorite and ozone. Jensen [30] is of the opinion that the enzymatic activity displayed by molds should be included in the list of causes of fat spoilage. He has surveyed the literature for reports of the various microorganisms which have been found to possess lipolytic activity. In his *Microbiology of Meats,* he has also discussed the organisms found in various meat products.

Of the various dairy products, butter is most subject to mold spoilage, although *Geotrichum candidum* and *Scopulariopsis brevicaulis* are frequently causes of undesirable flavors in cheese. Moldiness in butter is largely dependent on the initial contamination of raw materials, on manufacturing procedures, and on the temperature of holding. Macy and Combs [34] found the sources of contamination (in order of descending frequency) to be the raw cream (which was always contaminated), dry parchment, piping and pumps of the creamery, water, starter cultures, and salt. Thom and Shaw [66] recognize three main types of moldiness, the smudged type with dark or smoky areas due mainly to species of Alternaria and Cladosporium; the green type, due to Penicillia; and the "Oidium" type, with patches of yellow or orange discoloration caused by *G. candidum.*

A consideration of mold spoilage of stored fruits and vegetables carries one into the domain of plant pathology, for some of the rots of such products are due to organisms which have invaded the fruit on the living plant. Even with those which invade during storage we must remember that the plant tissues are alive, and presumably possess a mechanism which can be overcome only by certain species having to a certain degree parasitic qualities. It is not surprising, therefore, that we find some species of fungi occurring characteristically on each kind of fruit or vegetable. Thus, various fruits, especially the plums and cherries, are spoiled by pathogenic species of Sclerotinia, which also cause disease in the trees. *R. nigricans* is especially important as a cause of spoilage of fruits and stored potatoes, especially sweet potatoes. The small fruits, especially strawberries, are particularly susceptible. The disease in strawberries is known as leak, because of the softening and dripping of the fruit. It occurs as a source of considerable loss in shipment and is prevented by refrigeration. In sweet potatoes, a characteristic soft rot is produced, the main factors determining which are injury to the potatoes and humidity of the storage bins. For a bibliography of the rots caused by *R. nigricans*, see Heald.[25] The common soft rot of apples in storage is due to *P. expansum*. Although other organisms may at times cause spoilage of apples, certainly in the great majority of cases this Penicillium is responsible. An injury to the skin is apparently necessary for infection to take place. The spoilage of citrus fruits is caused by two species, *P. digitatum* and *P. italcum*. *P. digitatum* is sometimes referred to as *P. olivaceum*, since it forms conidia of an olive-green color. On oranges the olive-colored area is generally surrounded by a broad white zone of mycelium which has not formed conidia. *P. italcum* produces spores of a light blue-green color. Both species may frequently be found growing on one orange. As with the apples, these organisms are wound parasites, and losses may be avoided by care in handling and packing. Mucors occur frequently on fresh fruits, especially during shipment. A hairy, greyish growth of these molds often develops on grapes, thus preventing their sale. A similar growth of Sclerotinia may also develop on grapes, the mycelium penetrating the skin and the mold obtaining nourishment from the juice. It causes a rapid evaporation of water from the juice, without having a deleterious effect on the flavor of the grapes. It thereby increases the concentration of sugar to such a degree that grapes too sour for the manufacture of wine become sweet enough for this purpose. However, the mold may cause economic loss if allowed to develop unchecked. Species of Dematium and Alternaria have also been observed on grapes.

G. candidum (*Oidium lactis, Oospora lactis*) is a very common and widespread mold, said to be extraordinarily resistant to heat and antiseptics. It grows everywhere where lactic acid is present—on sour milk, cheeses, butter, sauerkraut, silage, and pickles. It is said to oxidize lactic acid completely to carbon dioxide and water, thus reducing the acidity of the medium in which it is growing. This, however, has not been satisfactorily proved, for it is also actively proteolytic and the reduction of acidity of sour milk may well be due to neutralization of the acid by the ammonia produced, rather than to the oxidation of lactic acid.

G. candidum is of practical importance in the dairy industries for, because of its proteolysis, it may in some cases cause spoilage and off flavors. However, in others it must take part in causing the proteolysis which is necessary for the manufacture of certain kinds of cheese. We have invariably found this mold in all samples of domestic or foreign Brie or Camembert cheese which we have examined. It is especially troublesome in butter and cottage cheese. It is ordinarily only found in the presence of lactic acid. The presence of this organism in any abundance in most dairy products is a good indication of uncleanliness, since it gives evidence that vessels have been used without proper cleansing or sterilizing after milk has stood in them long enough to sour.

The Mucors are also found, very frequently in stale, moist breads and are often called bread molds on this account. These organisms are capable of hydrolyzing starch to sugar. *N. sitophila* is another important cause of trouble in bakeries, giving rise occasionally to "epidemics" of infected bread. The spores apparently come from the flour.

S. brevicaulis is a common species of some importance in food spoilage. The spores are yellowish brown. It is important as a cause of spoilage of various substances. Growing more slowly than many other molds, it takes part in the final disintegration of the product. It is very active in proteolysis, producing ammonia abundantly from organic nitrogen compounds. In the presence of sugars, it produces, from arsenical compounds, diethylarsine which has a very characteristic garlic-like odor. This reaction has been used as a test for arsenic, the reaction being said to be more delicate than the usual chemical tests. Only arsenious acid or its salts of the alkaline metals may be detected readily, salts of the heavy metals not so surely, and arsenic sulphide not at all. Disagreeable odors may be produced on other substrates, described as ammoniacal, like turnips or cabbages. According to Thom it is an important secondary invader and cause of spoilage of Camembert cheese and other dairy products. It may be found, along with other molds, in corks, and may give rise to very disagreeable odors in bottled products which have been stoppered with such contaminated corks, without any evidence of mold growth in the product itself.

MOLDS IN TEXTILE AND WOOD PRODUCTS

It is not surprising that molds, because of their ubiquity and their ability to grow under adverse conditions, should be found in textiles. They may develop, under what would be considered unfavorable conditions for growth, to cause discoloration of fabrics or to lower the tensile strength of the material. They have been found capable of affecting either the raw fibers or the finished fabrics.

As would be expected, the filamentous fungi found associated with cotton are largely those found in soil, Cladosporium, Fusarium, Alternaria, Sporotrichum, Aspergillus, and Penicillium.[45] The molds found on fresh samples of raw cotton were capable of utilizing cellulose and starch as the sole source of carbon more readily than those found in stored samples. Thaysen and Bunker [62] present evidence that seems to indicate that cottons vary in their resistance to microbial activity as the origin of the samples varies. They found that of the three types tested the American cotton was the most resistant, followed closely by the Egyptian samples; those from India were the least resistant.

The term mildew is applied to the growth of fungi on fibers and fabrics; it results in discoloration and sometimes in the weakening or even disintegration of the material on which the growths occur. One hundred and eighty molds isolated from mildewed fabric have been described by Galloway.[20] Often, the mildew patches on textiles are brightly colored, being black, brown, yellow, green, or pink, depending on the color of the conidiospores and the pigments secreted by the molds. If the development of the fungi is allowed to proceed unchecked, the cotton material suffers what is termed tendering (weakening of the fibers). Another way in which discoloration may occur is by the growth of the fungi on unprocessed fibers and, by giving off acids, changing the pH of the material. During the subsequent processing which may require dyeing, the color does not go on the material uniformly, owing to local changes in pH. Often, organisms found on mildewed fabrics are incapable of utilizing cellulose. These molds are, however, capable of developing on the starch in the size, thereby satisfying their carbon requirement.

A number of tests have been devised to detect damage in fabrics or fibers caused by molds. Only one type will be briefly mentioned here. Fleming and Thaysen,[18] Prindle,[47] and others have devised tests involving the swelling of the fibers with carbon disulphide-sodium hydroxide or suprammonium solutions (preceded by staining with Victoria Blue B where the latter swelling solution is used). The fibers are then examined microscopically. When treated with such swelling solutions, normal cotton fibers present an appearance like a string of beads. The layers of cellulose swell except where they are enclosed by the cuticles and thus are constricted. The fibers of mildewed fabrics, on the other hand, do not present this appearance because the cuticles have been damaged or destroyed and the cellulose has been altered.

Although the use of a number of antiseptics, organic compounds, copper or zinc organic salts, and mercuric compounds have been advocated in controlling mold growths, the only sure way by which textile or textile material destruction by microorganisms can be prevented is by maintaining the moisture content of the materials below 8 per cent. This method of preventing mold destruction of fabrics or raw fibers is not feasible in all cases where the materials must be outdoors or where the fibers have to be wetted during the processing.

Thom, Humfield, and Holman [65] have devised a test to measure the mildew resistance of cotton fabrics. Sterilized samples of test fabric are placed on mineral salts agar in Petri dishes and inoculated with the spores of *Chaetomium globosum*. After incubation for 14 days at 28° to 30° C. the strips of fabric are washed and raveled down so that they contain the same number of threads as one inch of the original sample contained. The tensile strength is then measured by a suitable apparatus. More recently, Greathouse and his associates [23] devised another test for evaluating fabric treatment for mildew resistance, a modification of one Greathouse and others [24] had used previously. Their test involves placing strips of the samples to be tested on cotton batting strips placed in bottles laid on their sides. Sufficient liquid nutrient medium is added so that the test sample is in contact with the liquid, 5 to 10 ml. of the free liquid being present. These workers used both *C. globosum* and *Metarrhizium* sp. in the test. The samples are incubated for 7 days at about 30° C. and then washed, dried, and broken on the Scott tester. Greathouse and his coworkers [24] discussed the difficulties involved in the evaluation of the results obtained from this test procedure.

Wool is made up primarily of proteins whereas cotton is made up of cellulose. Species of Alternaria, Stemphylium, Oospora and Penicillium have been found by Prindle [46] to be capable of having deleterious effects on wool fibers. Species of Trichoderma, Cephalothecium, Dematium, Fusarium, and Aspergillus are some of the molds which can alter the structure of wool.

Molds can be used in the aerobic retting of flax. After being cut the flax plants are spread out on the ground during the autumn and winter in mild climates. Various molds attack the more available compounds. The bast fibers, largely cellulose in nature, are less easily available to most molds than are the pectins, hemicelluloses, proteins, and starch. When the retting process is complete the bast fibers can be easily separated. The crude fibers are then washed, combed, and prepared for spinning. There is said to be less danger of the cellulose fibers being attacked in the aerobic retting process than in the anaerobic method, whereby the flax is immersed in streams and the retting (a Middle English word for soaking) is carried out by anaerobic bacteria.

For further information, the reader is referred to Thaysen and Bunker [63] for an excellent discussion of mildewing in cotton goods and also to Prescott and Dunn.[44]

Although they are not the greatest source of economic loss, filamentous fungi may render wood less valuable for certain purposes. Species of Phialophora, Alternaria, Fusarium, Penicillium, Aspergillus, Cladosporium, Rhizopus, and others may produce stains or discolorations on lumber. The stains may be due to the color formed in the mycelium of the molds, to soluble pigments secreted by the molds, or to chemical reactions between enzymes or other compounds formed by molds and wood. Drying wood, or submergence in water, or chemically treating wood are measures that are taken to prevent discolorations due to the filamentous fungi. The fungi capable of disintegrating and destroying wood are, of course, not always harmful. By destroying wood and other cellulosic materials and thus returning organic substances back to the soil the molds play an important, and beneficial, role in the economy of nature.

SOIL FUNGI

The mold flora of soils have been studied extensively by a host of workers since 1886. The large number of colonies and the varied flora which appear when soil is plated out in acidified agar media make the soil an excellent source of organisms for study. Many of the molds used for monographic treatments of certain groups have come from soils. That molds exist in the soil as growing cells rather than exclusively as chance spores brought in by wind was finally proved by Conn and others who, by direct microscopic methods, demonstrated mycelium below the surface of the soil, and by Waksman and McClennan by less direct methods. On the basis of work at Rothamsted Experimental Station in England, Russell [55] estimated that in fertilized soil there was 1700 pounds of living fungus cell material per acre (2,000,000 pounds of soil), about twice as much as the material from bacteria, algae, and protozoa combined. It is probable that the source of most of our common molds is the soil, or the decaying vegetation on the surface of the soil. The taxonomy and distribution of the various molds found in soils are discussed in a number of contributions. The student is referred especially to a book by Gilman [21] published in 1945 which gives brief descriptions of all species of molds that have been reported in soil, together with keys to genera and species, and rather poor sketches of each genus.

Well over 250 species of molds have been isolated from soils. The most common genera are Penicillium, Zygorrhynchus, Trichoderma, Fusarium, Aspergillus, Mucor, Rhizopus, Alternaria, and Cladosporium, but many others are frequently found. Recently a considerable flora of Oomycetes (and of Myxomycetes!) has been demonstrated by special techniques. The relative abundance of different molds varies considerably with climate and with season. Here in Minnesota with our continental climate of cold winters and hot summers we find a decided difference between our early spring and our late summer flora. In the spring we find that Penicillium will produce almost as many colonies as all the other genera combined but in the heat of the summer we get many more Aspergillus, Alternaria, Fusarium, and Cladosporium. This may be partly due to organisms brought in from the southwest by prevailing winds but controlled experiments indicate that this is only part of the explanation. It has been stated that in warm climates the soil Aspergilli outnumber the Penicillia and in cold climates the reverse.

Soil fungi play two important roles in maintaining soil fertility. They readily decompose complex organic substances, especially starch, cellulose, chitin, and proteins, thus rendering the elements contained in dead plant and animal tissues available to plants as food. They assimilate soluble inorganic nitrogen compounds and minerals, thus removing them temporarily from soil solution, and so prevent their leaching out when present in excess over the needs of green plants.

It has been shown that under aerobic conditions in acid soils the decomposition of cellulose is carried out entirely by molds, but in neutral or basic soils both molds and bacteria take part in this decomposition. Only when the soil becomes completely anaerobic do molds play no part. The amount of nitrogen available to the fungi is frequently the limiting factor of cellulose decomposition. The soil fungi are also very active in ammonification. Many of the molds will produce ammonia from proteins more rapidly than the most active of the ammonifying bacteria. Thus the molds are among the primary agents concerned in the decomposition of dead plant matter in the soil. On the other hand, Heukelekian and Waksman have shown that about one third of the not inconsiderable non-nitrogenous material decomposed is built up into mold mycelium. A proportion of the organic matter of the soil consists of this mycelium living and dead. It may be again rendered available to green plants upon the death and disintegration of the fungi. Thus the molds tend to stabilize the supply of plant food in the soil. Although various claims have been made, there is little to lead one to believe that molds play any part in the oxidation of ammonium salts to nitrates, or to the fixation of atmospheric nitrogen.

Further information on soil fungi may be obtained from the monograph of Niethhammer [41] or from the briefer discussions of Waksman [68] or Brierley.[6]

Mycorrhiza. In connection with soil fungi, mention should also be made of a relationship between certain fungi and the roots of higher plants, called the mycorrhizal relationship. It is found that the roots of many plants are invested by a fine network of mycelium (ectotrophic mycorrhiza), which in some cases also penetrates the root tissues or cells in their roots (endotrophic mycorrhiza). Many species of fungi have been shown to be able to cause mycorrhiza in some plant or other. The normal roots become much modified in appearance. The association is obviously of benefit to the plant and hence can be given as an example of symbiosis in the sense that it is an association of two organisms with mutual benefit.

A recent work by Björkman,[4] unfortunately unavailable to the authors, has appeared which seems to give a new and very logical concept of the function of the mycorrhiza. Through the personal courtesy of Dr. L. G. Romel the outstanding features of this theory have been made available to us. It seems that the fungi enter the plants in the roots but do not develop further unless for some reason the carbon-nitrogen ratio becomes wide. Increase of light, moderate nitrogen starvation, or strangulation causes an excess of carbohydrate. The mycorrhiza seems to remove this excess and so benefit the plant. It acts as a parasite but only as long as the carbohydrate is in excess, thus actually benefiting the plant by removing the excess, but never as a parasite by removing the carbohydrate when it is not in excess. Bacteriologists will note the resemblance of this concept to that of the relationship of the legume plant and the legume bacteria as suggested by Giöbel.

In some families of plants, e.g., the Orchidaceae (orchids) and Ericaceae (heath plants), the mycorrhizal relationship is obligatory for the normal development of the plants. In a few cases it has been necessary to bring the fungus to the seedling crop plant where the fungus was not found naturally in the soil. In orchids it is known that the mycorrhizal fungi are necessary for the development of the seedling. Soil from the natural habitat contains the fungus, hence some of this is used in the seed bed. Knudson has shown that orchid seedlings may be grown in a nutrient solution containing glucose, until they have sufficient chlorophyll to synthesize their own carbohydrate without mycorrhiza. With these plants it is obvious that the mycorrhiza has supplied the seedling orchid with carbohydrate from the organic matter of the soil, making it available to the seedling plant. There are possibly other ways in which mycorrhiza benefits other plants. For instance there is some evidence that in some cases it takes part in the transformation and transfer of organic nitrogenous soil materials from the soil to the growing plant. In addition to Björkman's thesis [4] the reader is referred to monographs by Melin [39] and Rayner. [50]

LITERATURE

1. BERNHAUER, K., Zum Problem der Säurebildung durch Aspergillus niger (Vorläufige Mitteilung), Biochem. Z., **153**, 517 (1924).
2. BERNHAUER, K., and N. BÖCKL, Zum Chemismus der durch Aspergillus niger bewirkten Säurebildungsvorgänge. VII, Biochem. Z., **253**, 16 (1932).
3. BERNHAUER, K., and A. IGLAUER, Über die Säurebildung aus Zucker durch Aspergillus niger, Biochem. Z., **286**, 45 (1936).
4. BJÖRKMAN, E., Über die Bedeutungen der Mykorrhizaabildung bei Kiefer und Fichte, Symb. Bot. Upsal., 6, No. 2 (1942).
5. BOSWORTH, A., Chemical studies of Camembert cheese, N. Y. Agr. Exp. Sta. (Geneva) Tech. Bull. 5, 1907.
6. BRIERLEY, W. B., See Russell et al.[55]
7. CAHN, F. J., Citric acid fermentation on solid materials, Ind. Eng. Chem., **27**, 201 (1935).
8. CALMETTE, A., German patent 146, 411, Oct. 3, 1921.

9. CHALLENGER, F., L. KLEIN, and T. K. WALKER, The formation of Kojic acid from sugars by *Aspergillus oryzae, J. Chem. Soc.,* 16 (1931).

10. CHALLENGER, F., V. SUBRAMANIAM, and T. K. WALKER, The mechanism of the formation of citric and oxalic acids from sugars by *Aspergillus niger,* I, *J. Chem. Soc.,* 200 (1927).

11. CHRZASZCZ, T., and J. JANICKI, Recent advances in the fermentation industries, *J. Soc. Chem. Ind.,* **55,** 884 (1936).

12. CIUSA, R., and L. BRÜLL, Sul meccanismo della fermentazione citrica—I, *Ann. chim. applicata,* **29,** 3 (1939).

13. CLUTTERBUCK, P. W., Recent developments in the biochemistry of moulds, *J. Soc. Chem. Ind.,* **55,** 55T (1936).

14. CURRIE, J. N., The citric acid fermentation of *Aspergillus niger, J. Biol. Chem.,* **31,** 15 (1917).

15. CURRIE, J. N., and C. THOM, An oxalic acid producing Penicillium, *J. Biol. Chem.,* **22,** 287 (1915).

16. DOELGER, W. P., and S. C. PRESCOTT, Citric acid fermentation, *Ind. Eng. Chem.,* **26,** 1142 (1934).

17. EHRLICH, F., Über die Bildung von Fumarsäure durch Schimmelpilze, *Ber.,* **44,** 3737 (1911).

18. FLEMING, N., and A. C. THAYSEN, The deterioration of cotton on wet storage, *Biochem. J.,* **15,** 407 (1921).

19. FRANZEN, H., and F. SCHMITT, Die Bildung der Citronensäure aus Ketipinsäure, *Ber.,* **58,** 222 (1925).

20. GALLOWAY, L. D., The fungi causing mildew in cotton goods, *J. Textile Inst.,* **21,** T277 (1930).

21. GILMAN, J. C., *A Manual of Soil Fungi,* Iowa State College Press, Ames, Iowa, 1945.

22. GOULD, B. S., The metabolism of *Aspergillus tamarii Kita* kojic acid production, *Biochem. J.,* **32,** 797 (1938).

23. GREATHOUSE, G. A., D. E. KLEMME, and H. D. BARKER, Determining the deterioration of cellulose caused by fungi, *Ind. Eng. Chem., Anal. Ed.,* **14,** 614 (1942).

24. GREATHOUSE, G. A., P. B. MARSH, and H. D. BARKER, Evaluating fabric treatment for mildew or rot resistance by pure culture methods, Symposium on Mildew Resistance, Oct. 21, 1943, *Am. Soc. Testing Materials,* Philadelphia.

25. HEALD, F. D., *Manual of Plant Diseases,* McGraw-Hill, New York, 2nd ed., 1933.

26. HERRICK, H. T., R. HELLBACH, and O. E. MAY, Apparatus for the application of submerged mold fermentations under pressure, *Ind. Eng. Chem.,* **27,** 681 (1935).

27. HERRICK, H. T., and O. E. MAY, The production of gluconic acid by the *Penicillium luteum-purpurogenum* group. II. Some optimal conditions for acid formation, *J. Biol. Chem.,* **77,** 185 (1928).

28. HOROWITZ, N. H., and A. M. SRB, Arginine metabolism in Neurospora, Abstracts, 108th Meeting, *Am. Chem. Soc.,* 48B (1944).

29. HOWARD, B. J., Microscopical studies on tomato products, *U. S. Dept. Agr. Bull. 581,* 1917.

30. JENSEN, L. B., *Microbiology of Meats,* Garrard Press, Champaign, Illinois, 1942.

31. KATAGIRI, H., and K. KITAHARA, The formation of Kojic acid by *Aspergillus oryzae, Mem. Coll. Agr., Kyoto Imp. Univ.*, No. 26, 1 (1933).

32. LEWIS, W. L., and J. YESAIR, *The Cause and Prevention of Molds on Meat and Meat Products*, Inst. Am. Meat Packers, Chicago, 1928.

33. LU CHENG HAO, E. I. FULMER, and L. A. UNDERKOFLER, Fungal amylases as saccharifying agents in alcoholic fermentation of corn, *Ind. Eng. Chem.*, **35**, 814 (1943).

34. MACY, H., and W. B. COMBS, Field studies of the sources of mold in butter, *Minn. Agr. Exp. Sta. Bull. 235*, 1927.

35. MACY, H., S. T. COULTER, and W. B. COMBS, Observations on the quantitative changes in the microflora during the manufacture and storage of butter, *Minn. Agr. Exp. Sta. Tech. Bull. 82*, 1932.

36. MAY, O. E., H. T. HERRICK, A. J. MOYER, and P. A. WELLS, Gluconic acid. Production by submerged mold growths under increased air pressure, *Ind. Eng. Chem.*, **26**, 575 (1934).

37. MAY, O. E., A. J. MOYER, P. A. WELLS, and H. T. HERRICK, The production of Kojic acid by *Aspergillus flavus, J. Am. Chem. Soc.*, **53**, 774 (1931).

38. MAY, O. E., G. E. WARD, and H. T. HERRICK, The effect of organic stimulants upon the production of Kojic acid by *Aspergillus flavus, Zentr. Bakt. Parasitenk. II*, **86**, 129 (1932).

39. MELIN, E., *Untersuchungen über die Bedeutung der Baummykorrhiza*, Fischer, Jena, 1925.

40. MOLLIARD, M., Sur une nouvelle fermentation acide produite par le *Sterigmatocytic nigra, Compt. rend.*, **174**, 881 (1922).

41. NIETHHAMMER, A., *Die Mikroskopischen Bodenpilze*, Junk, The Hague, 1937.

42. PORGES, N., T. F. CLARK, and E. A. GASTROCK, Gluconic acid production. Repeated use of submerged *Aspergillus niger* for semicontinuous production, *Ind. Eng. Chem.*, **32**, 107 (1940).

43. PORTER, J. R., *Bacterial Chemistry and Physiology*, Wiley, New York, 1946.

44. PRESCOTT, S. C., and C. G. DUNN, *Industrial Microbiology*, McGraw-Hill, New York, 1940.

45. PRINDLE, B., Microbiology of textile fibres. II. Cotton fibre, *Textile Research*, **5**, 11 (1934).

46. ——, The microbiology of textile fibres. IV. Raw wool, *Textile Research*, **5**, 542; **6**, 23 (1935).

47. ——, Microbiology of textile fibres. V. Method for the general histological examination of normal or mildewed cotton fibres, *Textile Research*, **6**, 481 (1936).

48. PRINGSHEIM, H., and S. LICHTENSTEIN, Versuche zur Anreichung von Kraftstroh mit Pilzeiweiss, *Cellulosechem.*, **1**, 29 (1920).

49. RAISTRICK, H., Certain aspects of the biochemistry of the lower fungi ("Moulds"), *Ergeb. Enzymforsch.*, **7**, 316 (1938).

50. RAYNER, M. C., *Mycorrhiza*, Wheldon and Wesley, London, 1927.

51. ROBBINS, W. J., The assimilation by plants of various forms of nitrogen, *Am. J. Botany*, **24**, 243 (1937).

52. ROBBINS, W. J., and F. KAVANAGH, The specificity of pyrimidine for *Phycomyces Blakesleeanus, Proc. Natl. Acad. Sci., U. S.*, **24**, 141 (1938).

53. ——, The specificity of thiazole for *Phycomyces Blakesleeanus, Proc. Natl. Acad. Sci., U. S.*, **24**, 145 (1938).

54. ROGERS, L. A., A. O. DAHLBERG, and A. E. EVANS, The cause and control of "buttons" in sweet condensed milk, *J. Dairy Sci.*, **3**, 122 (1920).

55. RUSSELL, SIR [E.] J., and MEMBERS OF THE ROTHAMSTED STAFF, *The Microorganisms of the Soil*, Longmans, Green, London, 1923.

56. SAITO, K., Über die Säurebildung bei *Aspergillus Oryzae* (Vorläufige Mitteilung), *Botan. Mag. Tokyo*, **21**, 240 (1907).

57. SCHREYER, R., Vergleichende Untersuchungen über die Bildung von Gluconsäure durch Schimmelpilze, *Biochem. Z.*, **240**, 295 (1931).

58. SKINNER, C. E., and A. E. MULLER, Cystine and methionine deficiency in mold proteins, *J. Nutrition*, **19**, 333 (1940).

59. STEINBERG, R. A., The so-called chemical stimulation of *Aspergillus niger* by iron, zinc, and other heavy metal poisons, *Bull. Torrey Botan. Club*, **61**, 241 (1934).

60. ———, Growth of fungi in synthetic nutrient solutions, *Botan. Rev.*, **5**, 327 (1939).

61. TAMIYA, H., Über die Verwendbarkeit von verschiedenen Kohlenstoffverbindungen im Bau- und Betriebsstoffwechsel der Schimmelpilze. Studien über die Stoffwechselphysiologie von Aspergillus oryzae IV, *Acta Phytochim.* (*Japan*), **6**, 1 (1932).

62. THAYSEN, A. C., and H. J. BUNKER, Studies of the bacterial decay of textile fibers. Variations in the resistance of cotton of different origins to destruction by microorganisms, *Biochem. J.*, **18**, 140 (1924).

63. ———, *The Microbiology of Cellulose, Hemicelluloses, Pectin, and Gums*, Oxford University Press, New York, 1927.

64. THOM, C., and S. H. AYRES, Effect of pasteurization on mold spores, *J. Agr. Research*, **6**, 153 (1916).

65. THOM, C., H. HUMFIELD, and H. P. HOLMAN, Laboratory tests for mildew resistance of outdoor cotton fabrics, *Am. Dyestuff Rptr.*, 581 (1934).

66. THOM, C., and R. H. SHAW, Moldiness in butter, *J. Agr. Research*, **3**, 301 (1915).

67. VAN TIEGHEM, P. E. L., Fermentation gallique, *Ann. sci. naturelles Botan.*, **8**, 240 (1867).

68. WAKSMAN, S. A., *Principles of Soil Microbiology*, Williams and Wilkins, Baltimore, 2nd ed., 1932.

69. ———, U. S. Patent 2,326,986, Aug. 17, 1943.

70. WARD, G. E., L. B. LOCKWOOD, O. E. MAY, and H. T. HERRICK, Production of fat from glucose by molds. Cultivation of Penicillium javanicum van Beijima in large-scale laboratory apparatus, *Ind. Eng. Chem.*, **27**, 318 (1935).

71. WEHMER, C., Morphologie und Systematik der Familie der Aspergillaceen, p. 192; Chemische Wirkungen der Aspergillaceen, p. 239; In LAFAR, F. *Handb. der Technischen Mykologie*, Vol. 4, Fischer, Jena, 1905–1907.

72. WELLS, P. A., H. T. HERRICK, and O. E. MAY, The chemistry of the citric acid fermentation. I. The carbon balance, *J. Am. Chem. Soc.*, **58**, 555 (1936).

73. WILLIAMS, C. C., E. J. CAMERON, and O. B. WILLIAMS, A facultatively anaerobic mold of unusual heat resistance, *Food Research*, **6**, 69 (1941).

74. YABUTA, T., The constitution of Kojic acid, a γ-pyrone derivative formed by *Aspergillus oryzae* from carbohydrates, *J. Chem. Soc. Japan*, **125**, 575 (1924).

CHAPTER IX

MORPHOLOGY AND CLASSIFICATION OF THE YEASTS AND YEAST-LIKE FUNGI

The term yeast is not one with an exact botanical meaning. Henrici [8] has stated: "Many bacteriologists with little experience in studying yeasts think that they know very precisely what a yeast is and define it as a unicellular fungus multiplying by budding. Actually such a definition will apply to only a small proportion of the organisms usually classified as yeasts and only to these when they are maintained under constant conditions and not studied too closely." Some yeasts do not multiply by budding and most yeasts if cultivated for long periods of time in giant colonies will produce fringes of mycelium. The following definition is fairly satisfactory: Yeasts are true fungi whose usual and dominant growth form is unicellular. This definition, however, does not exclude certain of the primitive fungi which are unicellular but are not yeasts, and it does not include certain forms sometimes considered as yeasts in which a mycelium is commonly produced.

Yeasts are phylogenetically a heterogenous group. Some of them seem to be derived from the Basidiomycetes, so degenerate as to have lost most of the characters of that group but retaining the ability to produce exogenous spores, which are forcibly projected like basidiospores. Others have degenerated from these and have lost even this character. If we eliminate the yeasts which are probably imperfect or degenerate Basidiomycetes, the rest fall into two natural groups, the sporogenous yeasts and those lacking ascospores. The former produce ascospores as a result of conjugation or by parthenogenesis. Both groups seem to be primitive or degenerated Ascomycetes.

Asexual Reproduction. The vegetative multiplication of the yeasts is accomplished by budding, by fission, or by a combination of these two processes. In simple budding the cell wall apparently softens at one point and the protoplasm bulges it out. The bud generally reproduces the form of the parent cell. When the bud is mature it may be separated from the parent cell by constricting its base. Some species may form several buds (multipolar budding)

264

simultaneously from different parts of the cell and these may give rise to new buds before they have become detached from the parent cells, so that a small cluster of cells is formed (Fig. 109d). Repro-

ASCOMYCETES   **FUNGI IMPERFECTI**

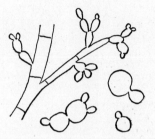

ENDOMYCOPSIS forms both mycelium and budding single cells. The
mycelium forms asci by fusion of
contiguous cells. Losing the power
to form spores, it becomes: ————

Losing the power to form mycelium,
it becomes: —————

CANDIDA. It forms both mycelium
and single budding cells, but fails to
form ascospores. Losing the power
to form mycelium, it becomes: —

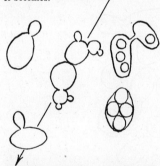

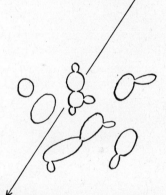

SACCHAROMYCES, ZYGOSACCHA-
ROMYCES, HANSENULA etc., not
forming mycelium, existing as single
budding cells. Ascospores are produced
in a cell formed by two conjugating cells
or in its progeny. Losing the power to
form spores, they become: —————

CRYPTOCOCCUS and other asporogenous genera. These yeasts grow as
single cells, reproduced by budding, do
not form either mycelium or spores.

FIG. 108.

duction by fission is the same process as occurs in bacteria. After sufficient elongation, a crosswall is laid down, and this then splits in the middle, giving rise to two cells of equal size (Fig. 109a). In the combination process buds develop as above but, instead of being separated from the parent cell by constriction, they develop a cross-wall in the pedicel.   See Fig. 110.

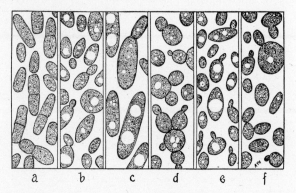

FIG. 109.   Vegetative cells of yeasts: *a, Schizosaccharomyces Pombé; b, Zygosaccharomyces Bailii; c, Saccharomyces guttulatus; d, S. cerevisiae; e, S. cerevisiae* var. *ellipsoideus; f, S. fragilis.*

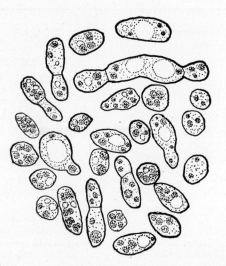

FIG. 110.   *Schizobastosporion Starkeyi-Henricii,* showing reproduction by combination of budding and fission.   Redrawn from original pencil drawing published by Starkey and Henrici, *Soil Science,* **23,** 33 (1927).

Sexual Reproduction. In addition to these methods of vegetative multiplication, yeasts may reproduce by intracellular spore formation.   These spores are somewhat like those of bacteria in that they are more resistant to heat and drying than are the vegetative cells, but unlike bacterial spores in that they are generally multiple and

therefore truly reproductive, and in that they are not formed readily
as soon as the culture has reached a certain age, but only under
exceptional circumstances. Unlike bacterial endospores, yeast ascospores are sexual spores, known to be haploid in most cases, and to
result from a union of gametes with subsequent reduction division.
Blastospores, arthrospores, conidia, and basidiospores are formed by
some yeasts, but general usage has justified the use of spore to mean
ascospore. Likewise sporogenous and asporogenous yeasts are really
ascosporogenous and anascosporogenous yeasts respectively, but
these latter terms are little used. To demonstrate yeast spores it is
usually necessary to subject a vigorously growing culture rather
suddenly to unfavorable conditions, as described in Chapter III.

Yeast spores germinate when transferred to a favorable medium,
generally by simple imbibition of water and a gradual swelling to
assume the form of vegetative yeast cell. In one group the spore
has a double membrane and on germination the outer membrane is
ruptured and cast off, the inner membrane serving as the cell wall of
the new vegetative cell. In some cases the ancestry of the yeasts
in the molds is still further indicated by the spores sending out a
short filament of mycelium (promycelium) on germination, from
which vegetative yeast cells are formed by lateral budding.

Sexual reproduction, first carefully studied by Guilliermond in 1902,
has been studied by him almost to the present time. He observed
isogamous conjugation and the immediate development of ascospores
in yeasts belonging to the genus Schizosaccharomyces (Fig. 12).
Later both isogamous and heterogamous conjugation were found in
certain other genera. Moreover Guilliermond observed a conjugation
of spores two by two within the ascus in Saccharomycodes Ludwigii,
confirming observations made by Hansen in 1893. Most of the
yeasts of industrial importance, however, were found to form their
ascospores with no evidence of conjugation. The process of spore
formation in these yeasts was thought to be parthenogenetic. Since
1935, however, researches of Winge and Laustsen [8] have demonstrated that there is usually an actual conjugation many vegetative generations previous to spore formation, and that probably
no yeasts form their spores exclusively by parthenogenesis. They
demonstrated frequent fusion of nuclei, two by two within the ascus,
which resulted in the formation of diploid spores. This is comparable to the process of conjugation of spores within the ascus observed by Hansen and by Guilliermond. This was found to be more
general than was thought previously. Moreover, if the ascospores
(or nuclei) do not fuse, the germinating haploid budding cells are

morphologically different from their parents. They are small and round and not so vigorous as the parent cells. These proliferating haploid yeast cells may conjugate with each other or with an asco-spore that has not fused. From either of such unions or a union of two spores or nuclei within the ascus, there develops the ordinary yeast cell, which is diploid. Eventually on the proper substrate these develop ascospores, after reduction division. Ascospore-form-ing yeasts are then of two types, one of which consists of those in which the usual growth form is haploid and in which spores form immediately after conjugation of the ordinary cells (Fig. 12). These have been called haplobiontic and are typified by Zygosaccharomy-ces or Schizosaccharomyces. The other type consists of yeasts which are called diplobiontic. In these the usual cell is diploid and the union of cells (and presumably of nuclei) takes place in the ascus or among the budding progeny of the haploid spores. Since the diploid cells are large and vigorous, those cells which have conjugated tend to crowd out the unfertilized

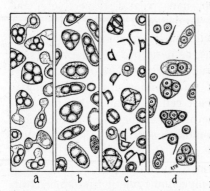

FIG. 111. Asci and ascospores of yeasts: a, Zygosaccharomyces sp. from soil; b, Saccharomyces cerevisiae var. ellipsoideus; c, Hansenula anom-ala; d, Pichia sp. from soil.

haploid cells in the culture. The terms haplobiontic and diplobiontic are not well chosen because they have been used in another sense by biologists.

Lindegren and Lindegren [10, 11, 12, 13] have continued the work of Winge and Laustsen. They have confirmed the work of the Danish investigators, but find that yeasts such as Saccharomyces are hetero-thallic. If a single spore is isolated and grown on media, the small haploid cells which develop do not conjugate with each other at all readily. If and when they do conjugate, the ascus which eventually develops has usually only two spores. These spores are mostly non-viable. If these germinate, the cells resulting from this union are still less likely to conjugate. However, when pure cultures, having developed from single spores of opposite sex, are mixed, mating takes place readily. The resulting proliferating diploid cells eventually form spores (usually four) which are found to be viable. Thus the heterothallism of these yeasts is only partial, but in nature it must be usual. There are only two sexes and the sexes are morphologically indistinguishable.   Most industrial yeasts reproduce sexually by isogamous, heterothallic conjugation of haploidal yeast cells or ascospores to form the ordinary diploid cells.

A single yeast cell may be heterozygous and variants may be produced after sporulation as characters segregate. A single-cell yeast culture thus does not necessarily yield a "pure culture" but single-spore cultures are obviously pure.

Yeasts may be used for genetic studies. If four ascospores are picked and cultured, they may result in different types of growth or of cultural characters due to segregations. But if one of these cultures is mixed with another single-spore culture from another source, artificial crosses can be made. One may discover thus which characters are dominant, which recessive, and which lethal. Yeasts are found to behave like other plants and animals with regard to the laws of heredity. Also new strains can be developed by making hybrids and phylogenetic relationships may be determined. Several new hybrid yeasts, some of industrial importance, have been so produced and research is now going on in this field. This knowledge also suggests the relationships of genera and species of sporogenous yeasts. Strains closely related hybridize readily and produce fertile progeny, but those distantly related either do not mate or they produce a large percentage of spores which do not germinate. Closely related genera usually produce sterile spores although one fertile intergeneric hybrid has been produced. More distantly related genera do not mate at all. Both Winge and Laustsen and the Lindegrens have published details of breeding techniques.

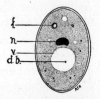

Cytology of Yeasts. The   structure   of   the yeast cell has been studied in some detail. It consists of a protoplast contained in a cell wall. The cell is said to contain a single nucleus although the two bodies which Badian pictures and which he interprets as chromosomes may actually be nuclei. Numerous granules and vacuoles representing various kinds of reserve foodstuffs are also found. When young, i.e., when the culture is actively growing, the cell wall is thin and the protoplasm is fairly free

Fig. 112. Diagram showing the structure of a yeast cell: *n*, nucleus; *v*, v a c u o l e ; *d.b.*, "dancing body"; *f*, fat vacuole.

of these reserve substances. After growth ceases, the cells develop thicker walls and become filled with granules and vacuoles. Occasional cells in old cultures develop extraordinarily thick walls and become distended with a large amount of reserve material. These are referred to in German literature as "Dauerzellen" and are, functionally at least, identical with the chlamydospores of mycelial fungi.

Since yeasts behave like higher organisms with regard to genetics, the importance of the nucleus has had renewed interest in recent years. What is known, however, is not in proportion to the importance of the subject. Bacteriologists, particularly, are interested because yeasts seem but a step higher than bacteria in complexity as well as size. Most of the work on nuclei in yeasts, like nearly all of it with bacteria, will have to be discounted since volutin (often called yeast nucleic acid) has not been distinguished from the chromatin which is characteristic of the nucleus. Most of the drawings and photographs in textbooks labeled nuclei may as well be and probably are metachromatic granular material. While the early cytologists may in some cases have demonstrated the nucleus (Moeller in 1893 probably, and Guilliermond in 1901 almost certainly, demonstrated them), the Feulgen reaction in the hands of Rochlin and Badian has established its presence beyond reasonable doubt. Although the presence of nuclei in yeasts is established, the size (less than 1 micron in diameter) is such that we still lack accurate knowledge on details as to chromosomes and behavior during budding, fission, conjugation, and spore formation. The remaining structures in the protoplast are reserve foodstuffs and may be discussed under three heads: fat, carbohydrates, and proteins.

Fat appears at times in old cultures as highly refractile vacuoles. At first these are usually numerous and small, but as the cell grows older they tend to coalesce and form one large vacuole which may nearly fill the cell. Such large fat vacuoles are very characteristic of certain species of yeasts. Their fatty nature may be readily demonstrated by staining with Sudan III. Carbohydrate, as in the more complex fungi, is stored as glycogen and can be demonstrated by suspending some of the culture in dilute Lugol solution and examining microscopically under a cover glass. The glycogen granules stain a deep reddish brown, the rest of the cell a pale yellowish brown. Protein occurs in the cytoplasm in the form of fine granules which have been studied by Kohl and by him designated albuminous granules. They may be demonstrated by overstaining with the basic dyes and then differentiated by some decolorizing agent. For this purpose Gram's stain serves admirably.

In connection with these albuminous granules some observations by R. and W. Albert and by Henrici are of interest, since they perhaps throw some light on the nature of Gram's stain as well as of the granules in question. If fresh preparations of young yeast cells are stained by Gram's method, all the cells stain a uniform deep blue-black. The Alberts showed that, if yeast cells were killed by a procedure which did not destroy their enzymes (treatment with acetone) and were then suspended in water, they would undergo autolysis. If now one makes preparations of these autolyzing cells and stains by Gram's method, it will be found that, as autolysis proceeds, part of the protoplasm fails to retain Gram's stain, and large numbers of Gram-positive granules appear in the Gram-negative matrix. As autolysis proceeds, these granules become fewer in number and finally disappear. The disappearance of the granules is accompanied by increasing amounts of protein in the water, i.e., there is a correlation between the Gram-staining of the granules and their resistance to autolysis.

If now one prepares a series of slides of fresh, non-autolyzed yeasts, stains by Gram's method, and decolorizes with different strengths of acid alcohol instead of the plain alcohol ordinarily used, an exactly similar series of preparations is obtained. That is, a slide of fresh yeast decolorized with say 1 per cent acid alcohol will appear like a slide of yeast which has autolyzed say 1 hour; if decolorized with 5 per cent acid alcohol it will appear like a slide of yeast which has autolyzed 2 hours; and so on. Thus one may demonstrate in the protoplasm of the freshly fixed yeast cell a whole series of fine protein granules which vary in their tenacity of Gram's stain, and this variation is correlated with their resistance to autolysis after the cell has died. These studies also indicate that the Gram-staining property is not resident in the membrane, as has been claimed, but in proteins contained in the protoplasm, at least as far as yeasts are concerned.

Another very prominent feature of the yeast cell is the presence of material known as volutin or metachromatic material. It occurs in all the higher fungi and in bacteria as well, but is especially prominent in the yeasts. Practically every cell contains at least one vacuole filled with this material situated near the nucleus (Fig. 112). These granules are less refractile than the fat vacuoles. Generally the vacuoles contain a small granule which exhibits an active Brownian movement, frequently referred to as the dancing body. This Brownian movement indicates that the vacuole contains fluid of not very high viscosity. The granule within the vacuole may sometimes suddenly disappear, and after a time as suddenly reappear. This fact, together with the fact that both the fluid of the vacuole and the granule behave identically toward certain vital stains, indicates that they are both of the same nature. The granules represent some of the material of the vacuole which has temporarily coagulated. In older cells additional smaller vacuoles are found, and sometimes granules of the same material not within a vacuole.

In slides fixed by the usual procedures, the material in the vacuoles coagulates and becomes shrunken and distorted, appearing as irreguar masses in the cytoplasm. They take the basic dyes intensely and in general stain as does the chromatin, but may be differentiated from the nucleus by various methods. They are most beautifully demonstrated, however, by vital staining with neutral red. Some of the cells suspended in water are placed under a cover glass and a drop of 1 per cent aqueous solution of neutral red is applied to one edge of the cover slip. As this seeps under, a solution of graded concentration is formed, and in some part of the field the right concentration will be found. Dead cells stain a uniform red with this dye, but in living cells only the volutin vacuoles and granules will stain, the former a light pink, the latter a deep red.

It is generally agreed that the volutin of the yeasts and bacteria is a reserve substance identical with the yeast nucleic acid of the biochemists and is closely related chemically with the thymonucleic acid found in the nucleus. It differs from thymonucleic acid in that it yields d-ribose rather than d-desoxyribose and uracil rather than thymine among its hydrolytic products. The amount of volutin developed in the cells appears to be proportional to the amount of nucleic acid which can be extracted, and also to a certain extent to the phosphorus available in the medium. The volutin may be absent in very young cultures, accumulates in large amounts in old cultures, particularly in the "Dauerzellen," and is used up or disappears in spore formation.

Classification of Yeasts. The yeasts have been variously classified. Formerly the system of Guilliermond [7] found in his excellent monograph was widely used and is still very useful. Recently, however, two monographs, one on the spore-bearing yeasts by Stelling-Dekker [26] and one on the asporogenous yeasts by Lodder,[14] have appeared. It is to be hoped that the third volume * promised by the "Centraalbureau voor Schimmelcultures" of Baarn, Netherlands,

---

* This volume was published in 1942 but was not distributed until late in 1945 in the United States: H. A. Diddens, and J. Lodder, *Die anaskosporogenen Hefen*, 2te Hälfte, 511 pp., N. V. Noord-Hollandsche Uitgevers Maatschappij, Amsterdam, 1942.

which institution is responsible for the two works mentioned above, on the little understood asporogenous yeasts with mycelium, will be available before long. We shall follow, in the main, the classification of these workers as to the yeasts themselves and that of Martin [17] down to the families.

ORDERS AND FAMILIES OF HEMIASCOMYCETES

A. Hyphal cells becoming chlamydospores, each of which germinates to become a single ascus. Parasitic on vascular plants. Order *TAPHRINALES*

B. Zygote or single cell transformed into an ascus directly or after proliferation of diploid yeast cells. Order *ENDOMYCETALES*

   1. Spore sacs (asci?) multispored; gametangia when present sometimes multinucleate. Family *ASCOIDEACEAE*

   2. Asci with eight ascospores or fewer; gametangia when present, always uninucleate. Family *ENDOMYCETACEAE*

Martin recognizes another family which Stelling-Dekker has combined with the Endomycetaceae. To determine the genera and species of the Endomycetaceae it is necessary to study both morphological and physiological characters. Among these are size and shape of vegetative cells; nature of cell division—by budding, fission, or a combination of the two; formation of buds at any place on the cell (multipolar) or only at ends of the cell (bipolar); formation of true mycelium or pseudomycelium, a condition resulting from bipolar budding cells becoming elongated and remaining attached to one another; mode of ascospore formation; number, shape, and size of spores; appearance of growth in liquid media; type of growth on agar slants or giant colonies; fermentation of various sugars; utilization of various organic compounds, especially alcohol, as sole source of energy; utilization of various chemicals, especially nitrate, as sole source of nitrogen; dominance of "fermentive" or "oxidative" character. By fermentive Stelling-Dekker means anaerobic production of carbon dioxide and alcohol; by oxidative, she means aerobic production of carbon dioxide. Methods of studying these characters will be found in Chapter III. Stelling-Dekker's monograph was published before Winge had published his papers on the sexuality of yeasts, hence the term parthenogenetic, as she uses it, must be understood to include spore formation by yeasts in which the usual growth form is diploid. It will be noted that Stelling-Dekker was compelled to include yeast-like fungi with yeasts as she could find no line of demarcation between organisms which produced mycelium only under exceptional conditions and those which produced it regularly.

GENERA OF ENDOMYCETACEAE

(Adapted from Stelling-Dekker)

Class *ASCOMYCETES*   Order *ENDOMYCETALES*

Subfamily A. *EREMASCOIDEAE.* Growth form, only mycelium. Ascospores formed by isogamous conjugation, hat-shaped, 4 to 8
per ascus. Entirely oxidative. But one genus, *EREMASCUS,*
description as for the subfamily.

Subfamily B. *ENDOMYCOIDEAE.* Growth form, either mycelium and
arthrospores or arthrospores alone. Spores formed by isogamous or heterogamous conjugation, or parthenogenetic. Oxidative or fermentive.

Genus I. *ENDOMYCES.* Both mycelium and arthrospores. Spores
by heterogamous conjugation or parthenogenetic, round to
hat-shaped, 4 per ascus. Oxidative or fermentive.

Genus II. *SCHIZOSACCHAROMYCES.* No mycelium, only arthrospores. Spores by isogamous conjugation, 4 to 8 per ascus.
Dominantly fermentive.

Subfamily C. *SACCHAROMYCOIDEAE.* Either mycelium with blastospores,
or only budding yeast cells, the latter often with pseudomycelium. Multiplication by fission, by multipolar budding,
or by bipolar budding. Spores by heterogamous or isogamous
conjugation or parthenogenesis. All transitions from purely
oxidative to purely fermentive forms.

Tribe a. *ENDOMYCOPSEAE.* Mycelium with blastospores, occasionally
arthrospores. Multiplication by fission or multipolar budding.
Spores parthenogenetic or by isogamous conjugation; round,
oval, sickle-shaped, or hat-shaped, 1 to 4 per ascus. Dominantly oxidative. But one genus, *ENDOMYCOPSIS,* description as for the tribe.

Tribe b. *SACCHAROMYCETEAE.* Mycelium rare or lacking, budding
yeast cells the usual growth forms. Multipolar budding.
Spores parthenogenetic or by isogamous or by heterogamous
conjugation.

Genus I. *SACCHAROMYCES.* Round, oval, or cylindrical cells.
Spores round, kidney-shaped, or hat-shaped, smooth, 1 to 4
per ascus. More or less strongly fermentive in all cases, in
addition to oxidative.

Subgenus *SACCHAROMYCES* sensu stricto. Spores parthenogenetic.

Subgenus *ZYGOSACCHAROMYCES.* Spores by isogamous or
heterogamous conjugation.

Genus II. *TORULASPORA.* Round cells. Spores formed after unsuccessful attempts to conjugate. Spores round, smooth, 1 to
3 per ascus. Dominantly fermentive.

Genus III. *PICHIA.* Cells oval to long cylindrical. Pseudomycelium
formed. Spores parthenogenetic, or by isogamous or heterogamous conjugation, angular or hemispherical, 1 to 4 per ascus.
Dominantly oxidative, weakly fermentive. Nitrates not reduced.

Subgenus *PICHIA* sensu stricto. Spores parthenogenetic.

Subgenus *ZYGOPICHIA*. Spores by isogamous or heterogamous conjugation.

Genus IV. *HANSENULA*. Cells oval or long cylindrical. Seldom round. Pseudomycelium formed. Spores parthenogenetic or by isogamous conjugation, hemispherical or spherical with a band, 2 to 4 per ascus. Oxidative. Nitrates reduced.

Subgenus *HANSENULA* sensu stricto. Spores parthenogenetic.

Subgenus *ZYGOHANSENULA*. Spores by isogamous conjugation.

Genus V. *DEBARYOMYCES*. Round, occasionally oval cells, at times pseudomycelium. Spores by isogamous, more frequently heterogamous, conjugation, round, more or less warty, 1 to 2 per ascus. Most species exclusively oxidative, some also fermentive.

Genus VI. *SCHWANNIOMYCES*. Cells oval. Spores formed after unsuccessful attempts at conjugation, round, warty, banded, 1, rarely 2, per ascus. Dominantly fermentive.

Tribe c. *NADSONIEAE*. Growth forms yeast cells, occasionally pseudomycelium, no true mycelium. Multiplication by bipolar budding. Buds with a broad base. Spores parthogenetic or by heterogamous conjugation.

Genus I. *SACCHAROMYCODES*. Cells lemon-shaped or sausage-shaped. Vegetative reproduction by combination of budding and fission. Spores parthenogenetic, round, smooth, 4 per ascus. Spores conjugate upon germinating. Both oxidative and fermentive.

Genus II. *HANSENIASPORA*. Cells lemon-shaped. Spores parthenogenetic, round, or hat-shaped, 2 to 4 per ascus. Both oxidative and fermentive.

Genus III. *NADSONIA*. Cells egg to lemon-shaped. Vegetative reproduction by a combination budding and fission. Spores heterogamous. After fusion of nuclei of mother cell and bud, a new bud is formed which becomes the ascus. Spores round, warty, 1 per ascus. Both oxidative and fermentive.

Genus IV. *ZYGOSACCHAROMYCODES*. Cells oval. Vegetative reproduction by combination of budding and fission. Spores by isogamous conjugation or, rarely, parthenogenetic. Spores round, 1 to 4 per ascus.

Subfamily D. *NEMATOSPOROIDEAE*. Growth forms both mycelium and yeast cells. Multiplication by multipolar budding. Spores formed by isogamous conjugation or parthenogenetically. Spores needle-shaped or fusiform, with or without flagella. Both oxidative and fermentive.

Genus I. *MONOSPORELLA*. Cells oval. Spores parthenogenetic, needle-like, 1 per ascus.

Genus II. *NEMATOSPORA*. Cells oval, elongated, irregular, or mycelium-like. Spores parthenogenetic, fusiform, flagellated, 2 to 8 per ascus. Both oxidative and fermentive.

Genus III. *COCCIDIASCUS*. Round to oval cells, spores by isogamous conjugation, fusiform, 8 per ascus. Entirely oxidative.

Eremascus, Endomyces, and Endomycopsis. These genera are of interest mainly in that they obviously connect the yeast with the other Ascomycetes. Like the other Ascomycetes, they possess a well-developed true mycelium, and as in the yeasts the ascospores are formed in yeast-like cells without the formation of binucleate ascogenous hyphae. Arthrospores are formed in Endomyces. In Endomycopsis, in addition to vegetative growth by mycelium, blasto-spores are produced which bud off the mycelium and these may continue to proliferate by budding as in the ordinary yeasts. See Fig. 13. Recently [28] it has been demonstrated that *Endomycopsis fibuliger* has the ability to excrete considerable quantities of amylase. The use of this organism instead of malt for the saccharification of mashes has given higher yields of fermentable sugar. Industrial applications are obvious. See page 337. Endomycopsis is often included in Endomyces.

Schizosaccharomyces. The genus Schizosaccharomyces seems mainly to be a group of tropical yeasts. Species have been isolated from various tropical fruits, from African beer made from millet, from Javanese, Formosan, and Jamaican molasses, from soil, and from various insects. This genus forms four to eight spores by isogamous conjugation. See Fig. 109 for the vegetative reproduction by fission which is characteristic of the genus. Stelling-Dekker uses the term "oidia (arthrospores) formation," rather than fission. Occasionally a cell splits into more than two cells but usually the fission is binary.

Saccharomyces. The genus Saccharomyces includes most of the yeasts of industrial importance. Vegetative reproduction is by budding. Pseudomycelium in most species is produced only in giant colonies or in agar slant cultures several months old. Mycelium appears in scattered strands at the edge of the growth. Saccharomyces is a typical diplobiontic yeast. The spores are round and two to four are found per ascus. A key derived from Stelling-Dekker is given for determination of species.

KEY TO THE SPECIES OF SACCHAROMYCES

(Adapted from Stelling-Dekker)

1. Fermenting glucose and galactose.
   a. Long pseudomycelium in young wort culture.   *S. dairensis*
   b. Cells single or in twos in young wort cultures.
      I. One spore per ascus.   *S. unisporus*
      II. Several spores per ascus.   *S. globosus*

2. Fermenting glucose, sucrose, and one third of the raffinose.
   a. Cells elongated. *S. muciparis*
   b. Cells round or oval. *S. Chevalieri*
      and varieties: *Lindneri* and *torulosus*
3. Fermenting glucose, sucrose, raffinose, and melibiose.   *S. microellipsoideus*
4. Fermenting glucose, galactose, sucrose, and one third of the raffinose.
   a. Cells small, round, or slightly oval. *S. exiguus*
   b. Cells larger, oval. *S. Mangini*
      and variety: *tetrosporus*
5. Fermenting glucose, sucrose, and maltose. *S. heterogenicus*
6. Fermenting glucose, sucrose, maltose, and one third of the raffinose.
   a. Cells egg-shaped. *S. oviformis*
   b. Cells elongated. *S. Bayanus*
7. Fermenting glucose, galactose, sucrose (weakly), and maltose.
      S. Chodati
8. Fermenting glucose, galactose, sucrose, maltose, and one third of the raffinose.
   a. Cells in young wort cultures round, oval, egg-shaped, or pear-shaped.
      S. cerevisiae
      and varieties: *ellipsoideus, turbidans,*
      Marchalianus, pulmonalis, festinans
   b. Cells in young wort cultures oval to sausage-shaped.   *S. intermedius*
   c. Cells in young wort cultures long oval, very large.   *S. Villianus*
   d. Cells in young wort cultures oval, but elongated, sausage-shaped, on agar.
      S. Odessa
   e. Cells much elongated (up to 30μ) on agar.   *S. tubiformis*
   f. Cells in young wort cultures round to oval, on agar becoming irregular cell-
      complexes. *S. paradoxus*
9. Fermenting glucose, galactose, sucrose, maltose, raffinose, and melibiose.
   a. Cells in young wort cultures elongated, sausage-shaped, forming long strands
      of pseudomycelium. *S. Pastorianus*
   b. Cells in young wort cultures single or in twos and threes.
      I. Cells oval. *S. carlsbergensis*
         and varieties: *monacensis, valdensis,*
         mandshuricusii, polymorphus
      II. Cells much elongated. *S. validus*
      III. Cells long oval. *S. Logos*
      IV. Cells oval on wort, filamentous on agar. *S. uvarum*
10. Fermenting glucose, galactose, sucrose, lactose, and one third of the raffinose.
       S. fragilis

It will be noted by the key that the familiar *Saccharomyces ellipsoideus,* the wine yeast, has been reduced to a variety. Elongated yeasts ordinarily diagnosed as *S. ellipsoideus* isolated from fermenting fruit juices tend to lose on cultivation their characteristic elongated oval shape and tend to become indistinguishable from the round *S. cerevisiae,* a common ale and bakery yeast. The differences between the species and the variety are not such as make a clear delineation. The differences are tendency of *S. cerevisiae* var. *ellipsoideus* to elliptical shape when first isolated and *S. cerevisiae* to round shape, and "fairly good" growth of the former in media whose only carbon source is alcohol and "scant to fairly good growth" of the latter. All gradations from the species to the variety are found. Nature does not seem to have divided the beer and the wine yeasts into distinct species.

There are two types of industrial yeasts that can be separated fairly satisfactorily. These are the top yeasts and the bottom yeasts, recognized as separate entities by Pasteur and by Hansen. The top yeasts grow throughout the fermenting liquid evenly distributed, gas is produced abundantly early in the fermentation, and the evolution of gas tends to bring the yeasts to the surface. The bottom yeasts tend to settle to the bottom of the liquids and gas production is slower in the early stages of fermentation. Nearly all the top and bottom yeasts of industrial importance may be separated into two species with several varieties of each on the basis of melibiose fermentation. *S. carlsbergensis* and varieties and a few rare species, bottom yeasts, ferment melibiose, while *S. cerevisiae* and varieties and a few rare species do not ferment this disaccharide. They ferment only one third of the raffinose.[27] See page 63. These are top yeasts. Baking yeasts, most distillery and wine yeasts, and those used in the production of many English ales are top yeasts. Bottom yeasts are of little use other than in the brewing industry. Most American, Czech and German beers are produced with bottom yeasts. The top yeasts occur much more frequently in nature. Mrak and associates [18, 19] made a careful study of yeasts occurring naturally on grapes and fermenting fruits in California and found very few strains of Saccharomyces which fermented raffinose completely. In the past three or four years, out of perhaps over two hundred isolations of Saccharomyces from infusions of apples, pears, grapes, raisins, prunes, raspberries, strawberries, and various spoiled jellies and jams, here in Minnesota, we have not isolated a single melibiose-fermenting strain.

It must be noted that although bottom and top yeasts are melibiose-fermenting and non-fermenting respectively, there are exceptions, and top yeasts have been developed experimentally from bottom yeasts, possibly by a segregation of characters incidental to sexual reproduction of heterozygous yeasts in cultures. It should be noted also that *S. cerevisiae* is the term usually given by the industry to most brewery yeasts whether top or bottom. For instance, most brewers of American beers insist that they use a strain of *S. cerevisiae*. Actually most American beers are made with bottom yeasts, and indeed the trade term for brews made with top yeasts is ale. According to

Stelling-Dekker and most other authorities on yeast classification, such strains should, in most cases, be termed *S. carlsbergensis.* Hansen's original *S. carlsbergensis* was a bottom yeast, isolated from the inoculum used in Denmark. *S. cerevisiae* was isolated from English ale and was a top yeast as described by Hansen.

There are many varieties, races, and strains in both these species, and these strains find their use in various industrial processes. For certain purposes certain strains are desired. Those producing a high alcoholic content in the mash are desired in distillery yeasts whether for distilled alcoholic liquors or for industrial alcohol; baking quality, high yield from inexpensive media, and high vitamin content are qualities desired in compressed yeasts; ease of clearing and flavor imparted are qualities necessary in beverage yeasts. The flavor of wines and beers is known to be partly due to the particular yeasts responsible for the fermentation, and in many cases, especially in the brewing industry, this is controlled. Mutations are said to occur, but more likely it is a segregation of characters due to sexual reproduction, and new races are being produced by artificial breeding. The older races have been given various trade names. Brewing yeasts are generally designated by names indicating the brewery from which they had their origin, as Carlsberg Bottom Yeast No. 1. The Saaz, Logos, and Frohberg yeasts are particularly well-known strains.

Other species of Saccharomyces are more rarely encountered. Some of these occur regularly in certain types of natural fermentations and are desirable. Often they occur as "weeds" and may impart undesired flavors, e.g., *S. Pastorianus.* This is a frequent contaminant in brewing and may often be obtained from commercial yeast cakes. It forms large sausage-shaped cells and a scum in old cultures. It gives rise to disagreeable flavors in beer, and seems to be a common organism in American "home brew."

There are in use in various parts of the world, particularly southeastern Europe and adjacent Asia, fermented beverages made from milk. Kefir and koumyss are the best known of these. The fermentation is a complex one, as pure cultures are not used, and there are various bacteria and usually several species of yeast present. Not all of the latter are capable of fermenting lactose, but depend upon bacteria for the preliminary conversion of the lactose to glucose and galactose. These hexoses are then fermented to carbon dioxide and alcohol by the yeasts. There are, however, some yeasts which form lactase as well as zymase, and can carry on the alcoholic fermentation by themselves. Of these the best known is *S. fragilis.* The cells are oval to elliptical. From two to four spores are formed.

It is a bottom yeast although it does not ferment melibiose. Certain asporogenous yeasts, *Cryptococcus kefyr* and *C. sphaerica* are also frequently found in fermented milk preparations. Another asporogenous lactose-fermenting species of yeast is well known. It forms pseudomycelium and has been called *Torula cremoris*. Lactose-fermenting yeasts have been found in souring figs also. Only a small amount of alcohol (4 per cent or less) is ordinarily formed, but carbon dioxide is formed in abundance. The resultant beverages are effervescent rather than intoxicating. In cream they are frequently the cause of considerable economic loss as "foamy cream." It has been shown by Rugosa [25] that lactose-fermenting yeasts and yeast-like fungi require an exogenous source of nicotinic acid for growth. One hundred fourteen strains of lactose fermenting yeasts and related fungi were studied. Strains of Saccharomyces and Cryptococcus, lactose non-fermenters, did not require nicotinic acid.

Zygosaccharomyces. (See Fig. 111.) This is a large genus and has been much studied since conjugation takes place regularly. It is also of some economic importance. Stelling-Dekker did not recognize the importance of the distinction between yeasts in which the usual growth form is diploid from those in which it is haploid and so she placed Zygosaccharomyces as a subgenus of Saccharomyces. Morphologically they are much alike, except that spores of Saccharomyces are formed after proliferation of diploid yeast cells and Zygosaccharomyces forms spores immediately after conjugation of ordinary haploid cells in most cases, although heterogamous conjugation is sometimes seen. It has been suggested that Zygosaccharomyces is merely a growth form of haploid Saccharomyces strains and that the spores formed are non-viable, but this has by no means been established.

A considerable number of the species of Zygosaccharomyces are able to withstand very high sugar concentrations and are therefore frequently found as the causative agent in the spoilage of honey. Lockhead and associates have made a careful study of honey yeasts. Many species are unable to grow in a medium containing less than 32 per cent honey. They are osmophilic, and other sources of sugar than honey, or salts may be used to produce a high osmotic pressure. Osmophilic yeasts including species of Zygosaccharomyces and asporogenous yeasts were found in all 191 samples of honey examined from all parts of Canada. Dilution, numbers of cells present, and an activating substance in honey were factors in the development of the yeasts. Similar organisms were isolated from the nectar of most flowers examined, but they were not found in any of the soils examined save those about apiaries.

Species of Zygosaccharomyces and certain asporogenous yeasts were also found to be responsible for the alcoholic fermentation of musts (unfermented grape juice) abnormally high in sugar. In the Rhine regions during warm and dry autumns, the grapes may become overripe and shriveled ("Edelreif"). On these there frequently grow certain molds. If either or both of these moldy and non-moldy sorts of grapes make up a considerable portion of the crop, the must is unusually rich in sugar, 30 to 60 per cent. The resulting wines ("rheinische Ausleseweine") are quite different from the usual Rhine wines. The grapes, the must, and the fermenting wines yielded a large number of osmophilic yeasts, especially species of Zygosaccharomyces which, rather than the ordinary wine yeasts, were responsible for the fermentation. These osmophilic yeasts are also in many cases responsible for the spoilage of other products high in sugar such as dried fruits, dates, and figs.[8]

Species of Zygosaccharomyces are frequently encountered and the reader is referred to Stelling-Dekker for description of species. The statement made in 1943 [10] that relatively few Zygosaccharomyces are found in nature is not in accord with the experience of the authors, and apparently not in accord with the publications of Lockhead, Mrak, and others. A monographic treatment [20, 21] of the genus is being published piecemeal by Nickerson, and no doubt this, when completely published, will be the standard authority on Zygosaccharomyces.

Pichia and Zygopichia. (See Fig. 111.) These are among the film-forming yeasts, that is, they tend to remain attached to one another after budding, and they grow in a pellicle on the surface of liquid media. They also tend to be oxidative rather than fermentive, and little alcohol but rather esters and carbon dioxide are produced. Alcohol is usually utilized readily. Pichia and Zygopichia, as well as asporogenous film-forming yeasts (which are possibly imperfect forms of film-forming, sporogenous genera), frequently cause a spoilage of fermented beverages in the later stages of the fermentation by other yeasts. However, in some cases this secondary action of these ester-producing yeasts is needed to provide the characteristic flavor of certain wines, sherry, for example. These yeasts are also common in pickle brine and can be readily isolated from the scum of ordinary cucumber pickle brine during the initial salting, or from sauerkraut, silage, dill pickles, and other foods whose acid comes from bacterial lactic acid fermentation. Mrak and Bonar have made some careful studies of these and other film-forming yeasts from a number of different kinds of pickle brine. A review of the literature will be found in their paper.[8]

Pichia and Zygopichia are distinguished by the fact that the former forms spores after proliferation of diploid cells or is parthenogenetic and the latter forms spores immediately after conjugation. The cells of both genera are elongated and sausage-shaped. Each spore, which is round, hemispherical, or angular, usually has a highly refractile fat globule which is of diagnostic value.

Hansenula and Zygohansenula. The latter is haplobiontic and the former is diplobiontic or parthenogenetic. They are also film-forming yeasts which form esters rather than alcohol, they are dominantly oxidative and they utilize alcohol. The spores are angular or hemispherical. These genera are found in the same habitats as Pichia and Zygopichia. As more species are being found the morphological differentiation of Pichia and Zygopichia from Hansenula and Zygohansenula is breaking down. However, the utilization of oxygen from nitrates resulting in the reduction of nitrates to nitrites by Hansenula and Zygohansenula and the lack of this ability by the other two genera points to a fundamental difference in metabolism and, for the time being at least, it seems desirable to recognize all four genera. If this criterion breaks down, species of Hansenula may have to be transferred to Pichia, and Zygohansenula to Zygopichia.

The best-known species *Hansenula anomala*, has characteristically hat-shaped spores (Fig. 111). This species resembles *Endomycopsis fibuliger*, which also produces ethyl acetate, is film-forming and oxidative, and possesses hat-shaped ascospores. Thus the relationship to the higher Ascomycetes may be traced from the yeasts through Hansenula and Endomycopsis, the latter of which, unlike the former, has a well-developed true mycelium. Both Hansenula and Zygohansenula are frequently referred to in the literature as Willia. Bedford[1] has made a study of Hansenula and has recognized seven species and three varieties. A determinative key is given.

Debaryomyces. This genus is also a film-forming yeast and is frequently found in the same habitat as the four preceding genera. One or, rarely, two spores are found per ascus. These are rough and warty. This roughness can best be seen if the cultures are incubated at low temperatures as explained in Chapter III.

Saccharomycodes and Hanseniospora. These are apiculate yeasts, that is, lemon-shaped with a small button-shaped production at each end. In Saccharomycodes, the round spores conjugate during germination and in Hanseniospora, which is much more common, the spores are formed by what Stelling-Dekker describes as parthenogenesis. Hanseniospora is common on grapes, grows rapidly, and is abundant during early fermentation. Since this yeast is sensitive to alcohol, it disappears as the fermentation proceeds. Off flavors may be imparted to the wine if these yeasts are too numerous. The ability to form spores is quickly lost on cultivation, and the corresponding genus Kloeckera, non-spore-forming apiculate yeasts, is probably Hanseniospora which has lost its ability to form spores. Both genera form buds by a process of budding combined with fission. The buds are thus formed on a broad base.

Nadsonia. The genus Nadsonia contains rather peculiar yeasts. The vegetative cells are large and frequently apiculate. In old cultures many of the cells form two large buds, one at each end. One of these may be cast off. The nucleus of the other fuses with the nucleus of the parent cell; then, according to Guilliermond, a spore is formed. But apparently the entire cell becomes the spore, which becomes filled with an enormous fat globule. The membrane of such a cell is greatly thickened, and after a time the outer lamella of this wall peels off irregularly, leaving a roughened or verrucose outer surface.

The growth of *Nadsonia fulvescens* in young cultures is white and very mucoid in character. The cells are very large. With the development of the fat globules in the spores the growth gradually becomes tan and then reddish brown in color. In many cultures white sectors appear in the old cultures, and these are found to contain non-sporogenous cells free from fat globules, which when subcultured yield a similar pure white growth.

Schwanniomyces and Torulaspora. In each of these genera the cells produce, under conditions which favor sporulation, slender tubular outgrowths as though they were about to undergo sexual fusion, but actual conjugation does not occur. In Schwanniomyces the cells then develop a single or, rarely, two ascospores each, which show an oil drop as in most Pichia species and a prickly surface as in Debaryomyces. In Torulaspora spores (one or two per ascus) are round and smooth. Both these genera are dominantly fermentive.

Monosporella, Nematospora, Ashbya, Coccidiascus. Monosporella is the generic name of the yeast found by Metchnikoff parasitic in the microscopic arthropod Daphnia. It forms a single needle-shaped spore which penetrates the digestive tract and enters the body cavity. It was with this organism that Metchnikoff made some of his observations of phagocytosis. Another species has been found in the larva of an insect. Nematospora contains species of yeasts which form oval to elliptical cells which reproduce by budding. This genus forms eight spindle-shaped ascospores. These possess a flagellum each, by which they are motile for a time. This disappears when they germinate. Ashbya is a yeast very like Nematospora but the flagellated spindle-shaped spores are formed in the mycelium. The ascus is a part of the mycelium and thus the genus hardly belongs to the Endomycetaceae. However, the similarity of Ashbya to Nematospora makes it desirable to consider it here. Coccidiascus is parasitic on the fruit fly Drosophila. The vegetative cells are round and they reproduce by budding. Eight spindle-shaped or banana-shaped spores are formed.

Asporogenous Yeasts. The asporogenous yeasts, that is, those which do not produce ascospores, are a heterogenous group. Some seem to be derived from Basidiomycetes, others from Ascomycetes. We shall first consider the larger group, those probably derived from Ascomycetes. Some may be strains resulting from union of haploid cells derived from the same ascospore as suggested by Lindegren and Lindegren.[10, 12, 13] Those are known to form spores with difficulty and it is quite probable that this power may be lost entirely with cultivation. The loss of spore formation may be a form of degeneration resulting from cultivation. Long-cultured strains of yeasts frequently lose their ability to form spores readily. Also it is possible that some of them are haploid forms of heterothallic yeasts. Winge and Laustsen, in investigating this possibility, tried to make crosses with all the asporogenous yeasts they could obtain, and got no spores. Still it remains a possibility. It has occurred to us that since intergeneric hybrids are usually sterile, the asporogenous yeasts in some cases may be such naturally occurring hybrids continuing to multiply vegetatively as diploid cells, i.e., they are sterile hybrids. Many asporogenous species have the size and vigor of diploid cells.

All the asporogenous yeasts probably derived from the Ascomycetes may be included in two families, Cryptococcaceae (Torulopsidaceae) and Nectaromycetaceae of the Fungi Imperfecti. Lodder [14] excludes yeasts forming true mycelium, but includes those forming pseudomycelium, a distinction difficult to make in practice, and one which Stelling-Dekker avoided by including both types in her system of sporogenous yeasts. The family Cryptococcaceae is divided into two subfamilies, the Cryptococcoideae (Torulopsidoideae), including those yeasts with no, or only primitive, pseudomycelium and the Candidoideae (Mycotoruloideae) which form pseudomycelium (and often true mycelium in fact).

The following key shows the relationship of the asporogenous yeasts.

CLASSIFICATION OF NON-ASCOSPORE-FORMING YEASTS AND YEAST-LIKE FUNGI

(Adapted from Lodder)

Order *MONILIALES*   Class *FUNGI IMPERFECTI*

Family I. *CRYPTOCOCCACEAE*. Yeast forms only or with pseudomycelium and/or true mycelium. Not forming carotinoid pigments.

Subfamily A. *CRYPTOCOCCOIDEAE*. Without pseudomycelium, or with only traces. No blastospores budding from mycelium.

I. Cells lemon-shaped, bipolar budding.

Genus *KLOECKERA*

II. Cells triangular, budding from angles.

Genus *TRIGONOPSIS*

III. Cells flask-shaped, single buds with a broad base.

Genus *PITYROSPORUM*

IV. Cells round, oval, or cylindrical.

A. No pellicle in liquid media, or a soft moist pellicle after a long time.   Genus *CRYPTOCOCCUS*

B. Pellicle dry, wrinkled, in liquid media.

1. Cells cylindrical, buds not separated by fission from mother cell.   Genus *MYCODERMA*

2. Cells polymorphous, buds separated by fission from mother cell.   Genus *SCHIZOBLASTOSPORION*

Subfamily B. *CANDIDOIDEAE*. Yeast forms with pseudomycelium and/or true mycelium, forming blastospores, arthrospores or both.

I. Blastospores regularly produced, arthrospores not produced.

Genus *CANDIDA*

II. Both blastospores and arthrospores produced.

Genus *TRICHOSPORON*

III. Arthrospores regularly, blastospores rarely, if ever, produced.

Genus *GEOTRICHUM*

Family II. *NECTAROMYCETACEAE*. Forming pseudomycelium, and conidia on the aerial surface of the colonies.

Genus *NECTAROMYCES*

Family III. *RHODOTORULACEAE*. No conidia. Yeast forms with or without pseudomycelium. Carotinoid pigments formed, non-fermentive, not germinating by repetition.

Genus *RHODOTORULA*

Family IV. *SPOROBOLOMYCETACEAE*. Yeast forms without true mycelium, reproducing by budding and also germinating by repetition, as do the basidiospores of many of the Tremallales of which these forms may be regarded as imperfect species. Non-fermentive.

A. Vegetative growth with rose, red, or salmon carotinoid pigments. Spores more or less compressed laterally, kidney- or pear-shaped, asymmetric.   Genus *SPOROBOLOMYCES*

1. No pseudomycelium.

Subgenus *SPOROBOLOMYCES*, sensu stricto

2. Pseudomycelium produced.

Subgenus *BLASTODERMA*

B. Vegetative growth white, cream, straw, or yellow with no trace of red. Spores round, ovoid, or globular, symmetrical.

Genus *BULLERA*

Cryptococcoideae, Cryptococcus. Most of the asporogenous yeasts without pseudomycelium will be found to belong to one of two genera, Cryptococcus and Mycoderma. The latter forms a heavy pellicle on liquid media, the former no, or only a slight, film. In some of the older literature Torula is used as the generic name rather than Cryptococcus. This is incorrect. Most mycologists use the name Torula to refer to certain of the Dematiaceae. See page 111. Although most workers have given up the generic name Torula for yeasts, there

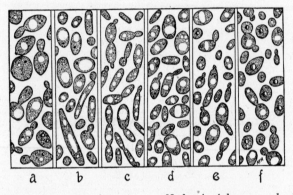

Fig. 113. Vegetative cells of yeasts: *a, Nadsonia fulvescens; b, Hansenula anomala; c, Pichia membranaefaciens; d, "Torula cremoris"; e, Rhodotorula glutinis; f, Cryptococcus pulcherrimus.*

is a difference of opinion as to the proper name to replace it. Most medical mycologists use Cryptococcus, but nearly all industrial workers who have abandoned Torula use Torulopsis. To use any one of these three generic names thus goes contrary to current usage. We have no choice but to adopt the generic name which seems to us to be in accordance with International Rules of Nomenclature, namely Cryptococcus.

Cryptococcus is a budding yeast with little or no pseudomycelium. Essentially it is very like Saccharomyces except that ascospores are never formed and there are non-fermenting as well as fermenting species. Cells of most species of Cryptococcus are spherical or nearly so, but in some they are ovoid or elongated. In many strains of several species of this and other genera of asporogenous yeasts, abortive copulation tubes are formed as in Torulaspora.[18] See page 283. Spore formation, however, does not follow this abortive attempt at copulation as it does in Torulaspora. This tendency to form abortive copulation tubes may be increased by exposure of cells to camphor.

There is no need of a separate genus Asporomyces to take care of these strains.

The fermenting species of Cryptococcus are nearly, if not quite, as active as species of Saccharomyces. Although of less industrial importance than Saccharomyces, some species are of economic significance. Some species are a source of trouble in breweries, others

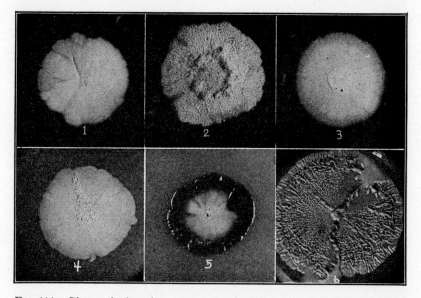

Fig. 114. Giant colonies of yeasts: 1, *Saccharomyces* sp. from soil; 2, *Pichia membranaefaciens;* 3, *Hansenula anomala;* 4, *"Torula cremoris";* 5, *Cryptococcus pulcherrimus;* 6, *Rhodotorula glutinis.*

in dairy establishments. Lactose-fermenting species may cause defects in cream or may be used to produce certain fermented milk drinks. See page 279. Some strains take part in natural alcoholic fermentations. Spoilage of dehydrated and fresh fruits is sometimes, in part at least, due to species of Cryptococcus. See following chapters.

Cryptococcus pulcherrimus is the only highly pigmented species and has been extensively studied. The pigment, a dark maroon, according to Beijerinck is secreted as a colorless chromogen which becomes dark red in the presence of iron salts and of air. On agar slant cultures with glucose one usually obtains a cream-colored growth with a dark maroon zone extending into the agar for some distance below the surface, at times forming a ring in the butt of the tube. With some media the growth itself becomes darkly colored.

This probably varies with the amount of iron occurring as impurities. Very faint traces of iron are sufficient to produce the color. This yeast may be easily distinguished from the common yeasts of the genus Rhodotorula by the color. It is maroon rather than pink or coral, and is not a carotinoid. Moreover, this yeast is fermentive in contrast to Rhodotorula species. In old cultures the cells develop very large fat globules which distend the cells and change its form from oval to round. See Fig. 113*f*. Beijerinck states that this yeast may be commonly found on grapes. It has been frequently isolated from other sources as well, but is probably not very common. Being so noticeable when growing on agar plates it is likely to attract attention and to be isolated. Punkari and Henrici have made extensive studies on variations of this yeast, and Roberts is now working on this problem. Pseudomycelium is produced by rough variants.

Recently Windisch[29] has described ascospore formation in *C. pulcherrimus* and Roberts[24] has also demonstrated them. Spores are found only in old and dried cultures and are not numerous. Castelli[2] was unable to find spores and one of us could not find them after tedious search in a stock culture. We are convinced that ascospores are really formed by some strains, at least, but it is evident that workers cannot depend upon them for diagnosis. And since Roberts after extended and careful work was unwilling to assign this species to a perfect genus, we also shall classify it among the asporogenous yeasts.

The so-called black yeasts were discussed on page 111.

Since species of Cryptococcus are so frequently isolated, and since some of them are of some importance, the following key, largely derived from Lodder,[14, 19] is given. It should be emphasized that every effort should be made to induce sporulation before placing an isolate in the genus Cryptococcus.

KEY TO THE SPECIES OF CRYPTOCOCCUS *

(Adapted from Lodder)

1. No sugars fermented.
   a. Nitrates utilized.
      I. Agar slant cultures mucoid.
         A. Cells round, or slightly oval. Agar slant cultures yellowish.
                                    C. albidus
         B. Cells round in wort, oval in agar. Cultures tinged with red.
                                    C. rotundatus
      II. Agar slant cultures not mucoid.   *C. aerius*

* New combinations are published elsewhere.

b. Nitrates not utilized.
  I. Agar slant cultures mucoid.
    A. Cells round or slightly oval.   *C. neoformans*
    B. Cells oval or elongated.
      AA. Diameter more than half the length.   *C. flavescens*
      BB. Diameter less than half the length.
        AAA. Lactose utilized, alcohol not.   *C. Laurentii*
        BBB. Alcohol utilized, lactose not.   *C. luteolus*
  II. Agar slant cultures not mucoid.
    A. Glucose only utilized.   *C. uvae*
    B. Other sugars also utilized.
      AA. Cells round.   *C. candidus*
      BB. Cells oval, very large.   *C. lipoferus*
      CC. Cells oval, small.   *C. minor*

2. Glucose only fermented.
  a. Agar slant culture not mucoid.   Red pigment in media containing traces of
    iron.   *C. pulcherrimus*
  b. Agar slant cultures not mucoid; no red pigment.   *C. Molischianus*
3. Fermenting glucose and sucrose.
  a. Cells large.
    I. Nitrates utilized.   *C. utilis*
    II. Nitrates not utilized.   *C. dattilus*
  b. Cells small.
    I. Pseudomycelium in wort; only peptone utilized.
      A. Cells oval to elongated.   *C. bacillaris*
      B. Cells round.
        AA. Asparagine and ammonium sulphate utilized.   *C. dactiliferus*
        BB. Asparagine and ammonium sulphate not utilized.
                                  C. stellatus
    II. Cells single or in twos; ammonium sulphate and asparagine also utilized.
                                  C. Gropengiesserii
4. Fermenting glucose, galactose, and sucrose.   *C. Holmii*
5. Fermenting glucose, sucrose, and maltose.   *C. colliculosus*
6. Fermenting glucose, sucrose, and lactose.   *C. kefyr*
7. Fermenting glucose, galactose, sucrose, and lactose.   *C. sphaericus*
8. Fermenting glucose, galactose, sucrose, and maltose.
  a. Raffinose not fermented.   *C. californicus*
  b. One third of raffinose fermented.   *C. fermentans*

Mycoderma. This is now usually accepted as the correct generic name for asporogenous film-forming yeasts and should not be used for acetic acid bacteria as it has been by some bacteriologists or for yeast-like fungi which form arthrospores as it has been by Vuillemin and a few other mycologists. Mycoderma species form a heavy pellicle and are oxidative rather than fermentive. They may be the imperfect stages or asporogenous strains of Pichia, Hansenula, Debaryomyces, and other sporogenous film-forming yeasts. Indeed, Baltatu obtained thirteen cultures of Mycoderma from well-known European culture museums and was able to induce sporulation in all of them. If this observation can be confirmed, it would seem that the generic term Mycoderma must be dropped in favor of the genera described on the basis of their perfect stages. Mycoderma species are found in the same habitats as the perfect film-forming yeasts, as sherry and certain Arbois wines and various pickle brines, and seem to be of equal or greater importance. There is a large literature on these organisms, much of which is confused and contradictory. Classification of species has not been satisfactory and the genus (if it is a genus) needs thorough study. Lodder [14] has made an excellent start but she has so far treated only cultures of which were available to her and strains with poorly developed or no mycelium. Whether the many strains of asporogenous film-forming yeasts with better developed pseudomycelium should be placed in separate genera or combined with Mycoderma will be clearer when more work is done. A monographic treatment of the genus is to be hoped for.

Pityrosporon. Pityrosporon is a very small yeast which grows on the skin, being particularly abundant in scalps in which there is an abundance of oily secretion. Although it is present in almost all scalps in which there is a normal amount of oil, it has been mostly studied because of its frequent association with seborrhea, and it has been considered by some investigators to be the cause of this condition. The experimental data cited to support this supposition are invalid because they are based on an erroneous identification of the organism used.[15] Actually, *Pityrosporon ovale* is a tiny yeast, characterized by a peculiar type of budding in which the bud is not constricted at its base but is attached to the parent cell on a broad surface. It will not grow on ordinary media unless some fatty substance such as lanolin, butter, oleic acid, or the secretions from the scalp are added to the surface of the medium. (See Chapter III.) A high concentration of glycerol in Sabouraud broth (up to 40 per cent) inhibits the growth of bacteria and most molds, but *P. ovale* grows on and about the epidermal scale used as inoculum and can be transferred to a slant of Sabouraud agar which has been covered with an ether extract of lanolin. This organism is sometimes called the bottle bacillus. Another species, *P. pachydermatis* has been described. It was isolated from the skin of a rhinoceros.

Kloeckera. This term replaces the familiar Hansenia which is invalid for these yeasts since it has been used earlier for another organism. Cells of Kloeckera are mostly lemon-shaped or apiculate. Sometimes the cells are elliptical or round. They reproduce by budding, are asporogenous, single, or in small clusters. In sugar media, acid is formed. Like the sporogenous apiculate yeasts, Kloeckera species are found in considerable numbers in the early fermentation of fruit juices. Apiculate yeasts often lose their ability to form spores very quickly on cultivation and it seems reasonable to consider Kloeckera as probably asporogenous strains of Hanseniospora. Lodder describes ten species and one variety.

Trigonopsis and Schizoblastosporion. In Trigonopsis young (24-hour) cultures show mostly round or elliptical yeast cells but a few appear as triangles. After a few days the sides of most of the cells are definitely triangular. Budding takes place at the apex. Schizoblastosporion was created by Ciferri to include asporogenous yeasts which reproduce by the type of budding combined with fission described on page 265. Only a few strains have been isolated, from soil and from grape leaves. See Fig. 110.

Comparison of Saccharomyceteae and Cryptococcoideae. As our knowledge of the yeasts has become systematized, the great similarity between yeasts with and without ascospores becomes more and more apparent. The fermenting species at least, of Cryptococcus, seem to be asporogenous forms of species of Saccharomyces. Likewise, there is great similarity between Mycoderma and Pichia, Schizoblastosporion and Saccharomycodes, Kloeckera and Hanseniaspora, Asporomyces and Torulaspora. The similarities often hold in biochemical as well as in morphological characteristics. With increased study it is probable that more and more of these asporogenous yeasts will be found to belong to the spore-forming genera. We can well think of these genera as form genera, and recognize that they are created to help systematize our knowledge of the isolates that we must consider. We must recognize that some of the names are possibly temporary for, as we find means of inducing sporulation, fewer and fewer forms may have to be placed in these genera. The statement of Lindegren and Lindegren that Torula is "probably an invalid genus" is correct only in so far as any genus of imperfect fungi is invalid. Species of Cryptococcus (Torulopsis) may be imperfect forms of Saccharomyces (and of other genera as well), but for the present, at least, nothing is gained by refusing to recognize form genera for those strains which cannot be induced to sporulate. We can hardly assume that all Cryptococcus species are imperfect stages of Saccharomyces any more than we can assume that all species of any other form genus of imperfect fungi belong to one perfect genus. Experience has taught that this is an unsafe assumption.

Candidoideae. We have seen that many diverse types of fungi may at times assume a unicellular form, frequently the single cells being hardly distinguishable from yeasts. Since these forms also produce other well-defined reproductive bodies, there is little question concerning their classification. But there exists quite a group of fungi which produce at times mycelium, at times free yeast-like cells, which do not form conidia or other bodies serving to identify them, or which may produce conidia that grade so imperceptibly into the free yeast-like cells that it is frequently difficult to tell which is which. Yeast-like cells are formed so regularly and comprise so prominent a part of the microscopic picture that, in spite of their non-specific characters, they are given considerable attention in classification. Such forms are looked upon as being transitional between the molds and the yeasts proper. Because they are transitional types, we find a great deal of confusion and contradiction regarding their proper nomenclature and classification. The same organism has been placed in half a dozen different genera depending upon the interpretation given by this author or that to the yeast-like cells. We must include in this transitional group a very heterogenous mixture of fungi whose true systematic relationships are obscure. "Transitions may be troublesome in taxonomy, but they are a part of Nature and we have to classify them." (Diddens and Lodder.)

The microorganisms to be considered have been mostly referred to as the genera Oidium, Monilia, or Mycoderma although many other generic names have been used. These three generic names are themselves used in different senses. As we have seen Mycoderma is used to mean (1) film-forming asporogenous yeasts, the apparently correct usage, (2) acetic acid bacteria, and (3) certain yeast-like fungi. Oidium and Monilia have been used in many different senses also and various authors have used different and mutually contradictory methods for differentiating these genera. Castellani differentiates Monilia from Oidium on the basis of production of gas from glucose, Stevens on the lack of ability to invade tissues of plants, Gilman and Abbott on the branching of conidiophores, and Henrici on the basis of blastospore as opposed to arthrospore production. Too often phytopathologists have been unaware of the medical mycological literature and as often medical mycologists have ignored rules of nomenclature and general mycological literature. Hence the same organism has frequently been designated by eight, ten, or more generic names. Recently, efforts of Ciferri and Redaelli,[8] Langeron and Talice,[9] Diddens and Lodder,[8] and others have begun to construct some order out of a virtual chaos and soon we may hope to find the classification of these organisms as simple as that of the Cryptococcoideae, for instance. But this will not be obtained by ignoring the literature of any branch of applied mycology whether it is phyto- or zoopathological.

Recently, Diddens and Lodder have given us an indication of how they are treating the Candidoideae in their forthcoming monograph. In the main, we follow their system since it seems the best and very much the simplest of any of the many recent schemes devised by several outstanding specialists in the group. The Candidoideae consist of yeast-like anascosporogenous fungi with pseudomycelium, true mycelium, or both and reproduction by blastospores, arthrospores, or both. The division of the subfamily into genera is accomplished on the basis of the kinds of spores formed. Those with blastospores but no arthrospores can be classified as Candida, those with both blastospores and arthrospores as Trichosporon, and those with arthrospores only or possibly rarely with blastospores as Geotrichum. This is a broad interpretation of genera but it seems best, at least for the present. The pathogenic genus Blastomyces (Chapter VI) is actually a mold, but it is often considered a yeast-like fungus.

Candida. This is a large diverse and important genus and as used here contains organisms of medical and industrial importance. Formerly, many of these organisms were known as Monilia. Monilia as understood by the bacteriologist or medical mycologist is quite a different entity from the genus known as Monilia to the general mycologist. To the latter the term at once suggests the non-sexual multiplication of the ascomycetous parasite of plums and other fruits, Sclerotinia. Here we have to deal with an essentially mold-like organism producing no yeast cells, which forms conidia in chains (sometimes branched) on aerial conidiophores, the individual spores connected by characteristic small intervening cells known as disjunctors. This seems to be the proper usage of the term. To the medical mycologist the term suggests an essentially yeast-like organism occurring on mucous membranes or skin lesions, which forms mycelium at least in media with low nutrient content. Recently, by agreement among many medical mycologists, Candida has come into fairly general use for "Monilia" used in this sense. Candida may have to be validated as a "nomen conservandum" by an authoritative international congress because another name, Syringospora, appears to have priority, and Mycotorula is believed to be the valid name by other well-known mycologists. However, Diddens and Lodder who specialize on the yeast-like fungi maintain that Candida is valid and correct for this group without authorization.

In many species of Candida, especially those of medical importance, the yeast cell is the predominant growth form, mycelium being produced in some species only under particular conditions. If it is grown on glucose agar slants, for instance, there occurs a creamy white growth of pasty consistency and yeast-like odor. Microscopic examination of such a culture shows only round or oval budding cells which cannot be distinguished from true yeasts. In old agar slant cultures, however, one may find the growth dipping down into the agar in the form of narrow bands or fine filaments; and microscopic examination of this part of the culture will reveal, in addition to the budding yeast cells, some filaments of mycelium. The nature of the mycelium depends in part upon the culture medium. In corn meal agar a true mycelium is formed and in several species of Candida it is very extensive. A pseudomycelium may also be formed and in some media with some species it is only mycelium that is formed.

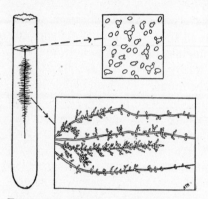

FIG. 115. Diagram illustrating the characteristics of the pathogenic Candidas. In a gelatin stab culture, only yeast-like cells are found at the surface, but filaments of mycelium radiate from the depths of the stab; these give rise to yeast-like cells by budding.

One may demonstrate a mycelium by making a stab in beef peptone gelatin. At the point of puncture there appears a heaped-up colony of buttery consistency, composed entirely of yeast cells. But after a few days there develop along the course of the stab many fine tufts of mycelium that radiate into the gelatin at right angles to the line of the stab, giving the growth a characteristic fir-tree appearance. If the tube is cut and microscopic preparations are made from these lateral projections, they will be found to be composed of mycelium, from which yeast cells are budded off in clusters along the sides and at the tips (Fig. 115). Such a stab culture may be used to differentiate these "medical" species of Candida from true yeasts. Corn meal agar is more convenient (see page 53) and on this medium mycelium growth may usually be demonstrated from the surface growth penetrating into the substrate. In glucose pour-plate cultures the surface colonies appear exactly like yeast colonies, and contain in many species only single budding cells. The deep colonies are usually at first lens-shaped and contain only yeast cells, but after a few days they send out fine streamers of mycelium which give them a star-like appearance. In liquid media, growth may be largely confined to the bottom of the tube (as in *Candida albicans*) or a surface film may form (as in *C. Krusei*). The manner of growth in broth varies not only with the species but also with the rough and smooth variants of a given species. Free budding cells or mycelium may develop, depending upon the species, composition of the broth, and the age of the culture. In lesions produced by species of Candida, both mycelium and yeast-like cells will be found.

There has been considerable speculation and investigation concerning the factors which determine the morphology of these organisms, i.e., as to when they will form mycelium and when assume the yeast form. Such investigations have been carried on almost entirely with the organism of thrush, *C. albicans*, but the results will undoubtedly be found applicable to other members of this group as well. In general, it would seem that the form of the organism is more or less an expression of the rate of growth. Where conditions are favorable for rapid multiplication, as with an easily assimilable or fermentable carbohydrate and abundant aeration, the yeast form predominates. When conditions are not so favorable, mycelium is formed.

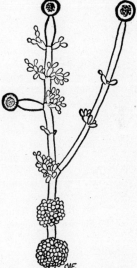

FIG. 116. *Candida albicans.* Blastospores and chlamydospores. Grown on corn meal agar.

The yeast cells budded from the mycelium in cultures are referred to as blastospores, oidia, or yeast-like cells. In addition chlamydospores, both intercalary and terminal, are occasionally formed. Fischer and Brebeck, and also Vuillemin, recorded observations of ascospores, and on this basis some authors have included these organisms in the ascomycetous genus Endomyces (Endomycopsis). But these observations made long ago have never been confirmed and moreover recent work [23] in Italy has shown that these bodies are clearly chlamydospores. There have also been noted round to oval bodies formed within the mycelium that have been designated endospores. These are probably fat granules.

Authorities do not agree upon the number of species of "medical Monilias" isolated from normal and pathological animal sources to

be included in the genus Candida. Henrici, in the first edition of
this book (1930) recognized only one pathogenic species, *Monilia
albicans*, and one saprophytic species, *M. candida*. Castellani [8] and
Dodge,[4] on the other hand, have recognized a large number of specific and even generic names, many of which certainly are synonyms.
Perhaps the following key derived from the work of Martin and
associates [16] and Langeron and Guerra [8] will be more satisfactory
than either extreme. Moniliases will be discussed in Chapter X.

CLASSIFICATION OF CANDIDA SPECIES ENCOUNTERED IN MEDICAL MYCOLOGY

("Medical Monilias")

A. Dry, flat, wrinkled colonies on Sabouraud agar, heavy pellicle on liquid media.
        Candida Krusei (= *Monilia Krusei*)
B. Moist, creamy colonies on Sabouraud agar, slight or no pellicle on liquid media.
  1. Glucose only fermented.   *C. parakrusei* (= *M. parapsilosis*)
  2. Glucose and other sugars fermented.
      a. Sucrose fermented; blastospores in verticals or in loose clusters.
        aa. Raffinose not fermented.
          * Maltose, not lactose, fermented.
                      C. tropicalis (= *M. candida*)
          ** Lactose, not maltose, fermented.
                      C. pseudotropicalis (= *M. mortifera*)
        bb. Raffinose fermented.   *C. Guilliermondi* (= *M. Guilliermondi*)
      b. Sucrose not fermented, blastospores in dense globular clusters.
                      C. albicans (= *M. albicans*)
                              (= *M. psilosis*)

The above key includes only organisms isolated from pathological
lesions or from the normal body. None of these is of exclusive parasitic habitat except possibly *C. albicans*. From non-animal sources
the other species in the above key frequently may be isolated, especially *C. tropicalis* (*M. candida*).

Some species of Candida, not included in the above key, are of
particular industrial importance. These are species sometimes rele-
gated into a separate genus, Brettanomyces.[8] They have a tendency
to develop only a primitive pseudomycelium, but the multipolar
budding cells cling together in clusters. Blastospores vary considerably in size and shape. Alcoholic production is slow and under
aerobic conditions so much acid is produced as eventually to kill
the cells. The cultures may be maintained by preventing accumulation of acid by maintaining them under anaerobic conditions or by
adding calcium carbonate to the medium. These Brettanomyces
species of Candida are concerned in the after-fermentation of Bel-

gian lambic beers and English stock beers (porter, stout, pale ale).
It takes several months for the fermentation to come to completion
but the final product may have as much as 10 per cent alcohol.
Conditions must be kept anaerobic to prevent acid formation. A

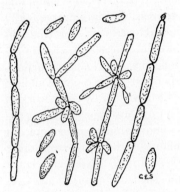

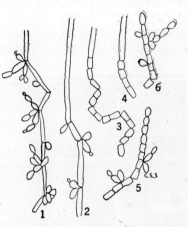

FIG. 117. *Candida* (*Brettano-myces bruxellensis* var. *non-membranaefaciens*). Camera lucida.

FIG. 118. *Trichosporon cutaneum:*
1 and 2, blastospores; 3 and 4,
arthrospores; 5 and 6, blastospores
and arthrospores. Camera lucida
from slide.

thesis, not consulted by the authors, has been published by Custers [8]
in the Dutch language on these organisms.

For the so-called *"Monilia nigra"* see page 111 and for *M. sitophila*
see page 115.

Trichosporon. This intermediate genus consists of those forms
which produce both blastospores and arthrospores. It is of some
medical importance. See Chapter X. Fonseca and Arêa Leão [5] have
reported the formation of ascospores in one species and have transferred it to the perfect genus Piedraia. In most species the perfect
stage has not been described. Puntoni [22] has recently added considerably to our knowledge of this group of microorganisms and undoubtedly much more study will be given to this genus in the future.
Trichosporon with a variant spelling as Trichosporum must be distinguished from the totally different Trichosporium, one of the
Dematiaceae. There has been some confusion of these genera in
the literature.

Geotrichum. This genus is less like what is ordinarily termed
yeast than any of the other genera mentioned in this chapter. It

probably should not be considered as a part of the Cryptococcaceae at all. The mycelium is definitely a true mycelium, blastospores are scarcely if ever produced, but arthrospores are formed regularly. In liquid media the best-known species *Geotrichum candidum*, produces a rather firm, felt-like mass, pure white in color. On solid media this is at first rather firmly adherent. Later it becomes soft and creamy. Microscopic examination shows both septate branched mycelium and numerous large square-ended arthrospores, the latter frequently joined together in short chains at alternate corners in zig-zag arrangement. The aerial arthrospores are more rounded and are called conidia by some workers and are distinguished from the cylindrical submerged oidia, but many workers, realizing that there are all gradations, make no such differentiations. As arthrospores become numerous, the growth becomes soft and creamy and takes on the appearance and odor of an ordinary yeast culture. The fragmentation of the mycelium into arthrospores has been observed by means of motion pictures.

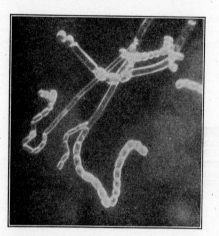

FIG. 119. *Geotrichum candidum*, showing development of oidia. Photomicrograph by dark field illumination.

A word about nomenclature. *G. candidum* is probably most often known as *Oidium lactis*, and nearly as often as *Oospora lactis*. The term Oidium to the general mycologist or phytopathologist means the imperfect stage of certain ascomycetous fungi, the powdery mildews. These are exclusively organisms parasitic on plants and they have true conidia borne on conidiophores. *G. candidum* has only superficial resemblance to these organisms, and hence *Oidium lactis* has to be placed in another genus. Geotrichum was created in 1809 for this very species as *G. candidum*. Geotrichum antedates Oospora (which itself is used in many different senses) by 24 years. Rarely *Mycoderma lactis* is also used but, as stated earlier, this is now generally regarded as a misuse of the term Mycoderma. We have no choice but to adopt the earlier term *G. candidum* which is becoming more familiar in the field of applied mycology. See Chapter VIII for a discussion of the industrial importance of this fungus.

The three genera of the Candidoideae, as we have given them, are large and inclusive. In the future it is possible that it may be found advisable to follow the lead of several eminent mycologists [3, 4, 9, 14] and recognize in addition to Candida, Trichosporon, and Geotrichum some of the following genera: Pseudomycoderma, Blastodendrion, Mycotorula, Euantiothamus, Pseudomonilia, Bret-

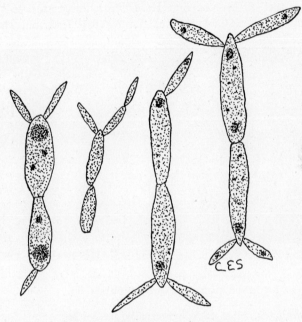

FIG. 120. Nectaromyces from nectar.

tanomyces, Proteomyces, Redaellia, Mycotoruloides, Mycocandida, Geotrichoides, or possibly others! And although the three generic names that we use are those employed by Diddens and Lodder, even these are not universally accepted. Geotrichum seems to be clearly valid but Candida and Trichosporon may have to be validated by authoritative congresses or replaced by other names. It is easy to see why these forms are so poorly understood by the average bacteriologist. It might be emphasized that real progress is being made in the understanding of these forms, and a usable classification will undoubtedly follow.

Nectaromyces. The family Nectaromycetaceae has only a single genus, Nectaromyces,[8] formerly called Anthomyces. These yeasts are found in the nectar of flowers, in which they appear characteristically in groups of four (occasionally more) long slender cells. These are arranged somewhat like an airplane with its outspread wings. The investigation of Gruess indicates that these "airplane forms" are produced by a growth in media of low nutrient value. In ordinary sugar media as used for yeasts, only large oval budding forms develop. But if the concentration of nutrients is greatly reduced, the form characteristic of the nectar growth also appears in artificial cultures. Nadson and Krassilnikov suggest that the airplane form is an adaptation which has resulted from natural selec-

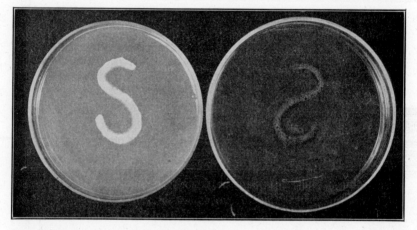

Fig. 121. *Sporobolomyces salmonicolor.* Petri plate culture showing development of "mirror colony" on the lid.

tion, enabling the yeast to adhere easily to the hairs on insects and so be transported to new flowers.

The latter authors observed sectorial mutations to occur in giant colonies, in some of which short filaments of true mycelium occurred which developed globular conidia on slender lateral branches appearing much as in the mold Verticillium. They also made cytological studies and found but a single nucleus in all the various growth forms. These findings should be confirmed. If they are not confirmed, there seems to be no reason for not relegating species of Nectaromyces to the genus Candida.

Sporobolomyces and Bullera. The anascosporogenous yeasts derived from the Basidiomycetes are classified in two families, the Sporobolomycetaceae and the Rhodotorulaceae.[8] The characteristics of the families and the genera are given in the key on page 285.

The peculiar characters of Sporobolomycetaceae were first recognized by Kluyver and van Niel. If one inoculates a Petri plate culture with a culture of Sporobolomyces in a characteristic pattern and incubates the plate, there is formed a faint duplicate of the colony pattern upon the lid of the dish (Fig. 121). These mirror colonies are formed by a deposition of the spores which are forcibly discharged from the surface of the colony.

Microscopic examination of a young colony shows only the presence of ordinary oval, budding yeast cells. But later, as spores develop (manifested by the occurrence of a powdery coat on the surface of the colony), many cells will be found with fine pointed projections exactly like the sterig-mata which are found on the basidia of a mushroom. On these there appear typical kidney-shaped cells which reproduce very closely the form of the basidiospores of some mushrooms. The discharge of these spores has been observed by Kluyver and van Niel and by Buller who report a mechanism which exactly parallels that in the Basidio-mycetes. The discharge of the spore is accompanied by the development of a drop of water at the point of attachment of the spore with its sterigma. When this drop

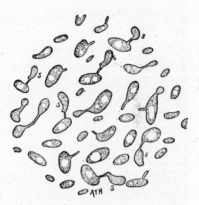

FIG. 122. *Sporobolomyces salmoni-color.* Basidiospores attached to sterigmata are marked *s.*

has reached a certain size, the spore is suddenly and forcibly propelled into the air. Buller has observed the successive production and discharge of as many as three spores from one sterigma and assumes that four may be formed. Occasionally more than one sterigma may form from a single cell.

The Sporobolomycetaceae have been considered as imperfect stages of species of the Tremallales [17] of the Heterobasidiomycetes (see page 33). In this order, the basidiospores reproduce by budding and repetition, this one stage of the Tremallales closely resembling the whole life cycle of the Sporobolomycetaceae. We have seen how the basidiospores (sporidia) of the smuts also proliferate.

Two species of Bullera and seven of Sporobolomyces are recognized by Derx and several additional species were described by Ciferri and Verona. These genera are not very common but may be isolated from straw or leaves. We have on two occasions isolated Sporobolomyces from bananas.

Rhodotorula. The family Rhodotorulaceae consists of asporogenous yeasts, non-fermentive and possessing carotinoid pigments, both of which characters are found in Sporobolomyces as well. There is only one genus,[8, 14] Rhodotorula, strains of which have been given a variety of specific names as *glutinis, mucilaginosa, rubra, sanguinea,* which serve to indicate the most striking characters of the group, namely, a sticky or mucoid growth and a red color. All species except one which is yellow are some shade of red or orange. A study of the chemistry of the pigments in one species has been made by Fromageot and Tchang.[6] Species have been created on the basis of morphological variations of the cells, i.e., their tendency to form oval or elliptical cells or to produce pseudomycelium; upon differences in consistency of the growth; upon variations in the shade of color produced, and sometimes apparently for no reason at all! The reason for considering Rhodotorulae as degenerated Basidiomycetes is that they are so very like Sporobolomycetaceae. Cultures of Sporobolomyces lost their ability to form the typical forcibly discharged spores and were then indistinguishable from Rhodotorula. And other cultures of Rhodotorula suddenly acquired the faculty of producing these basidiospores and became "Sporobolomyces." Both the Sporobolomycetaceae and the Rhodotorulaceae are distinguished from all other yeast-like organisms in their production of carotinoid pigments, and from many other yeasts in their total lack of any fermentive activity.

Lodder recognizes thirteen species and ten varieties of Rhodotorula and Harrison and Ciferri and Radaelli have recognized more. These twenty-three taxonomic entities were obtained by Lodder from thirty-seven strains labeled to represent thirty-five species and one variety sent to her from various culture collections. If so few strains represent so many species, the chances are that only a fraction of the species are described and most strains which one isolates are likely to be unnamed species or varieties. Although there is possibly good taxonomic justification for the recognition of these species and varieties, little is gained in identifying species of Rhodotorula except by the specialist. If only one species is recognized it is *Rhodotorula glutinis.* See Figs. 113 and 114.

Rhodotorulae are common air contaminants, not known to be of much economic importance. They do not occur frequently in soil, and their natural habitat is unknown. A serious discoloration of sauerkraut has been reported as due to these yeasts. They are frequently isolated from dairy products. Conditions of high acidity, low nitrogen content, and high salt content, which keep down bacterial growth, favor the growth of these yeasts. It has been reported that in samples of 3 per cent boric acid solutions purchased from pharmacies, from 48 to 38,400 pink yeasts per milliliter were obtained by plating! Out of thirty-seven strains of Rhodotorula studied by Lodder, twelve representing seven species and varieties were isolated from human or animal pathological materials, but it is doubtful that any of these was the causative agent of a disease. Thirteen species and varieties of yeasts which would be diagnosed as Rhodotorula have been listed by Dodge [4] in his *Medical Mycology*.

LITERATURE

Except for the Candidoideae the morphology and taxonomy of the yeasts has been fairly well covered by the monographs of Guilliermond,[7] Stelling-Dekker,[26] and Lodder.[14] Henrici [8] has made a survey of recent work up to 1941 in an 87-page review which, together with the three monographs, is recommended to all students particularly concerned with yeasts. In the interests of conservation of space, only such literature is cited here as was not cited by Henrici in the first edition of this book or in his review.

1. BEDFORD, C. L., A taxonomic study of the genus Hansenula, *Mycologia,* **34,** 628 (1942).
2. CASTELLI, T., Considerazione sulla Torulopsis pulcherrima, *Arch. Mikrobiol.,* **11,** 126 (1940).
3. CIFERRI, R., and P. REDAELLI, Studies on the Torulopsidaceae. À trial general systematic classification of the asporigenous yeasts, *Ann. Mycol.,* **27,** 243 (1929).
4. DODGE, C. W., *Medical Mycology,* Mosby, St. Louis, 1935.
5. FONSECA, O. O. R. DA, JR., and A. E. DE ARÊA LEÃO, Sobre os cogumelos da piedra brasileira (cited by Dodge), *Mem. inst. Oswaldo Cruz. Suppl.,* **4,** 124 (1928).
6. FROMAGEOT, C., and J. L. TCHANG, Sur les pigmentes carotinoides de Rhodotorula Sanniei, *Arch. Mikrobiol.,* **9,** 424 (1938).
7. GUILLIERMOND, A., *The Yeasts,* translated by F. W. Tanner, Wiley, New York, 1920.
8. HENRICI, A. T., The Yeasts. Genetics, cytology, variation, classification and identification, *Bact. Revs.,* **5,** 97 (1941).
9. LANGERON, M., and R. V. TALICE, Nouvelles methodes d'étude et essai de classification des champignons levuriformes, *Ann. parasitol. humaine et comparée,* **10,** 1 (1932).
10. LINDEGREN, C. C., and G. LINDEGREN, Segregation, mutation and copulation in Saccharomyces cerevisiae, *Ann. Missouri Botan. Garden,* **30,** 453 (1943).
11. ———, Selecting, imbreeding, recombining and hybridizing commercial yeasts, *J. Bact.,* **46,** 405 (1943).
12. ———, Sporulation in Saccharomyces cerevisiae, *Botan. Gaz.,* **105,** 304 (1944).
13. ———, Instability of the mating type alleles in Saccharomyces, *Ann. Missouri Botan. Garden,* **31,** 203 (1944).

14. LODDER, J., Die Anaskoporogenen Hefen, 1ste Hälfte, *Verhandel. Akad. Wettenschappen Amsterdam, Adfeel. Natuurkunde*, 2nd Ser., **32**, 1 (1934).

15. MACKEE, G. M., G. M. LEWIS, M. J. SPENCE, and M. E. HOPPER, Dandruff and seborrhea: 1. Flora of "normal" and diseased scalps, *J. Investigative Dermatol.*, **1**, 131 (1938).

16. MARTIN, D. S., C. P. JONES, K. F. YAO, and L. E. LEE, JR., A practical classification of the Monilias, *J. Bact.*, **34**, 99 (1937).

17. MARTIN, G. S., Outline of the fungi, *Univ. Iowa Studies Natural History*, Vol. 18, Suppl., 1941.

18. MRAK, E. M., H. J. PHAFF, and B. L. SMITH, Non-validity of the genus Asporomyces, *Mycologia*, **34**, 139 (1942).

19. MRAK, E. M., H. J. PHAFF, and R. H. VAUGHN, Yeasts occurring on dates, *J. Bact.*, **43**, 689 (1942).

20. NICKERSON, W. J., Studies in the genus Zygosaccharomyces. I. Transfer of pellicle forming yeasts to Zygopichia, *Farlowia*, **1**, 469 (1944).

21. ———, Studies in film-forming yeasts. Acid production by Zygopichia and Zygohansenula, *Mycologia*, **36**, 224 (1944).

22. PUNTONI, V., Studi sul genere Trichosporon, *Mycopath.*, **1**, 169 (1938).

23. REDAELLI, P., R. CIFERRI, and C. CAVALLERO, Sul presunto Endomyces albicans Vuillemin, *Mycopath.*, **2**, 116 (1939).

24. ROBERTS, C., A comparative study of *Torulopsis pulcherrima* and *Taphrina deformans* in culture, *Farlowia*, **2**, 345 (1946).

25. RUGOSA, M., Nicotinic acid requirements of certain yeasts, *J. Bact.*, **46**, 435 (1943).

26. STELLING-DEKKER, N. M., Die Sporogenen Hefen, *Verhandel. Akad. Wettenschappen Amsterdam, Adfeel. Natuurkunde*, 2nd Ser., **28**, 1–574 (1931).

27. WICKERHAM, L. J., A simple technique for detection of melibiose-fermenting yeasts, *J. Bact.*, **45**, 501 (1943).

28. WICKERHAM, L. J., L. B. LOCKWOOD, O. G. PETTIJOHN, and G. W. WARD, Starch hydrolysis and fermentation by the yeast *Endomycopsis fibuliger*, *J. Bact.*, **48**, 413 (1944).

29. WINDISCH, S., Entwicklungsgeschichtliche Untersuchungen an *Torulopsis pulcherrima* (Lindner) Saccardo und *Candida tropicalis* (Castellani) Berkhout. Ein Beitrag zur Systematik der Gärungsmonilien, *Arch. Mikrobiol.*, **11**, 368 (1940).

CHAPTER X

PATHOGENIC YEAST-LIKE FUNGI

Normal Occurrence of Yeasts in Man and Animals. Higher animals consume yeasts with their food, and these organisms have been demonstrated frequently in the alimentary tracts of animals and man. *Saccharomycopsis guttulatus* is apparently a constant normal parasite of the intestines of rabbits. Most of the species found in higher animals, however, are undoubtedly transitory organisms, not multiplying to any great extent in the body. Anderson [1] demonstrated that most species of yeasts are not injured by the digestive juices, but pass through the alimentary tract, and he described a number of species from human feces. Benham and Hopkins [4] isolated species of Candida, Cryptococcus, Geotrichum (Mycoderma), Saccharomyces, and Zygosaccharomyces from feces of normal persons. *Candida albicans* was isolated from 18 per cent and Geotrichum from 41 per cent of the cases examined. The frequent occurrence of yeasts in or on the human body has not been sufficiently considered by some authors who have described pathogenic yeasts.

Pathogenic Yeasts. It is very difficult to analyze the extensive literature on yeast infections in man. Many of the organisms reported have not been yeasts, but fungi of the type of *Candida albicans*. In many other cases the organisms have been so incompletely studied or described that it is impossible to determine whether the author was dealing with a true yeast or with a yeast-like form of a mycelial fungus. A large number of cases have been reported in which the pathogenicity of the fungus has been very imperfectly established, the mere presence of the yeast being considered sufficient evidence of its etiologic relationship to the disease. Where these fungi have occurred alone in deep-seated lesions, such evidence may be given weight, but in the numerous cases where yeasts have been found in superficial skin lesions, in the mouth and throat, sputum, or feces, associated with numerous other organisms, their presence can hardly be considered as evidence that they are the cause of the disease process under consideration. Even pathogenicity for laboratory animals, unless pronounced, should be considered guardedly, since various wild yeasts have been found to produce abscesses in lower animals when inoculated subcutaneously.

CRYPTOCOCCOSIS

(Torulosis, Torula Meningitis, European Blastomycosis).

History. The presence of an encapsulated yeast-like fungus in lesions and pathological material was reported by Busse in 1894 and 1895.[5] The patient was a woman who had a localized subperiosteal lesion of the tibia and in whom other osseus and visceral lesions subsequently developed. Busse called the disease saccharomycosis hominis and referred to the fungus which he found in the lesions as a yeast and as Saccharomyces, but he apparently did not use a binomial or specific name. In 1894 Sanfelice had isolated from fruit a fungus which was apparently like the one subsequently studied by Busse. He found that it was pathogenic for animals and he named it *Saccharomyces neoformans*.[18] Vuillemin[21] pointed out that the fungus differed from the true yeasts and transferred the species to the emended genus Cryptococcus, using the binomial *Cryptococcus hominis*. Another name, *Torula histolytica*, was added to the synonymy by Stoddard and Cutler[19] who, in reporting two cases of meningeal infection, interpreted the capsular material which surrounds the fungus cell as a space caused by a lytic action of the fungus. This name has been used widely in the United States. Other specific names and combinations of names have been used for this fungus, but the correct name appears to be *C. neoformans*.[3, 18]

Clinical. It is generally accepted, since the investigations of Benham[2] and of Lodder,[14] that cryptococcosis in the United States and in other parts of the world has a single common etiology, but that the disease in Europe is usually generalized, with skin lesions being a prominent feature, whereas in the United States it is primarily an infection of the central nervous system. The similarity between the fungi from the two types of lesions was noted in the first edition of this book. As additional cases have been reported from the United States it seems probable that this geographical differentiation has been overemphasized. It is true that meningitis is a common aspect of the disease as seen in the United States, but a review of the reported cases shows that in many instances there was widespread dissemination, and skin lesions are not uncommon. In many cases where meningitis was the principal feature, lesions were found in the lungs at autopsy and it is probable that in most cases the primary lesion was in the lungs.

Lesions of the Central Nervous System. The lesions consist of areas of destroyed or dissolved tissue containing an abundance of mucoid material and showing practically no inflammatory reaction. The complete absence of leucocytes is very striking, though giant cells may be formed.

The parasite appears in the tissues as round, budding cells, surrounded by a thick capsule of the mucoid material which is very evidently secreted by the yeast and not formed by the tissues. These yeast cells may be present in large numbers. In some cases they have been demonstrated in the spinal fluid before death. The capsules may be very clearly demonstrated by suspending some of the sediment from the centrifuged spinal fluid in a drop of India ink and examining the fluid under the cover glass. The yeast cells may show a marked variation in size.

There appears to be an association between cryptococcosis and Hodgkin's disease. The number of cases in which a concurrence of the two diseases has been reported far exceeds what might be expected on the basis of chance distribution. An adequate explanation for this association has not yet been made unless it is that certain aspects of cryptococcosis have been misdiagnosed as Hodgkin's disease. A thorough search for *Cryptococcus neoformans* in cases with the latter diagnosis is indicated.

Diagnosis. The differential diagnosis is made by the laboratory demonstration of *Cryptococcus neoformans* in the lesions. In ulcers the fungus is 2 to 15 microns in diameter. In spinal fluid the cells are usually smaller and in many cases are difficult to demonstrate, either because they are few and small or because they are mistaken for normal host cells. Attempts to isolate *C. neoformans* in culture from spinal fluid occasionally fail. This may be because of the periodic disappearance of the fungus from the spinal fluid, since it grows readily on acid dextrose (Sabouraud) agar and other usual culture media, and if present and viable should grow readily.

Prognosis and Treatment. The prognosis in cryptococcosis is very grave. There are few reported cases of arrest or recovery but, as with the other fatal mycoses, there is a probability that a mild unrecognized form of the disease exists and that only the terminal phases of the disease are known.

Iodides and other chemotherapeutic agents effective in other mycoses have not been useful. Symptomatic treatment, relief of pressure by spinal taps, and supportive therapy have occasionally been of benefit. There is some evidence that sulfadiazine is of value but it has not yet been tested in a sufficient number of cases for critical evaluation.

Morphology in Tissues. The cells of *Cryptococcus neoformans* are usually nearly spherical and this symmetry is not disturbed when the cell buds (Fig. 123). Unlike typical budding of most yeasts, the bud arises as a minute projection from the side of the parent cell and the connection between the mother and daughter cell always remains narrow. The bud secretes a capsule of its own, but frequently both

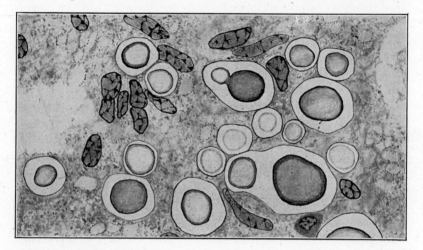

Fig. 123. Section through the meninges from a case of infection with *Cryptococcus neoformans*. Note the variation in size of the yeast cells, and the wide capsular spaces surrounding them. Drawing by Dr. J. C. McKinley.

encapsulated cells are surrounded also by a single enveloping capsule. The capsular material is produced in such quantity that frequently in tissue the total diameter of the capsule is as much as three times that of the cell proper. The budding cells, varying greatly in size and surrounded by the clear halos representing the capsules, may appear in considerable numbers and, by displacing host cells, particularly in certain tissues such as the meninges, form pockets in which the abundance of fungi and the absence of host tissue simulate a pure culture of the fungus. The cells vary in their reaction to Gram-staining.

Morphology in Culture. In culture *Cryptococcus neoformans* grows as spherical cells varying considerably in size and exhibiting the same peculiarities of budding as described above for the parasitic growth phase. In young cultures the capsule surrounding the cell may not be apparent unless the cells are mixed with dilute India ink or other capsule-demonstrating techniques are used. In most newly isolated strains the capsular material is produced in sufficient amounts to make the colony semi-fluid so that it tends to sag or flow slowly toward the bottom of the slant when the latter is incubated in a vertical position. The color is very light brownish tan.

In older cultures, and particularly in some strains, the capsule becomes very thick. It is usually eccentric so that it barely covers

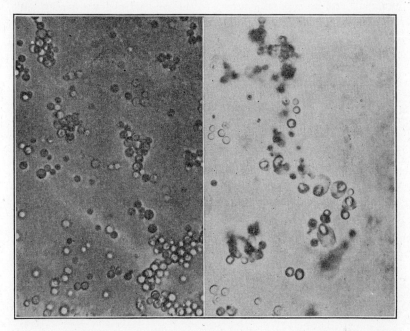

Fig. 124. *Cryptococcus neoformans:* left, young culture; right, old culture.

or even exposes the cell wall on one side, and it extends as a thick, striated, husk-like structure around the rest of the cell (Fig. 124). The thin area in the capsule marks the point where budding has recently occurred, where buds are still attached, or where budding may continue to take place. The thick capsule may, in other instances, enclose both parent cell and bud. In these old cultures there are exceptions to the previous statement that the bud communicates with the parent cell by a comparatively narrow opening. Occasionally in old cultures the neck is as wide as any portion of the bud and many bizarre forms are observed.

An examination of the culture may not give sufficient basis for the differentiation of *C. neoformans* from similar saprophytic species. In such cases it is useful to inject 0.05 ml. of a suspension of the fungus intracerebrally into mice. When so injected the pathogen produces typical gelatinous masses of budding cells in the meninges and within 5 to 15 days (depending upon the dosage and virulence of the strain) causes death of the animal.

Taxonomy. The thick capsule found in old cultures of *Cryptococcus neoformans* has been interpreted by some investigators as an ascus, and the small cell within the capsule as an ascospore. The fungus therefore was transferred to the genus Debaryomyces.[20] We have been unable to verify these observations. The manner of origin of the structures in question, their morphology, and their staining reactions seem to identify them rather with capsular material, stored food, and other vegetative structures. The large hyaline body which is conspicuous in many cells seems to originate by the coalescence of many small spherules and this material takes the fat stain. Until additional evidence bearing upon this point is brought forward it seems proper to refer the fungus to the imperfect yeasts under the name *C. neoformans*.

Distribution. The disease is widely distributed around the world and it is probable that apparent geographical localization is due actually to recognition rather than to an actual limitation of distribution.

Habitat in Nature. At about the same time that Busse and Buschke isolated this fungus from human lesions Sanfelice isolated it from fruit. Strains closely resembling it and believed to be avirulent strains of the species have been isolated from the surface of normal skin.[4] It seems probable that the natural habitat of the fungus is the surface of fruit and that from this and other vegetable material it may be transferred often to man.

Moniliasis. The commonest of the mycoses caused by yeast-like fungi is moniliasis, caused by *Candida albicans* (*Monilia albicans*). This fungus is primarily a parasite of the mucous membranes. Thus thrush occurs most frequently in the mouth, and not uncommonly in the vagina (in pregnancy). It may also extend through the gastrointestinal tract, and is very commonly found in sputum, although the level of infection in such cases is often unknown. Primary infections of the bronchi and lungs not associated with thrush have been reported, but the role of the fungus, whether primary or secondary, is a disputed point. In moniliasis the infections may involve the skin, producing eczema-like lesions of the moister parts such as the webs of the fingers, the groin, sub-mammary folds, and any skin crevice in which there are moisture and maceration. In all these conditions it may be questioned whether the fungus is of primary importance. It is known that *C. albicans* can be isolated from sputum in many types of pulmonary disease and that it can commonly be isolated from the feces.

Thrush. Thrush is one of the commonest of the mycoses of man. It is not so common or so serious nowadays as it has been in the past. It is most frequently a disease of nursing infants, particularly when they are undernourished or where there is a lack of cleanliness in their care. In older medical literature one reads of great epidemics of thrush in foundling asylums, with a relatively high mortality. We seldom see cases in such frequency or severity now. Thrush occurs also in adults, generally as a terminal event in such wasting diseases as typhoid fever, tuberculosis, or cancer, especially in patients who have been comatose or nearly so for a long time. It also occurs frequently as a mild infection of the vagina in pregnant women.

The majority of the cases are mild, and the infection remains localized to the affected mucous membrane, giving rise to no symptoms save local irritation. In such cases the disease appears as soft

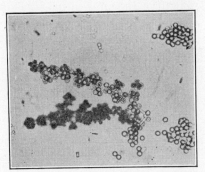

FIG. 125. *Candida albicans.* Characteristic chlamydospores in corn meal culture.

whitish patches on the mucous membranes of the mouth, on the tonsils, cheeks, or gums, occasionally on the tongue. These patches, composed mainly of the fungus growth, can generally be removed easily, leaving a slightly abraded surface. The membrane may be mistaken for diphtheritic membrane and, judging by the frequency with which this organism is found in throat cultures sent to diagnostic laboratories for examination for diphtheria bacilli, the disease must be confused frequently with diphtheria. Fineman [9] obtained some of her strains of the thrush parasite from such cultures, and Tanner and Dack investigated 22 strains of yeast-like fungi obtained from cases of sore throat which were for the most part *Candida albicans.*

In some cases the disease may become chronic and spread to other mucous membranes and the skin. There have been reported a small number of such cases in children, in which the organisms were present in the mouth over a period of some years, with occasional repeated infections, accompanied by eczematoid lesions of the skin, especially in the moist parts, between the thighs, in the bends of the elbows, and particularly between the fingers and toes. In several such cases loss of hair was a striking feature, although actual infection of the scalp could not be demonstrated. In these cases the organism could be regularly isolated from the feces in considerable numbers. These cases usually terminate fatally. The generalized cutaneous eruptions suggest that the condition is similar to that designated "trichophytide" in the ringworms, either an allergic manifestation or a blood-borne distribution in which for some reason the organism localizes in the skin only.[10] It is quite possible, however, that the fungus is in the alimentary tract and is carried from the mouth or the anus to the skin surfaces.

In a small number of cases (seven collected by Plaut) generalized infection by way of the blood stream with metastatic abscess in internal organs have occurred.

The diagnosis of thrush is established by microscopic examination of the membrane. This is best done by the use of unstained wet preparations. One finds a tangled mass of branched filaments of segmented mycelium, and scattered irregularly through them a number of yeast-like cells showing budding, together with leucocytes and desquamated epithelial cells. The fungus is easily isolated in pure culture on Sabouraud agar. It can be differentiated from similar fungi by the production on corn meal agar of hyphae bearing clusters of buds and chlamydospores, by its fermentation reactions, and by its pathogenicity for rabbits.

Fresh isolated strains are pathogenic for rabbits, producing localized abscesses in the kidneys and heart muscle, and occasionally generalized infection. When the fungus is injected intravenously the miliary abscesses in the cortex of the kidneys resemble closely those produced by *Aspergillus fumigatus*. In these lesions both mycelium and yeast cells may be found. Mice are very susceptible.

C. albicans (*Monilia psilosis*) is commonly present in the feces in tropical sprue, but is no longer thought to be of etiological importance in this disease.

Dermatomoniliasis. In addition to the cutaneous lesions observed in cases of thrush, *Candida albicans* has been isolated from various skin infections not associated with lesions of the mucous membranes. These have been for the most part conditions of an eczematoid nature in moist skin surfaces or in skin folds. They have been noted especially frequently in the webs of the fingers in washerwomen and housewives. The disease is known as erosio interdigitalis. An infection about the finger nails which occurs in workers in fruit canneries in the Northwest is, according to Kingery and Thienes,[12] caused by this fungus.

Bronchomoniliasis. *Candida albicans* is frequently isolated in great numbers from sputum. If the sputum has stood at room temperature for several hours the large numbers may be the result of multiplication of the fungus in the sputum after its collection. The fungus is capable of rapid growth in this medium and the examination and culture of old sputum may give a wholly erroneous impression of the mycological flora. If the fungus is found in large numbers in freshly collected sputum one should look for lesions in the mouth and throat. If it is definitely established that the fungus comes from the bronchi, its etiological importance still remains to be proved. *C. albicans* can be found in the sputum from very many types of pulmonary disease, where it appears to be of secondary or of no importance. The isolation of this fungus from sputum is therefore no valid reason for returning a laboratory diagnosis of moniliasis. It is probable that Candida infection of the lungs occurs and that it is sometimes of clinical importance, but the criteria for a diagnosis of bronchomoniliasis are still debatable.[6, 11]

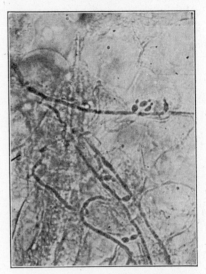

Fig. 126. Moniliasis of skin. *Candida albicans* in epidermal scales from "erosio interdigitalis."

Mycotic Endocarditis. Recently several cases have been reported in which drug addicts who were accustomed to taking heroin intravenously developed a condition which clinically appeared to be subacute bacterial endocarditis. From the blood stream or from lesions of the heart after death, yeast-like fungi were isolated and the fungus could be seen in the heart lesions. The fungus in all but one of these cases was *Candida parakrusei*. In one case it was *C. Guilliermondi.*[23]

Taxonomy. There is a voluminous literature on the taxonomy of these fungi.[7, 8, 13, 15, 16, 17, 22] It is generally recognized that the old name, Monilia, is invalid for them, and modern usage favors the generic name Candida.

LITERATURE

1. ANDERSON, H. W., Yeast-like fungi of the human intestinal tract, *J. Infectious Diseases*, **21**, 341 (1917).

2. BENHAM, R. W., Certain Monilias parasitic on man, *J. Infectious Diseases*, **49**, 183 (1931).

3. ——, The terminology of the Cryptococci with a note on *Cryptococcus mollis*, *Mycologia*, **27**, 496 (1935).

4. BENHAM, R. W., and A. M. HOPKINS, Yeastlike fungi found on the skin and in the intestines of normal subjects, *Arch. Dermatol. Syphilol. (Chicago)*, **28**, 532 (1933).

5. BUSSE, O., Ueber Saccharomycosis hominis, *Archiv path. Anat. (Virchow's)*, **140** (Hft. 1), 23 (1895).

6. CASTELLANI, A., *Fungi and Fungous Diseases*, Am. Med. Assoc., Chicago, 1928.

7. ——, A short general account for medical men of the genus Monilia, Persoon, 1797, *J. Trop. Med. Hyg.*, Dec. 1, 1937.

8. CONANT, N. F., The taxonomy of the anascosporous yeast-like fungi, *Mycopathologia*, **2**, 253 (1940).

9. FINEMAN, B. C., A study of the thrush parasite, *J. Infectious Diseases*, **28**, 185 (1921).

10. HOPKINS, J. G., Moniliasis and moniliids, *Arch. Dermatol. Syphilol. (Chicago)*, **25**, 599 (1932).

11. IKEDA, K., Bronchopulmonary moniliasis, *Arch. Path.*, **22**, 62 (1936).

12. KINGERY, L. B., and C. H. THIENES, Mycotic paronychia and dermatitis, *Arch. Dermatol. Syphilol. (Chicago)*, **11**, 186 (1925).

13. LANGERON, M., and P. GUERRA, Nouvelles recherches de zymologie médicale, *Ann. parasitol. humaine et comparée*, **16**, 36 (1938).

14. LODDER, J., Die Hefesammlung des Centraalbureau voor Schimmelcultures. II Teil. Die anaskosporogenen Hefen, *Uitgave van de N.V. Noord-Hollandsche Uitgevers-Maatschappij, Amsterdam*, 1934.

15. MACKINNON, J. E., and R. C. ARTAGAVEYTIA-ALLENDE, The so-called genus Candida Berkhout, 1923, *J. Bact.*, **49**, 317 (1945).

16. MARTIN, D. S., and C. P. JONES, Further studies on the practical classification of the Monilias, *J. Bact.*, **39**, 609 (1940).

17. MARTIN, D. S., C. P. JONES, K. F. YAO, and L. E. LEE, JR., A practical classification of the Monilias, *J. Bact.*, **34**, 99 (1937).

18. SANFELICE, F., Sull'azione patogena dei blastomiceti, *Ann. igiene*, **5**, 239 (1895).

19. STODDARD, J. L., and E. C. CUTLER, Torula infection in man, *Rockefeller Inst. Med. Res.*, Monograph 6, 1916.

20. TODD, R. L., and W. H. HERRMANN, The life cycle of the organism causing yeast meningitis, *J. Bact.*, **32**, 89 (1936).

21. VUILLEMIN, P., Les caractères specifiques du champignon du muguet, *Compt. rend.*, **127**, 630 (1898).

22. WICKERHAM, L. J., and L. F. RETTGER, A taxonomic study of *Monilia albicans* with special emphasis on morphology and morphological variation, *J. Trop. Med. Hyg.*, **42**, 174, 187, 204 (1939).

23. WIKLER, A., E. G. WILLIAMS, E. D. DOUGLASS, C. W. EMMONS, and R. C. DUNN, Mycotic endocarditis, *J. Am. Med. Assoc.*, **119**, 333 (1942).

CHAPTER XI

BIOLOGICAL ACTIVITIES OF YEASTS

ECOLOGY OF YEASTS

We find yeasts in nature wherever sugar is present, in the various foodstuffs of man, in the nectar of flowers, the exuded sap of trees, and above all on the surfaces of fruits. They are also found in soil, on the leaves of plants, and as symbionts or parasites in various animals, especially insects.

The constant occurrence of yeasts on fruits, especially grapes, naturally led to inquiries as to their origin. Pasteur showed that the immature fruits are free from yeasts, and that, if they are covered with cotton while ripening, no yeast will develop. Hansen believed, as a result of investigations with *Hansenia apiculata,* that the yeasts remain dormant in the soil during the winter and spring, probably in the form of ascospores, and are deposited on the fruit by the wind. The spores germinate and bud there to form new spores on the overripe fruit at the approach of winter. He found yeasts much more numerous in the soil of vineyards than elsewhere. However, Starkey and Henrici [42] found yeasts to be relatively infrequent in soil, being present in very small numbers in only 38 of 87 soil samples of all kinds, including a number from orchards. The varieties found were for the most part not those kinds found to be active in the spontaneous fermentation of fruit juices, only four cultures of Saccharomyces being found.

Yeasts have been found very frequently on insects and in their digestive tracts, and it is probable that insects are more important in distributing yeasts on fruits than is the chance distribution of infrequent yeasts from soil by the wind. Since yeasts are apparently distributed in nature largely through the agency of insects, it is not surprising to find yeasts frequently present in their alimentary tracts. Thus Berlse believed that the intestinal tract of Diptera was the normal habitat of many yeasts, including *"Saccharomyces ellipsoideus."* It has also been shown that the yeasts form an important part of the diet of certain insects, such forms as the fruit flies (Drosophila) for instance, depending for their nutrition not so much upon

315

the fruit as upon the yeasts growing there. In some insects, however, the yeasts penetrate the body cavity and live there, probably as symbionts, since they apparently do no harm to the insect, and are invariably present, being transmitted in the ova. These symbiotic yeasts are found particularly in the Homoptera, especially the cicadas, and are contained in a special mass of tissue, the pseudovitellus, so that microscopically they appear at first glance as some sort of gland. The species found are for the most part members of the genus Schizosaccharomyces. They have been especially studied by Sulc. In another homopterous insect, the locust, there occurs a pathogenic yeast which invades the blood and multiplies sufficiently to make the blood a milky white color instead of its normal clear straw color. It kills the insect and can be transmitted by inoculation.

Aside from the peculiar yeast, *Nectaromyces Reukaufii,* referred to previously, numerous other yeasts have been found in the nectar of flowers. Zinkernagel [54] has described 15 species obtained from various flowers, none of which formed ascospores. Lochhead and Heron,[28] studying the fermentations of stored honey, found these to be due in every case to yeasts of the genus Zygosaccharomyces, which could not only grow in high concentrations of honey but failed to develop in media of low osmotic pressure. Thus in tubes containing 10, 25, 50, 65, and 75 per cent honey, fermentation occurred in only the first three with "*S. ellipsoideus,*" and it occurred only in the last three with a yeast from fermented honey. An investigation of the nectar of flowers showed the occurrence of similar yeasts of high sugar tolerance belonging to the Zygosaccharomyces group.

Higher animals consume yeasts with their food, and these organisms have frequently been demonstrated in the alimentary tracts of animals and man. *S. guttalatus* is apparently a constant normal parasite of the intestines of rabbits. Most of the species found in higher animals are, however, undoubtedly transitory organisms, not multiplying in the body. Anderson [1] has demonstrated that most species of yeasts are not injured by the digestive juices, but pass through the alimentary tract, and has described a number of species from human feces. Rettger, Reddish, and MacAlpine,[39] however, found that baker's yeast was rapidly destroyed in the alimentary tract. The occurrence of yeasts in the normal throat has been studied by Tanner, Lampert, and Lampert.[46] They did not, however, clearly distinguish the strains they isolated from Candida. Yeasts were found in 10 per cent of the throats examined. Eighteen of forty-seven strains were pathogenic to mice. The frequent occurrence of yeasts in or on the human body has not been sufficiently considered by the various authors who have described pathogenic yeasts. See Chapter X.

NUTRITIONAL REQUIREMENTS OF YEAST

The yeasts, like other organisms, require adequate supplies of carbon, nitrogen, hydrogen, oxygen, phosphorus, sulphur, magnesium, and other elements.

Substances like sugars, organic acids, aldehydes, and glycerol can generally be used as sources of carbon for the growth of yeasts. There are some differences, of course, in the abilities of the various yeasts to utilize these substances. The carbon source is generally considered to be of importance in supplying the organisms with energy, i.e., the aerobic or anaerobic breakdown of carbon compounds yields energy which can be used by the yeast. Of course, some of the carbon is also used in building protoplasm, together with other elements.

Degradation products of proteins, such as proteoses, peptones, peptides, amino acids, and ammonia, as well as urea and amides, can, in most instances, serve as sources of nitrogen. Ammonium salts such as sulphate, phosphate, and chloride, are often employed in artificial media used for growing yeasts and are commonly used in the manufacture of compressed yeast. Nitrogen is, of course, a necessary component of amino acids which are built up into proteins, an indispensable constituent of protoplasm.

Obviously, oxygen and hydrogen are necessary, not only for the make-up of protoplasm, but also for the vital functions they perform in the general economy of the cell. Phosphorus, as phosphates, plays an important role in cell metabolism. The importance of phosphates will be described later in the discussion of the alcoholic fermentation. Phosphorus is also required for the make-up of nucleoproteins, phospholipids, and the like. Sulphur is an essential constituent of enzyme systems involving glutathione, thiamin, and so on. Magnesium is required for the operation of certain reactions catalyzed by enzymes (e.g., phosphorylation of glucose). Under certain conditions, manganese and cobalt may be substituted for it.

In addition to these substances, the yeasts may require other nutrients, the roles for which are not, in all cases, clearly understood at the present time. Wildiers' observation in 1901 that the addition of a small amount of organic matter, "bios," tremendously stimulated the growth of yeast cells in an otherwise chemically defined medium set off a series of far-reaching investigational researches, which are still going on today. He observed the ability of large inocula to initiate rapid growth in media which failed to support growths when small inocula were used. He concluded that bios, an organic substance of biological origin essential for the propagation of yeast cells, was carried over in large inocula from the previous cultures. He also found that other biological materials contained substances with marked stimulatory properties.

As already indicated, considerable research has been and is being done on the essential growth factors. These substances, when added to a medium complete in respect to carbon and nitrogen compounds and the other necessary nutrients, cause a stimulation of microbial growth all out of proportion to the minute amounts added.

The bios of Wildiers has proved to be a complex of growth-essential and stimulating substances such as thiamin, biotin, pyridoxine, inositol, and pantothenic acid. The role of the first-named compound is now known. The enzyme, carboxylase, which catalyzes the decarboxylation of pyruvic acid to carbon dioxide and acetaldehyde in the alcoholic fermentation, cannot function without its coenzyme, cocarboxylase. Cocarboxylase is known to be diphosphothiamin. The structures of the above compounds are as follows.

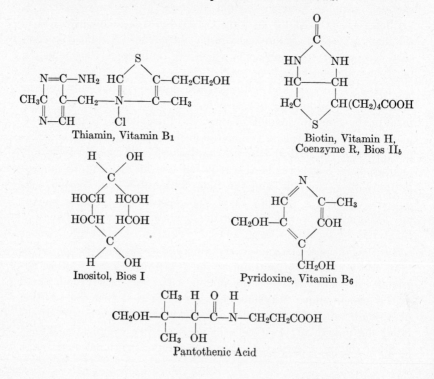

Thiamin, Vitamin B₁

Biotin, Vitamin H, Coenzyme R, Bios II_b

Inositol, Bios I

Pyridoxine, Vitamin B₆

Pantothenic Acid

Methods for the study of such nutritional requirements as are of use in taxonomy are given by Stelling-Decker and have been briefly treated in Chapter III.

THE PASTEUR EFFECT

That aerobic conditions inhibit the anaerobic breakdown of hexoses and other carbohydrates was noted by Pasteur in his *Études sur la Bière*.[35] He observed that the fermentation * carried on by cells of facultative organisms under anaerobic conditions disappeared or diminished and was replaced by respiration when such cells were placed under aerobic conditions, e.g., fermentation carried on by yeast cells (as indicated by the production of ethyl alcohol) under anaerobic conditions diminished (as indicated by the diminution of the production of alcohol) on aeration of the culture, and was replaced by respiration (as indicated by the increased amount of carbon dioxide formed). This phenomenon of the inhibition of fermentive processes by oxygen is the so-called Pasteur effect or Pasteur phenomenon.

One might regard this as a manifestation of a regulatory device whereby facultative organisms can use either their aerobic or anaerobic systems to obtain energy from the breakdown of sugar. Such a device is advantageous to the organism. In the presence of sufficient oxygen, the fermentive mechanism is blocked off and energy is obtained by the more efficient respiratory mechanism. Only in the absence of sufficient oxygen is the less efficient fermentive mechanism brought into play. Less sugar is required to develop the population of facultative organisms to a certain point under aerobic conditions than under anaerobic. The latter statement should not be misconstrued to mean that sugar consumption is lowered under aerobic conditions. For a given amount of sugar, provided there is an adequate supply of other nutrients, the population of facultative organisms in a culture will attain a higher point under aerobic conditions than under anaerobic conditions in a given period of time.

Many theories have been advanced concerning the mechanism and the exact locus of the Pasteur effect. None, however, has been generally accepted. Some claim that glucose is broken down to inter-

* The term fermentation will be used in this discussion of the Pasteur effect to refer to those processes whereby organisms obtain energy for their use by the anaerobic dissimilation of carbohydrates, i.e., anaerobic glycolytic processes, and the term respiration to those processes whereby organisms obtain energy by the aerobic breakdown of carbohydrates.

mediate fermentation products and that these are subsequently oxidized to carbon dioxide and water by the oxygen of air. One of the points in the dissimilation of sugar suggested as the locus of shunting off the fermentive process has been at the acetaldehyde (or pyruvate) stage where there is a competition between oxidation on the one hand and reduction with the formation of ethyl alcohol (or lactate) on the other.[44] It has also been suggested that the point of the Pasteur effect is at the triose phosphate stage.[5] In the alcoholic fermentation (see page 326) for the Embden-Meyerhof-Parnas scheme), hexose is initially phosphorylated. This is followed by the cleavage of the diphosphorylated sugar to two phosphorylated trioses. After further phosphorylation, the triose is oxidized at the expense of diphosphopyridine nucleotide, DPN (Coenzyme I) which is reduced to H_2-DPN. Under anaerobic conditions, H_2-DPN (reduced Coenzyme I) passes its hydrogen to acetaldehyde (reducing it to ethyl alcohol) and is itself oxidized to DPN. Under aerobic conditions, however, it is proposed that H_2-DPN does not pass its hydrogen to acetaldehyde but rather to an enzyme of the flavoprotein type (yellow enzymes) or to some enzyme, as yet unknown. If the hydrogen is passed to a flavoprotein enzyme, it in turn passes the hydrogen to molecular oxygen via the cytochrome-cytochrome oxidase system. Oxygen is the final hydrogen acceptor. Coenzyme I, shuttling back and forth between its oxidized and reduced states, oxidizes more phosphorylated triose molecules. The oxidation product of the phosphorylated triose is disposed of by oxidation through the intervention of oxidative enzymes.

Recently, it has been suggested that intermediates are not formed at all but that the locus of the Pasteur effect is at the hexose monophosphate stage. Engel'hardt[14] among others has proposed that the Neuberg ester is the critical compound. If this hexose monophosphate is further phosphorylated to the hexose diphosphate, the molecule undergoes fermentive breakdown. However, if this hexose monophosphate, instead of being phosphorylated, is oxidized to phosphohexonic acid, oxidative breakdown occurs. A somewhat related hypothesis has been advanced by Johnson.[22] He points out that both aerobic and anaerobic breakdown processes involve phosphorylative reactions. The aerobic processes carry on phosphorylations utilizing relatively large amounts of phosphates and may lower the phosphate concentration to the point where anaerobic glycolytic phosphorylations cannot occur. Therefore fermentive mechanisms are unable to operate. He does not, however, stipulate the point of the Pasteur effect, as does Engel'hardt.

Pasteur also made the observation, and it has been amply confirmed since, that aerobic conditions generally increase the rate and efficiency of the synthetic processes of the organism. Hence it has been suggested that the fermentation intermediates are used in the resynthesis of carbohydrates.

However, none of the above-proposed mechanisms nor the above-suggested loci of action is more than tentative. Considerable experimental work still remains to be done. For further information on this important subject the reader is referred to excellent reviews by Burk [9] and Lipmann.[27]

MANUFACTURE OF YEAST AND ITS USES

Compressed yeast is manufactured in tremendous quantities. Most of it is used for the baking, industrial alcohol, and brewing industries. Some of it is also used for vitamin preparations, enzymes, and the like.

Compressed Yeast Manufacture. The most commonly used method for the manufacture of yeast involves the use of the molasses-ammonia process. A dilute mixture of molasses, mineral salts, and ammonia is pitched, i.e., inoculated, with yeast. Concentrated wort, uninoculated mash, is added from time to time at such a rate that there is sufficient sugar for the growth of yeast but not for the unlimited production of alcohol. Sterile air is passed through the mash during most of the growth process to aerate it. Aerobic conditions inhibit the production of alcohol as noted above, but such conditions are difficult to attain in the presence of high concentrations of sugar and other organic matter. Therefore, small amounts of alcohol are produced. The pH of the mash is controlled by the addition of ammonia and sulfuric acid from time to time, a fairly low pH range of 4.0 to 4.5 being generally maintained. The periodic addition of ammonia is necessary because the yeast utilizes it for its nitrogen source. Temperature is controlled by the use of cooling coils in the tank. At the end of the growth period, the mature yeast is freed of the wort by centrifugation and/or filtration.

Yeast has also been prepared from sulphite liquor, a waste product in the manufacture of pulp from wood, mixed with small amounts of molasses (see page 339). Yeast for animal feed has also been prepared from dilute sugar solution prepared from wood by the Scholler-Tornesch process (see page 339). In both these instances, nitrogen in the form of ammonia and essential salts must be added.

The Uses of Yeast. Because of its ergosterol (provitamin D) content yeast is a good source for the production of vitamin D by irradiation. Yeast also contains thiamin, riboflavin, nicotinic acid, pantothenic acid, pyridoxine, biotin, and p-aminobenzoic acid, all considered vitamins of the B complex. It also contains large amounts of protein, fat, and mineral salts. Hence it is not surprising that there have been suggestions that yeast be used as a food supplement for humans. Strains of *"Torula utilis,"* yeasts belonging to the genus Cryptococcus (see page 286), have been proposed as suitable for this purpose. Irradiated yeast is used as a supplement in cattle feed.

Yeast is also a good source of the enzyme invertase, which hydrolyzes sucrose to invert sugar, glucose and fructose. This enzyme is used by the confectionery, baking, and syrup-manufacturing trades. Yeast has also been said to yield beneficial results in some cases when used therapeutically in the diet. Aside from the value derived from its vitamin content, however, such medical benefits are questionable.

It has been demonstrated that the yeasts, like some of the higher biological forms, convert carbohydrates into lipoidal materials. Yeasts normally produce lipids, but the rates of formation and the amounts stored are not generally of enough consequence to warrant industrial considerations. However, under national emergency conditions, it has been proposed that waste carbohydrate materials be used for the synthesis of lipids by yeasts. Lindner[25] carried on investigations in Germany during World War I in an attempt to produce, on an economically sound basis, fats from *Endomycopsis vernalis.* Fink and his coworkers[17] have also studied the production of lipids from Geotrichum. For further discussion on this subject, the reader is referred to Prescott and Dunn.[38]

More recently, yeast has been suggested for use in the microbiological assay of certain vitamins. Williams and his colleagues[52] claim that in a medium deficient in thiamin but containing all the other substances essential for the nutrition of yeast, the growth of yeast is directly proportional to the amount of this vitamin added to the medium. The development of yeast is measured turbidimetrically. A weakness of this method is that yeast is stimulated by both the pyrimidine and thiazole portions of the thiamin molecule as well as by thiamin itself. Frey and his associates have also suggested the use of yeast in ultramicrobiological[3] and microbiological[40] fermentation methods for the determination of thiamin. They have utilized the fact that thiamin is a component of the coenzyme cocarboxylase, for the enzyme carboxylase, which is essential for the production of carbon dioxide from the anaerobic breakdown of sugar,

(The enzyme system catalyzes the decarboxylation of pyruvic acid to carbon dioxide and acetaldehyde.) They claim that the amount of carbon dioxide produced in a microrespirometer or a fermentometer by yeast suspended in a salt-glucose solution is directly proportional to the amount of thiamin added. However, the compressed yeast recommended for this assay purpose can also be stimulated to produce gas by the pyrimidine fraction of the thiamin molecule as well as thiamin.[12] See page 318 for the structure of thiamin.

The use of yeast for assay of pyridoxine (vitamin B_6) has also been suggested by these two groups of workers.[4, 51] At the present time, the method of assay for pyridoxine using yeast and measuring the growth response turbidimetrically is the best available. It is superior to the assay method employing lactobacilli as the test organism.

Williams, Snell, and their associates have also described techniques for the microbiological assay of pantothenic acid,[36] inositol,[53] and biotin[41] employing yeasts as the test organisms and using the turbidity method.

THE ALCOHOLIC FERMENTATION

The final establishment of the fact that fermentation, as it occurs in nature, is caused by living cells comes from Pasteur's classical experiments with yeasts. His views were vigorously opposed, especially by the chemist Liebig, who held that ferments were not living cells but merely organic catalysts in a state of extreme disquietude, this state being transferred to sugar molecules, which then changed to forms more stable, alcohol and carbon dioxide. Pasteur's thesis that fermentations occurring in nature are due to living cells has been firmly established. However, his view that fermentation is a part of the vital phenomenon which cannot be separated from the life of the yeast cell, that fermentation is inseparable from the presence of living cells, has been proved fallacious. Buchner found that cell-free press juice, obtained by grinding yeast cells with sand and subjecting the ground cells to hydraulic pressure, could carry out the fermentation. From his studies, this investigator concluded that the production of alcoholic fermentation does not require as complicated an apparatus as the living yeast cell, and that the fermenting power of yeast juice is due to an enzyme, zymase. Actually, zymase has proved to be a battery of individual enzymes. Buchner's discovery of enzymes in the cell-free press juice of yeast has provided a technique for the study of the mechanism of fermentation—a technique whereby fermentive systems may be studied apart from the other chemical processes (e.g., assimilatory processes) of the cell. It has made possible the isolation and purification, at least partially, of the individual components of this battery of enzymes and the determination of some of their chemical properties.

The Role of Phosphates in the Fermentation. The studies of Harden and his associates [19] demonstrated the important fact that phosphates exert a stimulatory effect on the zymase fermentation of glucose, which proceeds more slowly than the fermentation carried on by intact cells. Harden and Young [20] found that inorganic phosphates disappear during the first stage of fermentation and are replaced by organic phosphates, esters of hexose. It was originally believed that the primary purpose of phosphorylation was to introduce two phosphate groups into the hexose molecule to form hexosediphosphate and, thus, model the molecule for cleavage into two triose phosphates.

Subsequent investigations, however, have assigned an even more important role to the phosphates. The phosphate ester bonds of hexose are changed, as the fermentation proceeds, to different types of linkages which serve as carriers of energy. Large quantities of energy given off by the oxidation-reduction reactions occurring in the fermentive breakdown of sugars are not dissipated haphazardly, but accumulate instead in energy-rich phosphate bonds † (Lipmann's terminology). The major portion of oxidation-reduction energy, made available, is converted into phosphate bond energy. Once the energy-rich phosphate bonds are produced, transphosphorylations, i.e., migration of phosphate groups from one compound to another, may occur through transport systems such as the adenylic acid system.‡

† Energy-rich phosphate bonds: linkages which when cleaved yield large amounts of energy, ca. 10,000 calories, e.g.,

$$R \cdot \overset{OH}{\underset{O}{CO \cdot P \cdot O}} \sim PO_3H_2, \quad R \cdot \overset{O}{C \cdot O} \sim PO_3H_2, \quad R : \overset{COOH}{C \cdot O} \sim PO_3H_2.$$

Energy-rich phosphate bonds will be designated in the text as: $\sim PO_3H_2$.

‡ Adenylic acid system: A coenzyme system consisting of two adenosine polyphosphates, adenosine triphosphate (ATP), and adenosine diphosphate (ADP); and adenosine monophosphate (AMP) or adenylic acid. ATP may donate an energy-rich phosphate group to a phosphate acceptor and itself become ADP. The ADP may in like manner give up an energy-rich phosphate group and become AMP. AMP, though containing a residual phosphate group, is incapable of giv-

The adenosine polyphosphates generated may serve as phosphate "donors" for the phosphorylation of hexose. Others may pass their phosphate groups to amino acids. The phosphorylated amino acids may then condense with other amino acids to form proteins with the regeneration of inorganic phosphates. Useful work, the synthesis of proteins, would thus be accomplished. Lipmann pictures a phosphate cycle with the following steps: (1) the assimilation of inorganic phosphate with the formation of the primary ester linkage, (2) the generation of energy-rich phosphate bonds by oxidation-reduction reactions, (3) the distribution of energy-rich phosphate bonds by cell catalysts such as the adenylic acid system with the phosphorylation of hexose and/or other compounds, e.g., amino acids, (4) utilization of energy in energy-rich bonds to do some useful work as the synthesis of proteins with the regeneration of inorganic phosphate. Only a superficial treatment of this fascinating subject has been attempted here. The interested reader is referred to excellent reviews by Kalckar,[24] Meyerhof,[32] and Lipmann[26] which deal with this subject.

The Alcoholic Fermentation Proper. Our present-day knowledge of the chemistry of the alcoholic fermentation is the result of investigations directed not only toward studying the mechanisms of the alcoholic fermentation per se but also toward studying the mechanisms involved in muscle metabolism. Correlative studies in the field of sugar dissimilation in muscle tissues have contributed a considerable portion of what is known today of the alcoholic fermentation. The findings of the various investigators have been summarized in the so-called Embden-Meyerhof-Parnas scheme for the dissimilation of sugar.

Essential features of this scheme are given in Table 4. The individual reactions consist of phosphorylations, intramolecular rearrangements, oxidation-reductions, dehydration, and decarboxylation. The elucidation of the nature of these reactions is due to Embden, Meyerhof, Parnas, Warburg, Lohmann, Cori, and others. The following is a brief résumé of the transformations that are believed to occur in the alcoholic fermentation.

The production of alcohol and carbon dioxide from glucose begins with the phosphorylation of the hexose molecule. Initially, a phosphate group donated by the adenylic acid system is introduced into the glucose molecule under the mediation of Mg^{++} (under certain

ing it up (as a regular part of the system). AMP and ADP can, by accepting phosphate groups, be converted to ATP.

TABLE 4

EMBDEN-MEYERHOF-PARNAS SCHEME FOR THE DISSIMILATION OF SUGAR

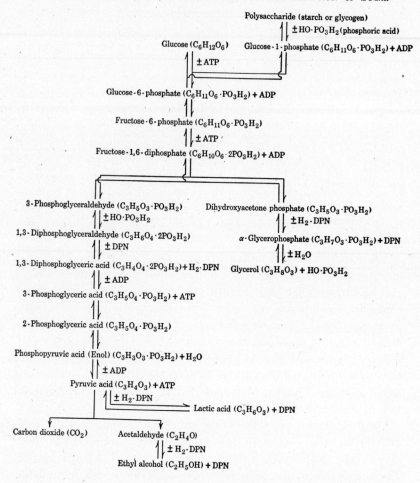

Polysaccharide (starch or glycogen)

$\pm HO \cdot PO_3H_2$ (phosphoric acid)

Glucose ($C_6H_{12}O_6$)   Glucose-1-phosphate ($C_6H_{11}O_6 \cdot PO_3H_2$) + ADP

$\pm$ ATP

Glucose-6-phosphate ($C_6H_{11}O_6 \cdot PO_3H_2$) + ADP

Fructose-6-phosphate ($C_6H_{11}O_6 \cdot PO_3H_2$)

$\pm$ ATP

Fructose-1,6-diphosphate ($C_6H_{10}O_6 \cdot 2PO_3H_2$) + ADP

3-Phosphoglyceraldehyde ($C_3H_5O_3 \cdot PO_3H_2$)   Dihydroxyacetone phosphate ($C_3H_5O_3 \cdot PO_3H_2$)

$\pm HO \cdot PO_3H_2$ $\pm H_2 \cdot DPN$

1,3-Diphosphoglyceraldehyde ($C_3H_6O_4 \cdot 2PO_3H_2$) α-Glycerophosphate ($C_3H_7O_3 \cdot PO_3H_2$) + DPN

$\pm$ DPN $\pm H_2O$

1,3-Diphosphoglyceric acid ($C_3H_4O_4 \cdot 2PO_3H_2$) + $H_2 \cdot DPN$ Glycerol ($C_3H_8O_3$) + $HO \cdot PO_3H_2$

$\pm$ ADP

3-Phosphoglyceric acid ($C_3H_5O_4 \cdot PO_3H_2$) + ATP

2-Phosphoglyceric acid ($C_3H_5O_4 \cdot PO_3H_2$)

Phosphopyruvic acid (Enol) ($C_3H_3O_3 \cdot PO_3H_2$) + H_2O

$\pm$ ADP

Pyruvic acid ($C_3H_4O_3$) + ATP

$\pm H_2 \cdot DPN$

Lactic acid ($C_3H_6O_3$) + DPN

Carbon dioxide (CO_2)   Acetaldehyde (C_2H_4O)

$\pm H_2 \cdot DPN$

Ethyl alcohol (C_2H_5OH) + DPN

conditions Mn^{++} or Co^{++} will also serve) and hexokinase where ATP is the phosphate donor (and, demonstrated in muscle tissue, under the mediation of Mg^{++}, hexokinase, and myokinase where ADP is the donor). The primary phosphorylation product formed is glucose-6-phosphate, the Robison ester. This compound exists in an equilibrium with fructose-6-phosphate, the Neuberg ester. The latter compound is then believed to be phosphorylated by one of the adenosine polyphosphates to fructose-1,6-diphosphate, the Harden and Young ester.

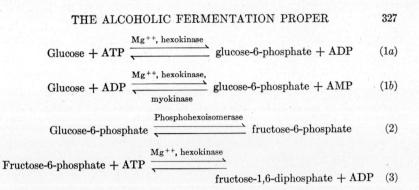

$$\text{Glucose} + \text{ATP} \xrightarrow{\text{Mg}^{++}, \text{ hexokinase}} \text{glucose-6-phosphate} + \text{ADP} \qquad (1a)$$

$$\text{Glucose} + \text{ADP} \xrightarrow[\text{myokinase}]{\text{Mg}^{++}, \text{ hexokinase},} \text{glucose-6-phosphate} + \text{AMP} \qquad (1b)$$

$$\text{Glucose-6-phosphate} \xrightleftharpoons{\text{Phosphohexoisomerase}} \text{fructose-6-phosphate} \qquad (2)$$

$$\text{Fructose-6-phosphate} + \text{ATP} \xrightarrow{\text{Mg}^{++}, \text{ hexokinase}}$$
$$\text{fructose-1,6-diphosphate} + \text{ADP} \quad (3)$$

This hexose diphosphate is acted upon by the enzyme zymohexase (aldolase) to form as cleavage products two triose phosphates—a molecule of glyceraldehyde phosphate and a molecule of dihydroxyacetone phosphate—an equilibrium existing between the two.

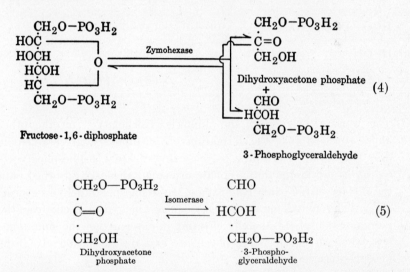

The glyceraldehyde phosphate, according to Warburg and Christian,[49] unites with inorganic phosphate to form 1,3-diphosphoglyceraldehyde.

$$\begin{array}{c} \text{CHO} \\ | \\ \text{HCOH} \\ | \\ \text{CH}_2\text{O—PO}_3\text{H}_2 \end{array} \xrightleftharpoons[\text{(H}_3\text{PO}_4)]{+\text{HO—PO}_3\text{H}_2} \begin{array}{c} \text{OH} \\ | \\ \text{HCO—PO}_3\text{H}_2 \\ | \\ \text{HCOH} \\ | \\ \text{CH}_2\text{O—PO}_3\text{H}_2 \end{array} \qquad (6)$$

3-Phospho-
glyceraldehyde   1,3-Diphospho-
                                       glyceraldehyde

This diphosphorylated triose is oxidized to 1,3-diphosphoglyceric acid by the removal of two hydrogen atoms. Prior to the introduction of the concept of phosphorylated intermediates, the explanation of the mechanism of dehydrogenation (oxidation) of an aldehyde group was to assume that the aldehyde group was first hydrated and then dehydrogenated. An examination of the oxidation of diphosphoglyceraldehyde to diphosphoglyceric acid obviates the necessity for such an assumption. In this oxidation step, one of the energy-poor phosphate bonds, § a low potential phosphate ester bond, is converted to an energy-rich bond by the energy generated by the oxidation. The two hydrogen atoms are accepted by Coenzyme I or diphosphopyridine nucleotide, DPN, which is converted to the reduced form, H_2-DPN.

$$
\begin{array}{lll}
\text{OH} & & \text{O} \\
\overset{\cdot}{\text{HCO}}\text{—PO}_3\text{H}_2 & \overset{\text{Triose phosphate dehydrogenase}}{\rightleftharpoons} & \overset{\cdot\cdot}{\text{CO}}\sim\text{PO}_3\text{H}_2 \\
\overset{\cdot}{\text{HCOH}} \qquad + \text{DPN} & & \overset{\cdot}{\text{HCOH}} \qquad + \text{H}_2\text{-DPN} \\
\overset{\cdot}{\text{CH}_2\text{O}}\text{—PO}_3\text{H}_2 & & \overset{\cdot}{\text{CH}_2\text{O}}\text{—PO}_3\text{H}_2 \qquad (7)
\end{array}
$$

1,3-Diphospho-glyceraldehyde   1,3-Diphospho-glyceric acid

The work of Meyerhof and Junowicz-Kocholaty,[33] on the other hand, suggests that the formation of 1,3-diphosphoglyceraldehyde does not occur. According to these investigators, 3-phosphoglyceraldehyde and inorganic phosphate are simultaneously adsorbed onto the surface of the oxidative enzyme, triose phosphate dehydrogenase. DPN then removes one hydrogen from the aldehyde and one from the inorganic phosphate, thereby effecting in one reaction the simultaneous oxidation of the triose phosphate and the formation of 1,3-diphosphoglyceric acid.

H_2-DPN, the reduced form of Coenzyme I, may reduce a molecule of phosphorylated triose to glycerophosphate (which on hydrolysis yields glycerol) and itself be regenerated to its oxidized form, DPN. However, by far the greater load of regenerating the oxidized form, DPN, is borne by the reaction involving the reduction of acetaldehyde to ethyl alcohol with the concomitant oxidation

§ Energy-poor phosphate bonds: linkages which when cleaved yield small amounts of energy, ca. 3000 calories (or actually require energy); those linkages where the phosphate residue is linked to an alcoholic hydroxyl group, e.g., hexose phosphate, triose phosphate, glycerol phosphate, etc. Energy-poor phosphate bonds will be indicated in the text as: —PO_3H_2.

of H_2-DPN. DPN is again available for the oxidation of another triose diphosphate (or triose phosphate) molecule.

The 1,3-diphosphoglyceric acid subsequently loses one phosphate group, the high-energy phosphate linkage to ADP (converting it to ATP), to become 3-phosphoglyceric acid.

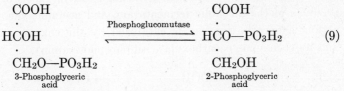

$$\begin{array}{ccc}
\overset{\overset{\displaystyle O}{\cdot\cdot}}{CO}\sim PO_3H_2 & & COOH \\
\mid & & \mid \\
HCOH & + ADP \rightleftharpoons & HCOH & + ATP \qquad (8) \\
\mid & & \mid \\
CH_2O-PO_3H_2 & & CH_2O-PO_3H_2
\end{array}$$

1,3-Diphospho-
glyceric acid   3-Phospho-
glyceric acid

This intermediate in turn is in equilibrium with 2-phosphoglyceric acid.

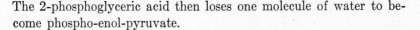

$$\begin{array}{ccc}
COOH & & COOH \\
\mid & \xrightarrow{\ \ \text{Phosphoglucomutase}\ \ } & \mid \\
HCOH & \longleftarrow & HCO-PO_3H_2 & \qquad (9) \\
\mid & & \mid \\
CH_2O-PO_3H_2 & & CH_2OH
\end{array}$$

3-Phosphoglyceric
acid   2-Phosphoglyceric
acid

The 2-phosphoglyceric acid then loses one molecule of water to become phospho-enol-pyruvate.

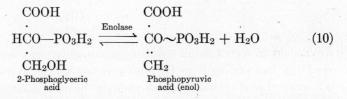

$$\begin{array}{ccc}
COOH & & COOH \\
\mid & \xrightarrow{\ \ \text{Enolase}\ \ } & \mid \\
HCO-PO_3H_2 & \longleftarrow & CO\sim PO_3H_2 + H_2O & \qquad (10) \\
\mid & & \mid\mid \\
CH_2OH & & CH_2
\end{array}$$

2-Phosphoglyceric
acid   Phosphopyruvic
acid (enol)

This transformation actually involves more than merely a simple dehydration. In the dehydration of 2-phosphoglyceric acid, a reaction catalyzed by the enzyme enolase and freely reversible, a change occurs in which the phosphate linkage, an ordinary ester linkage and, as such, a low-energy linkage on the glycerate side, becomes an energy-rich enol phosphate linkage on the pyruvate side. The total or the overall energy over the whole molecule is equal on both sides of the reaction. However, the dehydration changes the energy distribution within the molecule in such a way as to concentrate and make available a much larger portion of energy in the phosphate linkage on the pyruvate side.

At this point it is believed that the phosphopyruvate yields the energy-rich phosphate linkage to ADP or AMP to form ATP.||

$$
\begin{array}{ll}
COOH & COOH \\
| & | \\
CO{\sim}PO_3H_2 + ADP \rightarrow & C{=}O \quad + ATP \\
| & | \\
CH_2 & CH_3
\end{array}
\qquad (11a)
$$

2-Phosphopyruvic   Pyruvic acid
acid (enol)

$$
\begin{array}{ll}
COOH & COOH \\
| & | \\
2CO{\sim}PO_3H_2 + AMP \rightarrow & 2C{=}O \quad + ATP \\
| & | \\
CH_2 & CH_3
\end{array}
\qquad (11b)
$$

2-Phosphopyruvic   Pyruvic acid
acid (enol)

Pyruvic acid then yields carbon dioxide, one of the two main end products of the alcoholic fermentation, and acetaldehyde. This reaction, a decarboxylation, is catalyzed by the enzyme carboxylase and its coenzyme, cocarboxylase (diphosphothiamin).

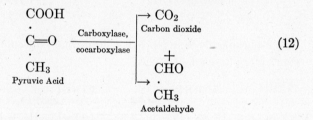

(12)

Acetaldehyde serves as an oxidizing agent (hydrogen acceptor) for H_2-DPN (converting it to DPN as previously described) and is itself reduced to ethyl alcohol, thus yielding the other main end product of this fermentation.

$$
\begin{array}{ll}
CHO & CH_2OH \\
| \quad + H_2\text{-}DPN \rightleftharpoons & | \quad\quad + DPN \\
CH_3 & CH_3
\end{array}
\qquad (13)
$$

Acetaldehyde   Ethyl alcohol

To recapitulate the above dissimilation scheme briefly, a hexose molecule is diphosphorylated. A cleavage occurs with the formation

|| Lardy and Ziegler (*J. Biol. Chem.*, **159**, 343–351, 1945) state that they have been able to demonstrate the enzymatic synthesis of phosphopyruvate from pyruvate. Previously the reaction, phosphopyruvate to pyruvate, had been considered irreversible.

of two molecules of phosphorylated triose. Phosphotriose is further phosphorylated to the diphosphorylated form and oxidized to diphosphoglycerate with the concomitant reduction of DPN to H_2-DPN. The diphosphoglycerate after dephosphorylation and dehydration is converted to phosphopyruvate. After dephosphorylation pyruvic acid is decarboxylated to acetaldehyde and carbon dioxide. Acetaldehyde is reduced to ethyl alcohol with the concomitant oxidation of H_2-DPN to DPN.

Thus are thought to be formed the two main end products of alcoholic fermentation, ethyl alcohol from the reduction of acetaldehyde and carbon dioxide from the decarboxylation of pyruvate. Evidence for the above-described transformations are by no means conclusive in every instance. However, our state of knowledge concerning the alcoholic fermentation is more advanced than for any other fermentation. For further detailed information see an excellent review by Werkman and Wood [50] or *Bacterial Chemistry and Physiology* by Porter.[37]

Enzymes Involved in Alcoholic Fermentation. Traube's proposal that fermentations are due to substances secreted by living cells was borne out by the experiments of Buchner. It has been pointed out that zymase has proved to be a battery of enzymes and coenzymes. The reactions the individual enzymes catalyze have been described above.

The chemical natures of some of the enzymes involved in the breakdown of sugar have been partially determined. Most of them have been shown to be proteins in close association with specific metals, such as magnesium, with the addition in some instances of adenylic acid or its di- or triphosphate derivatives.

The prosthetic group of diphosphoglyceraldehyde dehydrogenase, DPN or Coenzyme I (the dialyzable, thermostable coenzyme or cozymase of Harden and Young), has been shown by von Euler, Albers, and Schlenk [16] to be a dinucleotide made up of adenine, nicotinic acid amide, two molecules of phosphoric acid and two molecules of d-ribose. The manner in which it oxidizes diphosphoglyceraldehyde and is itself reduced to the dihydro form is as follows.

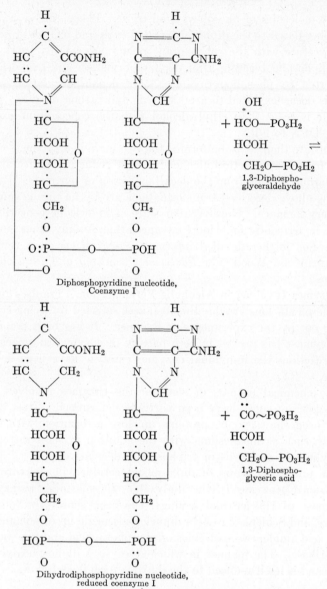

Diphosphopyridine nucleotide,
Coenzyme I

Dihydrodiphosphopyridine nucleotide,
reduced coenzyme I

The coenzyme for carboxylase, cocarboxylase, consists of thiamin—a pyrimidine nucleus attached through a carbon atom to a thiazole ring—and two phosphoric acids. The structure as proposed by Lohmann and Schuster [29] is as follows.

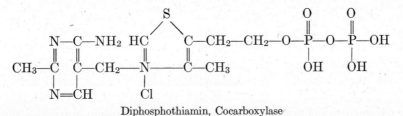

Diphosphothiamin, Cocarboxylase

The structures of the components of the adenylic acid system as proposed are as follows.

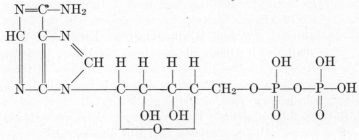

Adenosinemonophosphate (AMP), Adenylic Acid

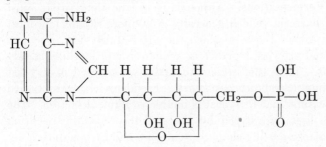

Adenosinediphosphate (ADP)

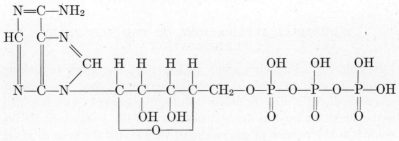

Adenosinetriphosphate (ATP)

Inhibitors for some of the above-described enzymes are known. Iodoacetic acid is known to inhibit the action of diphosphoglycer-

aldehyde dehydrogenase which catalyzes the oxidation of diphos-
photriose to diphosphoglycerate. Enolase, the enzyme that catalyzes
the dehydration of 2-phosphoglyceric acid to phospho-enol-pyruvate,
is inhibited by sodium fluoride. The mechanism of this inhibition
was worked out by Warburg and Christian.[48] They found that a
magnesium-fluor-phosphate complex is formed which inhibits the
action of the enzymes by combining with the protein.

For further details on the enzymes of yeast, the reader is referred
to *Chemistry and Methods of Enzymes* by Sumner and Somers.[43]

Symbiotic Fermentations. Although it is true that yeasts must
compete with bacteria (which generally grow more rapidly) in most
environments, except those in which the *p*H is fairly low, they are
sometimes found growing together in symbiotic relationships in certain situations. Thus the ferment of kefir is composed of a yeast
and a bacterium (*Streptococcus kefir*). Freudenreich, who studied
this ferment, claims that the yeast is unable to ferment lactose. The
milk sugar is first hydrolyzed by the streptococcus, the resulting
glucose and galactose being changed to alcohol and carbon dioxide by
the yeast. A similar relationship is present in the ginger beer "plant"
and in a curious ferment which has been used in rural America for
the manufacture of vinegar directly from molasses. In the latter
ferment the bacterial symbiont is apparently an acetic acid bacterium. The yeast first produces alcohol from the sugar; then the
bacterium oxidizes the alcohol to acetic acid. In all three of these
ferments the organisms grow together as curious irregular lumps of
cartilaginous consistency, part of the sugar being converted into a
gum which holds them together. These masses or grains are strained
out after the fermentation is complete, and will remain viable, after
drying, for considerable periods of time.

INDUSTRIAL APPLICATIONS OF THE ALCOHOLIC
FERMENTATION

Baking. The leavening agent used to raise the dough in making
bread is generally a strain of *Saccharomyces cerevisiae*. The amount
of gas produced is directly proportional to the amount of yeast added
to the dough, at least in the first few hours of the fermentation. Inasmuch as the volume of gas produced varies with the type of yeast
used, the baker must have a source of yeast of uniform, definite,
gas-producing qualities.

Starch in the dough is hydrolyzed to maltose by the wheat diastase
naturally occurring in the flour. Where low diastatic flour is en-

countered the grain miller generally fortifies the naturally occurring amylases with either wheat or barley malt (germinated wheat or barley). Other substances are often added to the dough. Although there is usually sufficient calcium and phosphorus in the dough to satisfy the nutritional requirements of yeast, they are usually component parts of so-called bread improvers or dough conditioners. Although the breakdown of wheat proteins by the proteolytic enzymes normally present in wheat or in the diastatic preparations added to the dough usually supplies the nitrogenous compounds, additions of slight amounts of ammonium compounds cause rapid increase in the production of gas. Propionates and diacetates (generally the sodium salts) may also be added to flour to inhibit the development of molds in the finished bread. They have the added value of retarding development of "rope" (an undesirable condition caused by certain strains of *Bacillus mesentericus*) in bread.

After the starch has been hydrolyzed to maltose, this dissacharide is acted upon by the maltase of yeast which converts it to glucose. The zymase complex attacks the hexose, carrying out the alcoholic fermentation with formation of carbon dioxide and alcohol. The former causes the dough to rise, the latter being driven off, for the most part, during the baking. Flavors are imparted to bread, in part, by minute quantities of esters which are also formed in the fermentation. The proteolytic enzymes of yeast are said to cause desirable changes in the wheat gluten.

Industrial Alcohol Produced by Fermentation. Large quantities of alcohol required for industrial purposes are produced by fermentation with yeasts. Raw materials may consist of any fermentable saccharine material or carbohydrate which can be hydrolyzed to fermentable sugars.

Ordinarily, the organisms used are strains of *Saccharomyces cerevisiae*, capable of tolerating high alcohol concentrations. However, strains of *Schizosaccharomyces Pombé* have also been used. The starter is prepared by growing and transferring the yeasts in successively larger volumes of cultures and mashes until the volume is large enough for pitching the main mash.

The Manufacture of Industrial Alcohol from Molasses. In the United States and Canada, blackstrap molasses, a by-product of cane sugar refineries, is the most common raw material. It contains sugar and, generally, most of the nutrients required for the growth of yeast cells which carry out the fermentation.

The mash is prepared so that the sugar concentration is between 10 and 15 per cent. Higher concentrations of sugar may have a deleterious effect on the growth of yeast. They may also be undesirable because the alcohol produced slows down the fermentation, a longer time then being required for the complete utilization of the residual sugar. On the other hand, concentrations of sugar lower than 10 per cent lead to loss of valuable fermentation space. The nitrogen deficiency is made up by the addition of ammonia, ammonium phosphate, or ammonium sulphate.

Since it would be costly to sterilize the wort, the manufacturer depends on the use of a large inoculum of yeast cells, ordinarily from 4 to 6 per cent of the final volume of mash, and the low pH to prevent contaminants from multiplying appreciably. The large inoculum overwhelms the relatively small numbers of undesirable organisms and prevents them from developing. Sulphuric or phosphoric acid is generally added to adjust the pH to approximately 4.5. The yeasts are able to propagate and dissimilate the sugar at this fairly low pH but undesirable bacteria are retarded in their development. Lactic acid is sometimes added to or produced in the mash by allowing a lactic acid fermentation to occur, prior to inoculation with yeasts. This organic acid inhibits the growth of the butyric acid bacteria which may develop as undesirable contaminants.

After the mash has been pitched, an aerobic condition is developed by aeration. It has been noted previously in the discussion of the Pasteur effect that aerobic metabolism is economically superior to anaerobic breakdown of sugar. Once the number of yeast cells has been brought up to a satisfactory point, aeration is ceased. Dissimilation of sugar then begins, anaerobic conditions are established, and alcohol and carbon dioxide are formed.

Although the initial temperature of the mash when pitched is usually between 21° and 27° C., the temperature rises because of the activities of the yeast. Therefore, cooling coils inside or sprays on the outside of the fermenting tanks must be used to control the temperature.

After a fermentation period of approximately 48 hours, the fermentation is generally complete, with a yield of about 90 per cent of theoretical on the basis of fermentable sugar.

A continuous process for preparing the starter [18] as well as a continuous process for the alcoholic fermentation of molasses [7] have been developed by Kolachov and his associates.

Alcohol is distilled off the "beer" (fermented mash). Fractions containing various concentrations of alcohol are separated during the distillation. Those fractions high in alcohol are called "high wines," those low in alcohol "low wines." The former are rectified to 95 per cent concentration whereas the latter are generally redistilled with new lots of beer. The "slop" (residual solids) may be used for fertilizers or added to stock feeds.

The Manufacture of Industrial Alcohol from Starchy Materials. Alcohol may also be prepared from carbohydrates which are hydrolyzable to fermentable sugars. Starchy materials can be used as the initial raw material. The starch in corn, wheat, and potatoes may be hydrolyzed either by acid or diastase hydrolysis. The starchy material is first macerated or ground. Where grain such as corn is used, the oil-bearing germ must first be removed.

When acid is used for the hydrolysis, sulphuric or hydrochloric acid is added to the mash to adjust the concentration to the appropriate strength. The amount to be added depends on the grain and the acid used. The mash is then subjected to steam under pressure. When the hydrolysis of starch to glucose is complete, the acid is neutralized with calcium carbonate, lime, or ammonium hydroxide. Where the acid to be neutralized is sulphuric, and the alkali is calcium carbonate or lime, a precipitate of calcium sulphate forms and is separated from the wort by sedimentation and filtration. The mash is fortified with ammonia (or ammonium salts) for the nitrogen source and other substances required for the growth of yeasts before use.

Starchy raw material can also be hydrolyzed by diastase. The amylase may be supplied by malt (germinating barley), by molds or mold enzyme preparations, or by the naturally occurring diastase where wheat is the raw material.

Malt is freshly ground and first added to the starch material in small amounts, approximately 10 per cent of the total to be used. This pre-malting step liquefies the mash, thus making it easily handled by pumping or blowing. The liquefied mash is then pumped to cookers where it is steamed to solubilize the starch. After rapid cooling (to prevent formation of non-fermentable substances from grain) to a mashing temperature of 50° to 65° C., the rest of the malt is added and the hydrolysis of starch takes place. The higher temperatures favor dextrinization, the lower temperatures, saccharification. Kolachov and his associates have developed a rapid continuous process for the conversion of corn starch.[18]

In the Amylo process involving the use of selected molds, the grain to be hydrolyzed is soaked in water for a few hours in order to soften it. After the addition of more water, it is heated under pressure to render the starch soluble. Either hydrochloric or sulphuric acid is added to facilitate the liquefaction. The sterilized mash is cooled to 38° to 40° C. and inoculated with a pure culture of a Mucor or Rhizopus. *Mucor Rouxii, Rhizopus japonicus,* or other related molds are some that have been used in this process. Sterile air is blown through the mash to develop the mold; the temperature is then lowered and the mash inoculated with yeast. In the Boulard process,[8] a modification of the Amylo process, acid is not added and the mash is inoculated simultaneously with both the mold and yeast.

Organisms of the *Aspergillus flavus-Oryzae* group have been used in the manufacture of diastatic preparations in Japan for hundreds of years. An efficient method has recently been developed by Underkofler and his coworkers [30] involving the use of certain strains of *A. Oryzae.* Air is passed up through the perforated bottom of the aluminum pans in which the moistened bran is held. The moisture content of the mixture is about 70 per cent. The temperature rise due to the growth of mold is controlled by the rate of aeration. After about 48 hours' incubation at a little below 45° C., the moldy bran is dried and ground before use, in the same manner as malt.

Where wheat meal or flour is the raw material, the Balls-Tucker process may be used, employing the naturally occurring amylases in wheat. The ground wheat, before cooking, is extracted with a weak solution (0.5 per cent) of sodium sulphite. This sulphite-diastase mixture is added to the cooked grain to saccharify the starch.

These hydrolyzates from starchy materials, after fortification with nutrients, are inoculated with suitable strains of yeast.

For further details on the manufacture of industrial alcohol, the reader is referred to *Industrial Microbiology* by Prescott and Dunn.[38]

The Manufacture of Industrial Alcohol from Cellulosic Materials. At least three processes have been developed in the attempt to utilize cellulose from waste wood. The United States has been in the fortunate position where it has not had to rely to any great extent upon this raw material for the source of fermentable sugars.

The Bergius-Rheinau process [6] involves, first, the shredding and drying of wood to a water content of about 0.5 per cent. The dried wood is then treated with a 40 per cent solution of hydrochloric acid at room temperature. The acid extract is distilled at about 36° C. under vacuum to separate off most of the acid, which can then be regenerated, reconcentrated, and re-used. The hydrolysate is further concentrated by spray drying and the resultant particles of dried material collected in a cyclone (a device which, by centrifugal force, gathers small particles in air). The solid hydrolysate contains a high percentage of fermentable sugar.

In the Scholler-Tornesch process,[38] the shredded wood, heated to about 170° C., is extracted with dilute (0.4 per cent) acid under pressure in contrast to the foregoing process. The wood is not dried and no attempt is made to recover the acid. The dilute hydrochloric acid extract is neutralized with calcium carbonate, allowed to stand in a tank to permit settling, and then filtered.

Sulphuric acid (0.5 per cent) is used in the Giordani-Leone process.[38] Quicklime may be used to neutralize part of the acid and the rest is recovered for further use.

The hydrolysates from the above processes are inoculated after fortification with nutrients for yeast. Acetic acid, lignin, and furfural are by-products of the above-described processes.

Sulphite liquor, a waste product in the manufacture of pulp from wood, has also been used in the production of alcohol[13] (the Heijkenskjöld method). Calcium carbonate or lime is added to raise the pH to above 5.5 and the free sulphur dioxide removed by heating to 90° C. and aeration for about two hours. The waste sulphite liquor is allowed to stand for some time to allow settling and, after fortification with nutrients, inoculated with yeasts.

Brewing. The production of malt beverages involves, essentially, the following steps of malting, mashing, fermentation, and finishing.

The malting step is concerned primarily with the production of amylases used for the liquefaction and saccharification of the starch in the grain. Selected barley is first washed and steeped in water of about 10° to 15° C. The grain is then allowed to germinate for a few days at a temperature of 20° to 25° C. The amylase content is higher in barley after it has been sprouted. This may be due either to formation of new enzymes or to the destruction of enzyme inhibitors. After the germination has proceeded to a satisfactory point, the malt is dried under carefully controlled conditions.

The solubilization and digestion of the desirable portion of the malt and malt adjuncts is the purpose of the mashing step. After the dried and crushed grains from the malting step have been transferred to cookers or mash tubs, water and malt adjuncts are added. The latter which may consist of corn, rice, and wheat products, and sucrose or invert sugar, is often added to malt to reduce the protein content of beer in the United States. The temperature of the mixture is initially low, about 40° C., and is gradually increased, depending upon the method used, to 60° or 70° C. The higher temperature favors dextrinization whereas the lower temperature favors saccharification by the amylases and the digestion of proteins by the proteolytic enzymes also present in the grain. The pH of the mixture when first mixed is about 5.8 but it falls during the process to 5.5 or 5.2. Toward the end of the mashing step, the spent grain and proteins settle out and the clear amber wort is filtered off. The spent grain is extracted or leached a number of times with hot water (usually 75° C.) in a process known as sparging. The sparged grain can be used as stock feed. The wort and spargings are pumped to copper kettles where hops are added and the whole boiled. Tannins, bitter acids, and resins are extracted from the hops in this process. The tannins react with proteins, forming complexes, and aid in clearing the wort. A characteristic flavor is imparted to the beer by substances extracted from the hops. Antiseptic principles are also extracted. The boiling process also destroys enzymes, coagulates proteins, and carmelizes the sugar. The wort is then filtered and cooled.

The wort is now ready to be pitched. Selected strains of bottom yeasts are commonly used in the manufacture of beer. The terms beer and ale are often used interchangeably. In the United States the industry terms brew made with top yeasts ale and those with bottom yeasts beer. See page 278 for top and bottom yeasts. As soon as the krausen stage is reached, as indicated by the appearance of white foam on the surface of the fermenting mixture, it is often pumped to another fermenter. This affects the removal of more proteins which have settled during the initial phase of fermentation. The temperature is generally kept at about 5° to 14° C. in the manufacture of beer, and at 13° to 22° for ale. Cooling coils have to be used in the fermenters because the activities of yeast tend to raise the temperature. After a fermentation period not longer than ten days, a product known as "green" beer is obtained. This is now stored for two weeks to several months. In this maturing process, undesirable substances are eliminated by settling, and mellowness is acquired.

The finishing process involves the carbonization of the mature beer. This may be accomplished either by carbon dioxide under pressure or by the krausening process. The latter process involves the addition of about 15 per cent of fermenting beer to the stored beer placed in pressure tanks. The gas evolved by the fermenting yeast cells carbonate the entire mixture. This process requires from three to four weeks and the beer is further stored for from three to eight weeks. Bottled beer is generally pasteurized at 63° C. for twenty minutes. For further details on brewing see Tauber [47] and Prescott and Dunn.[38]

Beer defects may be caused by any of a number of factors. Haze may be due to unstable protein, tannin-protein complexes, resins, or undesirable organisms such as wild yeasts or Sarcinae.

The Manufacture of Wine. Wine by official definition is the product of alcoholic fermentation of the juice of sound, ripe grapes. However, alcoholic beverages produced from other fruits, such as berries and citrus fruits, have also been called "wines."

Wines can be differentiated into the red or white wines. The former are those containing the coloring matter from the skin of red grapes and the latter are those made from white grapes or the juices of other grapes. Wines are also differentiated into the dry or sweet wines. The former are those in which fermentation has been allowed to go to completion so the sugar has been largely depleted; the latter are those in which fermentation has been stopped so there is considerable, relatively speaking, residual sugar. Space does not permit a detailed discussion of the classifications or manufacture of the various types of wines (grape). Only a brief outline will be given here of the general procedures followed in the manufacture of wine.

A fine wine is obtained only when grapes of good quality are used and sound manufacturing practices are followed. The characteristic bouquet and aroma of a given wine are often dependent on the grapes of a certain locality. Grapes may vary in their quality from year to year, even in the same locality; hence the interest of the connoisseur of wines in the year of the vintage. Accordingly, old wines are not necessarily better than more recent wines.

Selected grapes are crushed without stemming (Cruess advises leaving stems on the grapes) and then treated with potassium metabisulphite, sodium bisulphite, or sulphur dioxide. In the old days, sulphur was burned in the vats to furnish the sulphur dioxide. This pre-fermentation treatment of the grapes destroys or inhibits undesirable wild yeasts, bacteria, and molds but allows the wine yeast to develop.

Several hours after this treatment, the starter is added, selected strains of *Saccharomyces cerevisiae* var. *ellipsoideus* being used. The starter, which is about 2 to 5 per cent of the volume of crushed grapes to be inoculated, is prepared. "Must" (unfermented juice) which has been sterilized is often used as the culture medium of the original culture. Successively larger volumes are inoculated until the starter is prepared.

Generally, the crushed grapes furnish adequate nutrients for the development of yeast. According to Joslyn and Cruess [23] the optimum sugar concentration is 22° Balling. Higher sugar concentrations may favor the production of more than 13 per cent of alcohol by volume but higher concentrations of alcohol also inhibit the fermentation. Actually, the tolerance of yeast to alcohol is dependent in part on the temperature (the higher the temperature, the lower the tolerance) as well as on the strain of yeast. The sugar concentration can be adjusted either by the addition of water or sugar, or by the mixing of a must high in sugar with one low in sugar content.

Initially, mixing or stirring is resorted to in order to aerate the inoculated crushed grapes. Oxygen is required for the rapid growth of the yeast which carries out the fermentation. A "cap" of grape skins, seeds, and so on forms on the surface of the fermenting mixture, necessitating the punching of holes in the cap, or pumping juice from the bottom of the vat over it. The temperature is kept at 20° to 24° C. If it rises too high a "stuck" wine may result; the high temperature and alcohol inhibit the yeast and undesirable bacterial contaminants may develop. After three to five days of fermentation, the "free-run wine" is drawn off. The free-run wine is transferred to closed storage tanks and allowed to ferment still further, bungs being provided to allow the excess carbon dioxide to escape. The residual fermentable sugar is utilized to the desired extent in seven to eleven days at a temperature of about 21° to 29° C.

The new wine is now transferred to storage tanks made of oak, preferably, or redwood where it is stored for the aging process. The tanks are filled to the top and sealed to prevent the access of excess air. Undesirable organisms such as Acetobacter and "wine flowers," *Mycoderma vini*, may develop under strictly aerobic condition. Slight amounts of air are desirable, however, to oxidize the alcohol to acids. These in turn combine with alcohol to produce the esters which are necessary for the development of aroma and bouquet. The wine is periodically racked (drawn off), to separate it from the lees, the settleable solids. The aging process may require several years. Newer processes to hasten aging include such steps as flash pasteurization and filtration.

Wine defects may be caused by undesirable organisms such as mycodermas, tourne bacilli (lactobacilli), and mannitol-producing organisms. Mrak [34] has studied the wine defects caused by iron or tin salts, copper, zinc, aluminum, and so on. Sometimes these casses (turbidities) may be remedied by treatment of the wine with gelatin, bentonite, or casein preparations. The defects caused by bacteria may often be corrected by treatment with bentonite or filtration through infusorial earths, followed by a subsequent passage through bacterial filter. This in turn is followed by a treatment of the wine with metabisulphite or sulphur dioxide.

The reader is referred to *The Principles and Practice of Wine Making* [10] and *Commercial Fruit and Vegetable Products*,[11] both by Cruess, for further details.

The Manufacture of Distilled Alcoholic Products. Whisky, gin, brandy, cordials, and liqueurs constitute the principal distilled spirits. Bourbon whisky may be prepared from corn, malt, and rye. Rye whisky is generally manufactured from rye and barley or rye malt. Scotch whisky is made from barley malt. The fermentation is carried out with strains of *Saccharomyces cerevisiae*. The mash is sometimes also inoculated with lactic acid organisms. After the alcoholic fermentation is complete, the mash is distilled, the type of still and the method of distillation affecting the characteristics of the final product. The raw whisky should be aged in charred new oak containers.

Gin is obtained by the distillation of the mash with or over juniper berries. Rum is a distilled product manufactured from the fermentation of molasses. Brandy is obtained from the distillation of fermented juice or the mash of fruit. Cordials and liqueurs are prepared by mixing or redistilling spirits such as neutral spirits (alcohol), brandy, and gin, with or over fruits, flowers and plants.

Vinegar Manufacture. The manufacture of vinegar essentially involves two steps. The first is the breakdown of sugar in a fruit such as apple, or a malted starchy substance, to alcohol. The second is the transformation of the alcohol to acetic acid by certain desired strains of Acetobacter. The yeast is involved in the first step.

GLYCEROL FERMENTATION

An examination of the Embden-Meyerhof-Parnas scheme (see page 326) for the dissimilation of sugar shows that small amounts of glycerol are normally formed by yeasts in their breakdown of glucose. It was noted in the discussion of the alcoholic fermentation that phosphorylated triose can serve as the hydrogen acceptor for reduced diphosphopyridine nucleotide, H_2-DPN, and be itself reduced to glycerophosphate. The phosphoric acid is split off and glycerol is formed. In the normal alcoholic fermentation this does not occur because acetaldehyde acts as the hydrogen acceptor for H_2-DPN and is reduced to ethyl alcohol. Accordingly, only small quantities of glycerol are generally produced.

A few years before World War I, Neuberg and his associates in Germany, in attempts to elucidate the mechanism of ethyl alcohol fermentation by yeast, noted an appreciable increase in the amount of glycerol produced on the addition of sodium sulphite to the fermenting mash. In effect, an addition compound of acetaldehyde and sodium bisulphite had been formed in accordance with the following reactions.

$$Na_2SO_3 + H_2O + CO_2 \rightarrow NaHSO_3 + NaHCO_3$$
$$CH_3CHO + NaHSO_3 \rightarrow CH_3CHO \cdot HSO_3Na$$

$$Na_2SO_3 + CH_3CHO + H_2O + CO_2 \rightarrow CH_3CHO \cdot HSO_3Na + NaHCO_3$$

This rendered the acetaldehyde unavailable for serving as the hydrogen acceptor for H_2-DPN.

This was the basis for the Connstein and Ludecke (sulphite) process [31] developed in Germany. Beet sugar was used as the source of the sugar. Top yeast was found to be more resistant to sodium sulphite and hence more suited for this process. The more sodium sulphite added, the greater was the yield of glycerol and the smaller the yield of alcohol. Alcohol and acetaldehyde were removed by distillation and the excess sulphite precipitated out as the calcium salt. Glycerol was obtained by distillation under partial vacuum.

The Cocking-Lilly (sulphite-bisulphite) process developed in England is a modification of the foregoing process. Aqueous solutions of a mixture of sodium sulphite and sodium bisulphite are periodically added to the fermenting mash. Inasmuch as sodium bisulphite displays inhibitory properties, the proportion of this salt to sodium sulphite is low at the beginning of the fermentation. As the fermentation proceeds, the proportion of bisulphite in the mixture is increased. The fermentation time is shorter than in the sulphite process and higher yields of glycerol are obtained.

In the United States a process was developed by Eoff, Linder, and Beyer [15] from investigations initiated as a result of reports that glycerol was being produced by fermentation in Germany. The Eoff (sodium carbonate) process depends on the finding that an alkaline reaction increases the yield of glycerol. According to Neuberg, the following overall reaction could be written for the fermentation occurring in an alkaline medium.

$$H_2O + 2C_6H_{12}O_6 \rightarrow 2C_3H_5(OH)_3 + CH_3COOH + C_2H_5OH + 2CO_2$$

Evidently, the alkaline reaction favors dismutation (the Cannizaro reaction whereby one molecule of aldehyde is oxidized with a concomitant reduction of a second molecule) at the phosphorylated triose stage as follows.

Triose diphosphate $+$ DPN $\rightarrow$ diphosphoglyceric acid $+$ H$_2$-DPN

Triose phosphate $+$ H$_2$-DPN $\rightarrow$ glycerophosphate $+$ DPN

Triose diphosphate $+$ triose phosphate $\rightarrow$

glycerophosphate $+$ diphosphoglyceric acid

Special strains of yeast, "trained" to grow in alkaline medium, gave the highest yield of glycerol. Blackstrap molasses, corn sugar, and sucrose were all found to be suitable as the carbon source when the other essential nutrients were added. Soda ash, because of its low cost, was recommended for use but any substance which makes the mash alkaline can be used. Eoff recommended the addition of soda ash in five portions during the fermentation.

YEAST SPOILAGE IN FOOD PRODUCTS

In foods preserved from bacterial decomposition by low pH or high osmotic pressures, yeasts as well as molds may grow and cause considerable economic loss. Unlike the molds, however, yeasts are not at all active in the decomposition of proteins. They become undesirable because of the active fermentation of carbohydrates which they carry out with resultant gas production. In some cases, they probably act as does *Geotrichum candidum*, upon organic acids, raising the pH of the medium to a point where putrefactive bacteria may grow. Owing to their ubiquitousness, certain asporogenous yeasts (usually designated as Torula in industrial literature) and, in some instances, sporulating yeasts have been found undesirable contaminants in a wide variety of foodstuffs.

Yeasts are extraordinarily abundant in various dairy products, notably cream, butter, and cheeses. Yeasts occur quite regularly in cream, and the numbers rise considerably when the cream sours. They are naturally abundant in butter. In some cheeses, as Camembert, yeasts make up a large proportion of the microbic flora. Lactose-fermenting yeasts occasionally give considerable trouble in cream, producing a marked gaseous fermentation known as foaminess. These organisms are constantly present in cream, and the fermentation can be prevented by proper cooling.

Tomato catsup, honey, sugar syrup, and fruit juices are all susceptible to spoilage by fermenting yeasts. The chemical composition of these substances, as well as dairy products, make them readily subject to decomposition by yeasts.

However, other substances which one would not expect to be spoiled by yeasts are also attacked. Some yeasts are capable of growing in strong pickle brines, sauerkraut, and even on salted fish. Species of Rhodotorula may produce pink or red discolorations in fats of both vegetable and animal origin and in sauerkraut. Under certain conditions, certain strains of *"Saccharomyces ellipsoideus"* are said to develop a pink pigment. According to Jensen [21] the lipophilic *S. pulcherrimus* of Beijerinck (see page 287) produces a red pigment in the presence of soluble iron salts. Yeasts of the Candida and Rhodotorula genera have been found to be factors in the spoilage of beef. These organisms are capable of proliferating at temperatures close to −1° C. where chilled beef is stored. Occasionally, the slimes on sausages have been found to be due to yeasts.

No attempt has been made here to catalog the various genera of yeasts that have been reported in foodstuffs. For further details and procedures the reader is referred to Tanner's *Microbiology of Foods*.[45] The method of examining food for yeasts may be found in the *Official and Tentative Methods of Analysis of the Association of Official Agricultural Chemists*.[2]

LITERATURE

1. ANDERSON, H. W., Yeast-like fungi of the human intestinal tract, *J. Infectious Diseases*, **21**, 341 (1917).

2. ASSOCIATION OF OFFICIAL AGRICULTURAL CHEMISTS. *Official and Tentative Methods of Analysis of the Association of Official Agricultural Chemists*, Washington, D. C., 6th ed., 1945.

3. ATKIN, L., A. S. SCHULTZ, and C. N. FREY, Ultramicrodetermination of thiamine by the fermentation method, *J. Biol. Chem.*, **129**, 471 (1939).

4. ATKIN, L., A. S. SCHULTZ, W. L. WILLIAMS, and C. N. FREY, Yeast microbiological methods for determination of vitamins, *Ind. Eng. Chem., Anal. Ed.*, **15**, 141 (1943); **16**, 67 (1944).

5. BALL, E. G., Chemical reactions of nicotinic acid amide *in vivo*, *Bull. Johns Hopkins Hosp.*, **65**, 253 (1939).

6. BERGIUS, F., Conversion of wood to carbohydrates, *Ind. Eng. Chem.*, **29**, 247 (1937).

7. BILFORD, H. R., R. E. SCALF, W. H. STARK, and P. J. KOLACHOV, Alcoholic fermentation of molasses, *Ind. Eng. Chem.*, **34**, 1406 (1942).

8. BOULARD, H., *Société d'exploitation des procédes*, H. Boulard, 1931 (cited by Prescott [38]).

9. BURK, D., A colloquial consideration of the Pasteur and neo-Pasteur effects, *Symposia on Quantitative Biology*, VII, 420 (1939).

10. CRUESS, W. V., *The Principles and Practice of Wine Making*, Avi, New York, 1934.

11. ——, *Commercial Fruit and Vegetable Products*, McGraw-Hill, New York, 2nd ed., 1938.

12. DEUTSCH, H. F., The stimulatory effect of thiamine and certain of its derivatives on the assay of vitamin B by yeast fermentation, *J. Biol. Chem.*, **152**, 421 (1944).

13. EINESON, E. W., Yeast from wood, *Chem. Industries*, **38**, 573 (1936).

14. ENGEL'HARDT, W. A., and A. P. BARKASH, Oxidative breakdown of phosphogluconic acid (Russian-English summary), *Biokhimiya*, **3**, 500 (1938).

15. EOFF, J. R., W. V. LINDER, and G. F. BEYER, Production of glycerin from sugar by fermentation, *Ind. Eng. Chem.*, **11**, 842 (1919).

16. VON EULER, H., H. ALBERS, and F. SCHLENK, Über die Co-Zymase, *Z. physiol. Chem.*, **237**, 274I (1935).

17. FINK, H., H. HOEHN, and W. HOERBURGER, Über die Versuche zur Fettgewinnung mittels Mikroorganismen mit besonderer Berücksichtigung der Arbeiten des Institut für Gärungsgewerbe, *Chem. Ztg.*, **61**, 689, 723, 744 (1937).

18. GALLAGHER, F. H., H. R. BILFORD, W. H. STARK, and P. J. KOLACHOV, Fast conversion of distillery mash for use in a continuous process, *Ind. Eng. Chem.*, **34**, 1395 (1942).

19. HARDEN, A., *Alcoholic Fermentation*, Longmans, Green, New York, 4th ed., 1932.

20. HARDEN, A., and W. J. YOUNG, The influence of phosphates on the fermentation of glycose by yeast juice (prelim. communication), *Proc. Chem. Soc.*, **21**, 189 (1905).

21. JENSEN, L. B., *Microbiology of Meats*, Garrard Press, Champaign, Illinois, 1942.

22. JOHNSON, M. J., Role of aerobic phosphorylation in the Pasteur effect, *Science*, **94**, 200 (1941).

23. JOSLYN, M. A., and W. A. CRUESS, Elements of wine making, *Calif. Agr. Ext. Circ. 88*, Nov. 1934.

24. KALCKAR, H. M., The function of phosphate in enzymatic syntheses, *Ann. N. Y. Acad. Sci.*, **45**, 395 (1944).

25. LINDNER, P., Das Problem der biologischen Fettbildung und Fettgewinnung, *Z. angew. Chem.*, **35**, 110 (1922).

26. LIPMANN, F., Metabolic generation and utilization of phosphate bond energy, *Advances in Enzymol.*, **1**, 99 (1941).

27. ——, Pasteur Effect. A Symposium on Respiratory Enzymes, University of Wisconsin Press, Madison, 1942.

28. LOCHHEAD, A. G., and A. D. HERON, Microbiological studies of honey, *Can. Dept. Agr. Bull. 116*, new series (1929).

29. LOHMANN, K., and P. SCHUSTER, Untersuchungen über die Cocarboxylase, *Biochem. Z.*, **294**, 188 (1937).

30. LU CHENG HAO, E. I. FULMER, and L. A. UNDERKOFLER, Fungal amylases as saccharifying agents in the alcoholic fermentation of corn, *Ind. Eng. Chem.*, **35**, 814 (1943).

31. MAY, O. E., and H. T. HERRICK, Some minor industrial fermentations, *Ind. Eng. Chem.*, **22**, 1172 (1930).

32. MEYERHOF, O., Energy relationships in glycolysis and phosphorylations, *Ann. N. Y. Acad. Sci.*, **45**, 377 (1944).

33. MEYERHOF, O., and R. JUNOWICZ-KOCHOLATY, The equilibria of isomerase and aldolase and the problem of the phosphorylation of glyceraldehyde phosphate, *J. Biol. Chem.*, **149**, 71 (1943).

34. MRAK, E. M., D. C. CAUDRON, and L. M. CASH, Corrosion of metals by musts and wines, *J. Food Research*, **2**, 439 (1937).

35. PASTEUR, L., *Études sur la bière*, 1876, English translation by F. Faulkner, and D. C. Robb, *Studies on Fermentation*, Macmillan, London, 1879.

36. PENNINGTON, D. E., E. E. SNELL, H. K. MITCHELL, J. R. McMAHAN, and R. J. WILLIAMS, Assay method for pantothenic acid, *Univ. Texas Pub. 4137*, 14 (1941).

37. PORTER, J. R., *Bacterial Chemistry and Physiology*, Wiley, New York, 1946.

38. PRESCOTT, S. C., and C. G. DUNN, *Industrial Microbiology*, McGraw-Hill, New York, 1940.

39. RETTGER, L. F., G. F. REDDISH, and J. G. MacALPINE, The fate of baker's yeast in the intestine of man and of the white rat, *J. Bact.*, **9**, 327 (1924).

40. SCHULTZ, A. S., L. ATKIN, and C. N. FREY, Determination of vitamin B_1 by yeast fermentation, *Ind. Eng. Chem., Anal. Ed.*, **14**, 35 (1942).

41. SNELL, E. E., R. E. EAKIN, and R. J. WILLIAMS, Assay method for biotin, *Univ. Texas Pub. 4137*, 18 (1941).

42. STARKEY, R. L., and A. T. HENRICI, The occurrence of yeasts in soil, *Soil Sci.*, **23**, 33 (1927).

43. SUMNER, J. B., and G. F. SOMERS, *Chemistry and Methods of Enzymes*, Academic Press, New York, 1943.

44. SZENT-GYÖRGYI, A., Studies on Biological Oxidation and Some of its Catalysts, Rényi, Budapest, 1937.

45. TANNER, F. W., *The Microbiology of Foods*, Garrard Press, Champaign, Illinois, 1944.

46. TANNER, F. W., E. N. LAMPERT, and M. LAMPERT, On the presence of yeast-like fungi in normal throats, *Zentr. Bakt. I. Orig.*, **103**, 94 (1927).

47. TAUBER, H., *Enzyme Technology*, Wiley, New York, 1943.

48. WARBURG, O., and W. CHRISTIAN, Isolation and crystallization of enolase, *Naturwissenschaften*, **29**, 589 (1941); *Chem. Abstracts*, **36**, 4141 (1942).

49. ———, Isolierung und Kristallization des Proteins des oxydierenden Gärungsferments, *Biochem. Z.*, **303**, 40 (1939).

50. WERKMAN, C. H., and H. G. WOOD, On the metabolism of bacteria, *Botan. Rev.*, **8**, 1 (1942).

51. WILLIAMS, R. J., R. E. EAKIN, and J. R. McMAHAN, Assay method for pyridoxin, *Univ. Texas Pub. 4137*, 24 (1941).

52. WILLIAMS, R. J., J. R. McMAHAN, and R. E. EAKIN, Assay method for thiamin, *Univ. Texas Pub. 4137*, 31 (1941).

53. WILLIAMS, R. J., A. K. STOUT, H. K. MITCHELL, and J. R. McMAHAN, Assay method for inositol, *Univ. Texas Pub. 4137*, 27 (1941).

54. ZINKERNAGEL, H., *Untersuchungen über Nektarhefen*, *Zentr. Bakt. II*, **78**, 191 (1929).

CHAPTER XII

CLASSIFICATION, MORPHOLOGY, AND BIOLOGICAL ACTIVITIES OF THE ACTINOMYCETES

Henrici stated that "no group of microorganisms presents so much difficulty in classification as that now generally designated Actinomycetes." The difficulty which Henrici found, in 1930, has now, in 1945, partly because of his own writings, resolved itself into a more logical and orderly system. Of necessity, classification of any group of plants or animals precedes intimate knowledge of these forms. This preliminary classification stimulates research on the organisms classified. Later, when this knowledge has been obtained and has been disseminated, reclassification is necessary. In the interim and until the newer classifications are accepted, there is difficulty and confusion.

Classification. The actinomycetes contain organisms that are definitely mold-like and bacteria-like. The most mold-like actinomycetes resemble the Fungi Imperfecti more closely than they do the bacteria-like actinomycetes, and the most bacteria-like actinomycetes are closer to the tubercle and diphtheria bacilli than they are to the mold-like actinomycetes.

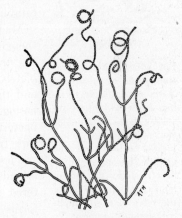

Fig. 127. Conidia and conidiophores of *Streptomyces coelicolor*. Drawn from slide culture. Note that both dextrorse and sinistrorse spirals are found in the same preparation.

Many of the actinomycetes possess a well-developed mycelium and reproduce by conidia, usually in chains. Occasionally some of the mycelium may segment into arthrospores. Most of the mycologists studying these organisms ignored the bacteria-like actinomycetes and have classified the whole group as Fungi Imperfecti, or have given them a rank as a separate class between the Fungi Imperfecti and the Schizomycetes. Thus Vuillemin, in his classification of the Fungi Imperfecti, first included the actinomycetes as a separate order under the name Microsiphonales, but later gave them the rank of a family (Nocardiaceae) in his order of Arthrosporales, giving more weight to the fragmentation of the mycelium as a character of taxonomic importance. Drechsler[6] could see no resemblance to bacteria and would include them without qualification as a group of the Fungi Imperfecti. Lieske[14] prefers to consider them an independent group of fungi, between the molds and the bacteria, but showing a more intimate relationship with the bacteria than with the higher fungi. Waksman[29] believes that "they should be looked upon as a group of fungi, to be classified separately from other groups till their exact systematic position has been definitely established."

FIG. 128. Smear preparation from a culture of *Actinomyces bovis,* showing bacterial forms resulting from fragmentation of myselium. When rapidly subcultured the growth becomes purely bacteria-like, no mycelium developing. Note the resemblance to diphtheroid bacteria.

Many of the actinomycetes, however, although they for a time have a definite branching mycelium, very soon fragment completely into bacillary or coccoid arthrospores and these continue to divide by transverse fission. At this stage they resemble ordinary bacteria very closely. The degree to which this fragmentation occurs varies with the species or with different cultures of the same organisms, but is most frequently encountered in the pathogenic species. In such forms the development of aerial mycelium may be very slight or completely lacking. On the other hand, when rapidly subcultivated, such forms may fail to develop any mycelium or the mycelium may be so fragile that it dissociates when mounted for examination, the growth appearing precisely like a somewhat pleomorphic bacterium, such as the diphtheroid organism. This observation led early to the view that the actinomycetes are but higher forms of bacteria. That they are closely related to the bacteria is also indicated by the occurrence of acidfast species of actinomycetes which bear a close resemblance to the tubercle bacilli, not only in morphology, but also in cultural characters, pathogenicity, and immunity reactions. This relationship is so clearly established that there can remain no doubt that some of the actinomycetes, at least, are phylogenetically very close to the Mycobacteria. Puntoni[20] has recently called attention to the biochemical, morphological, and immunological similarities between the anaerobic *Actinomyces bovis* and *Lactobacillus bifidus.*

We are unwilling to decide on the systematic position of the actinomycetes but since most bacteriologists classify them in the order Actinomycetales of Class Schizomycetes, we shall so consider them. The term actinomycete we write in the lower case to indicate that it is not used in a taxonomic sense but somewhat in the manner we would use yeast or mold. It includes all the Actinomycetales except the Mycobacteriaceae. See page 353.

Petruschky proposed some years ago an arrangement which is still followed at least in part by some textbooks in bacteriology. He made a separate class of fungi characterized by the formation of very fine filaments which he designated as Trichomycetes. This includes four genera: Actinomyces, having forms with true branching and forming "clubs" in infected tissues; Streptothrix, with true branching but not forming "clubs"; Cladothrix, with false branching; and Leptothrix, with no branching. But as will be pointed out later, the formation of "clubs" in the tissues is not a reliable character and certainly not sufficiently specific to be used for generic differentiation. And Cladothrix and Leptothrix are ensheathed iron bacteria bearing no similarity to the actinomycetes but rather closely related to the blue-green algae. There is, therefore, no good reason for continuing Petruschky's classification.

It is very difficult to read the literature on this group of microorganisms intelligently because of the multiplicity of names which have been applied, sometimes to the group as a whole, sometimes to portions of it. The following generic names are used synonymously with the actinomycetes: Streptothrix, Cladothrix, Oospora, Nocardia, Discomyces, Actinomyces.

The name Streptothrix was applied by Cohn to the first species of the group to be discovered, *Streptothrix Foersteri*. This name was, however, previously used to designate one of the higher molds and is, therefore, not eligible. It has, however, been used by many early medical authors to designate the entire genus and, as indicated above, by numerous bacteriologists, following Petruschky, to designate those pathogenic forms not producing "clubs" in tissues.

The name Cladothrix was first applied to a group of the iron bacteria of which *Cladothrix dichotoma* is the type species. This is an organism composed of chains of cells in a sheath, showing false branching. No one acquainted with this organism would consider it closely related to the actinomycetes. Nevertheless, Eppinger named the acidfast actinomycete which he discovered *C. asteroides*, under the mistaken impression that it exhibited false branching, and this name has been handed down through the literature.

The name Oospora has been applied to some members of the group by certain French bacteriologists, and Thaxter named the organism of potato scab *Oospora scabies*. The genus Oospora is rather poorly defined, but is usually considered to include certain of the higher molds with septate mycelium. The actinomycetes do not belong here. Nevertheless this name is preferred by Sartory.

The name Nocardia, given by Trevisan to the group to honor Nocard who discovered one of the important species, has been used by some French authorities to designate the whole group, by some writers to designate the saprophytic species. It has not come into general use except in France and must be ruled out for the whole group by the laws of priority. It is valid, however, for those aerobic forms which fragment readily into arthrospores; Nocardia will probably come into general use, but in this restricted sense.

Rivolta coined the term Discomyces for the causative agent of botryomycosis. Under the two mistaken impressions that the causative agent of botryomycosis is an actinomycete and that Actinomyces is not a valid name, a few writers, especially in France, have used Discomyces as the generic name for the actinomycetes. According to Buchanan [4] the organism described and named by Rivolta is a coccus and not a filamentous form at all.

The name Actinomyces was given to the organism of lumpy jaw in cattle by Harz. It has the advantage over all the other terms used in that it fulfills the law of priority, being the first name applied to a member of the group which had not been used for some other fungus, in that it is descriptive, and in that it is more widely used than the others. Fortunately the synonymy of the various terms is coming to be generally recognized, as well as the validity of the term Actinomyces. The name means ray fungus, and these organisms are frequently referred to in English literature as ray fungi, and in German literature as Strahlenpilze.

The somewhat involved question of synonymy and terminology of the actinomycetes is very thoroughly discussed by Breed and Conn [2] and by Buchanan.[4]

If only one genus is recognized, Actinomyces is the proper name and has now come to be rather generally used. However, the large number of described species running into the hundreds and the very great diversity of characters, both morphological and physiological, would seem to make a division into several genera advisable. The system of Waksman and Henrici appears to be the best of the many that have been proposed. Each of these authors has made a study of the genus extending over a quarter of a century and each has

resisted the temptation to divide the large and diverse genus Actinomyces until a real basis for this division became evident. The following key taken from their recent work has in it ideas from several
earlier workers, Ørskov, Jensen, Krassilnikov,[13] Brumpt, and others.
This reclassification of the actinomycetes was the last paper sent in
for publication by Henrici before his untimely death.

KEY TO THE GENERA OF THE ORDER *ACTINOMYCETALES*

(Adapted from Waksman and Henrici [30])

A. Mycelium rudimentary or absent.   Family *MYCOBACTERIACEAE*
                                          Genus *Mycobacterium*
B. Branched mycelium produced.
   1. Vegetative mycelium divides by segmentation into bacillary or coccoid ar-
      throspores. Conidia not produced. Family *ACTINOMYCETACEAE*
   a. Anaerobic or microaerophilic, usually parasites of animals, not acidfast.
                            Genus *Actinomyces*
   b. Aerobic, partially acidfast or not acidfast. Sometimes pathogenic to
      animals.   Genus *Nocardia*
   2. Vegetative mycelium normally not divided into arthrospores. Conidia pro-
      duced on proper media. Rarely if ever pathogenic to animals.
                      Family *STREPTOMYCETACEAE*
   a. Conidia found in chains from aerial hyphae.
                      Genus *Streptomyces*
   b. Conidia formed terminally singly or in small clusters on conidiophores,
   not in chains.   Genus *Micromonospora*

The above system is very similar to an earlier classification by
Puntoni. It differs in being more complete and in that International
Rules of Nomenclature are followed. Concise but lucid Latin descriptions of Puntoni's three genera in a paper,[21] which in effect sum-
marizes his work, shows how closely he anticipated the system above.
In our opinion, however, none of the generic names used by Puntoni
is valid as used.

Concerning the origin and evolution of the actinomycetes, three
possibilities have been considered: (1) that they are a higher development of the bacteria; (2) that they are degraded molds; and
(3) that they represent a common ancestral type from which both
bacteria and molds have developed. We hardly know enough about
them yet to warrant such speculation, but all three theories have
had their supporters. Lieske [14] leans toward the third viewpoint because of the fact that the actinomycetes are very labile and prone
to vary in their morphology, at times toward the bacteria, at other
times toward the molds. The following scheme taken from his book

illustrates the suggested relationship to the bacteria and to the higher fungi:

$$\text{Actinomycetes} \rightarrow \begin{cases} \text{Mycobacterium, Corynebacterium} \rightarrow \text{bacteria proper} \\ \text{Geotrichum} \rightarrow \text{the molds proper} \\ \quad\quad\downarrow \\ \text{Yeasts} \end{cases}$$

Lieske places organisms of the type of Geotrichum very close to the actinomycetes because of the fragmentation of the mycelium common to both groups. Vuillemin also held that these organisms were closely related.

Since the arthrospores or fragmentation spores of actinomycetes resemble bacteria so closely, and since some species of actinomycetes may at least temporarily fail to form mycelium and grow entirely in a bacteria-like form, one might rationally assume that bacteria bear the same relationship to actinomycetes as yeasts bear to larger molds, i.e., that they represent actinomycetes which have permanently lost the power to form mycelium. This may be considered as very probably true for the acidfast bacteria and the diphtheroid group. But it remains to be proved that the bacteria are themselves phylogenetically a homogenous group, and therefore it would be unwise to assume a relationship of all bacteria to the actinomycetes. It should be pointed out that the fungi too constitute a heterogeneous group and monophyletic origin for all fungi is not accepted by all mycologists.

The following diagram may have some value in depicting the relationships of the various genera of the actinomycetes to each other and to related organisms. It must be remembered that any attempts to show phylogenetic relationships must be a subject of personal judgment and opinion, and can never be certain. As Jaques Loeb is said to have remarked, in refusing to discuss evolutionary theories, "I do not know how to experiment with the past."

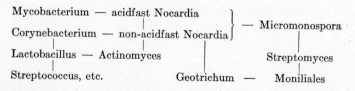

Morphology of Actinomycetes. Actinomycetes differ from nearly all the Eumycetes in the extreme fineness of their mycelium. This varies from usually less than two microns in diameter to less than one micron and is commonly about one micron. The mycelium is no thicker, in most cases, than the typhoid bacillus and reveals no more internal structure than does that organism. One must keep in mind the minuteness of the diameter of the cell in evaluating research on internal structures which various workers have found in the cells. One often has the feeling that the microscope has been used to detect structures which are beyond the resolution power of the instrument.

This mycelium is branched, and in some species rather twisted and curled. It forms a tangled mass like the mycelium of any of the higher molds. Although the branching has been described as dichotomous by some authors, it is not. There is a main or axial filament with lateral branches. In most actinomycetes examined the young hyphae of the mycelium appear to be homogeneous, i.e., undifferentiated, whether examined unstained or in fixed and stained preparations. In older parts of the mycelium it frequently becomes thicker and one can distinguish within it granules and vacuoles. In certain forms, especially in old cultures on rich media, these vacuoles may become quite numerous and relatively large.

There has been some difference of opinion concerning the occurrence of septa in the mycelium. Drechsler [6] states that septa are present, but that the cells so formed are very long. Most other investigators deny the existence of septa. It must be admitted that with such fine mycelium it is somewhat difficult to determine whether certain rather infrequent interruptions in the continuity of the mycelium are septa or vacuoles. The frequent occurrence of fragmentation of the mycelium into segments analogous to the arthrospores of organisms like *Geotrichum candidum* has been considered evidence of the occurrence of septa in the mycelium. This fragmentation occurs in the same manner as the fission of bacteria, i.e., the crosswall develops just preceding the division. This can be seen with pathogenic species quite readily. The presence of septa in those species which do not fragment has not been definitely established; if present, they are certainly not numerous. This formation of arthrospores occurs very early and regularly with some species, and rarely or not at all with others, and was first proposed as a basis for a major subdivision of the group by Ørskov.[18] In general, those species which tend to form pellicles on liquid media tend to undergo mycelial fragmentation, and those that grow in the bottom of the tube do not, but this is by no means an absolute rule.

The formation of arthrospores or fragmentation spores has been studied particularly by Ørskov. The fragments frequently occur in a characteristic zigzag arrangement, which is best seen in slide cultures. According to Ørskov, fragmentation begins at the center of the colony and proceeds peripherally. After the mycelium has split into elements of fairly uniform length, these undergo post-fission movements of precisely the same kind as those shown by the diphtheroid bacteria, one element moving through an arc to lie at an angle with the adjacent element. This Ørskov refers to as angular growth. It is particularly characteristic of the pathogenic species, and may be considered further evidence of a relationship to bacteria. Such a zigzag arrangement of the elements produced by fragmentation of the mycelium is also characteristic of *G. candidum*.

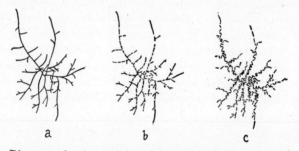

a b c

Fig. 129. Diagram showing origin of bacterial forms from mycelium in *Nocardia: a,* continuous mycelium; *b,* fragmentation; *c,* post-fission movements lead to "angular growth."

When smear preparations are made from fragmented cultures of actinomycetes, naturally the arrangement of the mycelial fragments is disturbed and they become irregularly scattered. Here and there will be found two cells in a V-shaped arrangement. The appearance of the slide is that of a rather pleomorphic bacterium, such as the diphtheroid organism. If in addition some conidia have been formed, these will appear very much like cocci in chains, and the resemblance to a smear preparation of mixed bacteria is very close indeed.

In preparations stained by certain methods, deeply stained granules may sometimes be demonstrated. There has been some discussion of whether or not these are to be considered nuclei. They may be completely absent in the younger mycelium, may first appear as small isolated granules, and may occur as numerous large masses in the older mycelium. Most authors are inclined to interpret them as volutin, and it is certain that most of these bodies are volutin granules. It has been demonstrated, however, in recent years that some of these are nuclei. Drechsler,[6] some twenty-five years ago, interpreted bodies which he found in developing conidia as nuclei but since his methods did not differentiate between nuclei and volutin granules, his findings have been generally discounted by critical bacteriologists. Recently, Newcomer and Kenknight[17] have demonstrated by the Feulgen stain what appear to be nuclei, definite and discrete. Von Plotho[19] has found discrete nuclei by the Feulgen method in the conidia and somewhat less discrete nuclei in the mycelium. Badian[1] has also demonstrated what appear to be nuclei in the spore-bearing mycelium and in the conidia.

In addition to the arthrospores or fragmentation spores many species of actinomycetes reproduce by the formation of conidia on aerial hyphae. Spore formation is, however, very irregular, with many species failing completely on some media. Cultures which have not been transplanted for some time frequently fail to form spores in the first subculture. It is not an uncommon experience to find conidia develop rather suddenly on a strain which has not shown any aerial mycelium during many months of subcultivation, and old laboratory strains, which formed conidia when first isolated, frequently have a tendency to lose the ability to form conidia readily. The formation of aerial mycelium and conidia is manifested by the development of a fine powdery coat on the surface of the culture.

The mechanism of spore formation and the arrangements of the sporogenous hyphae have been studied in some detail by Drechsler.[6] According to this author, conidia are formed by the development of septa in the terminal portions of the filaments. These septa are at first thick and stain deeply. Then a division occurs transversely through the septa separating the terminal portion of the filament into cylindrical segments which later may become rounded. But Lieske[14] believes that true septa are not formed. Instead, vacuoles or empty spaces appear in the hyphae, dividing the protoplasm into many segments which become separated by constriction to form the conidia. According to this author, the aerial spores are not true conidia, but merely a further development of fragmentation spores. It would seem, however, that the aerial mycelium and its spores are too minute to permit such fine differentiations to be made with certainty. It should be noted, however, that the presence of septa in the pathogenic species previous to formation of the fragmentation spores is definitely established.

A very striking character of the spore-bearing filaments is their tendency to be spirally twisted. This is more marked in some species than in others. Drechsler has noted that in some cases the filaments are coiled to the right, in other cases to the left, and he has maintained that this character is constant for the species. It is not always so, however; both Waksman and Henrici have demonstrated to one of us a single hypha bearing both dextro and sinistro coiled chains of conidia. The spiral curvature begins to develop as the spores are formed and increases during their development. When the spores are mature, the filaments untwist and this mechanism may serve to help discharge them into the air.

The spore-bearing aerial hyphae are branched, and this branching may also be characteristic of the different species and serve as a means of differentiation. Drechsler recognizes two main types: "(1) an erect dendroidic type in which the sequence of development of the sporogenous hyphae is sucessive; and (2) a prostrate, racemose type in which the development is more nearly simultaneous." In addition, Waksman has described a type in which the spore-bearing branches are given off from the main or axial filament in whorls. It remains to be demonstrated, however, that these characters of the conidia and conidiophores are sufficiently constant to serve as diagnostic characters. It has been claimed [1] that the conidia are diploid, union of nuclei taking place in the immature conidiophore and reduction division in the germinating spore. This has not been confirmed. Consult Knaysi [12] for cytology of the actinomycetes.

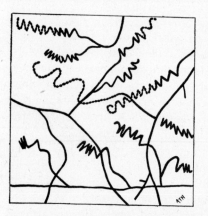

Fig. 130. Conidia and conidiophores of *Streptomyces viridochromogenus*.

Physiology of the Actinomycetes. The colonies of the aerobic actinomycetes must be familiar to all who have ever exposed agar plates to the air, either intentionally or accidentally, for their spores are ubiquitous. Small, round, flat, tenaciously adherent to the medium, often highly pigmented, the surface often covered with a white or greyish powdery film, the surrounding medium often dark brown in color, and very frequently accompanied by a most penetrating musty odor, colonies are easily recognized.

Older colonies vary considerably in appearance. In general, two main types may be recognized, corresponding to the forms that do and do not readily undergo fragmentation of the mycelium. The first type forms colonies which are very firm, almost cartilaginous in consistency, and very adherent to the agar. They are usually slightly conical in cross section, frequently have an elevated central papilla, and show marked radial foldings. Such forms are at first smooth and glistening on the surface, but later develop spores, when the surface develops the powdery appearance mentioned above. Not

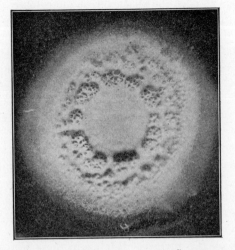

FIG. 131. Colony of mold-like actinomycete, *Streptomyces griseolus*.

FIG. 132. Colony of bacterium-like actinomycete, *Actinomyces bovis*.

infrequently the aerial hyphae do not develop all over the surface, but in concentric rings. In the second type the colonies are not so tenacious, but tend rather to be of a mealy consistency, and are not so adherent to the agar. Their surface is usually irregularly wrinkled in all directions, not showing the radial folds. These colony forms are not perfectly constant and species may be found which will form one type at one time or on one medium, and the other type at another time or on a different medium. The growth on agar slants in general varies as does the character of the colonies.

Colonies on agar media that do not promote conidia formation are somewhat difficult to distinguish from bacterial colonies, as are subsurface colonies of most actinomycetes. The radiating mycelium can often only be seen when the colony is examined under the microscope. The colonies of non-fragmenting species, however, are always adherent and after a little experience one can usually distinguish colonies of bacteria from those of actinomycetes without the use of a microscope.

On liquid media also, two general types of growth may be recognized, which again correlate roughly with the types of colonies described above. The non-fragmenting, tenacious colony types usually grow submerged in the liquid, and form small fluffy masses of mycelium either at the bottom of the tube or adherent to the sides. The fragmenting, mealy colony types tend to form a dry wrinkled pellicle floating on the surface. But again these characters are not altogether constant, and the correlation of these characters is by no means perfect.

One of the most striking and important of the cultural characters of the actinomycetes is their production of pigments. Three types may be recognized: that which develops in the spores, that which is retained in the mycelium, and that which diffuses into the medium. The spores are usually white or grey, sometimes a distinct brownish-grey or olive-grey. The mycelium may be nearly colorless, having a rather indefinite yellowish translucent appearance, or it may be brilliantly pigmented. Practically all the colors of the rainbow may be found if a number of species are studied; blue, green, yellow, orange, and red. The production of pigments by actinomycetes, especially by the genus Streptomyces, has been studied particularly by Krainsky, by Waksman, by Millard and Burr, and by Conn.[5] Pigment production is often used to distinguish species.

In addition to the pigments of the mycelium, many species form soluble pigments. These are usually of the same color as the pigment retained in the mycelium but they may be different. Yellow and orange are most frequently observed. One species, *Streptomyces coelicolor* (*Actinomyces violaceus-ruber*), shows regularly a very striking color change, being at first red and later a pronounced blue. This has been shown to be due to a change in the reaction of the medium, the pigment being very similar to litmus and changing from red to blue as the reaction of the medium changes from acid to alkaline. This pigment also diffuses into the medium.

A considerable number of species produce a very characteristic brownish discoloration of the agar. It is very pronounced on potato and gelatin, and easily noticeable in the water-clear peptone solution. At first yellowish, this medium becomes gradually light and then dark brown, and finally almost black. It was formerly believed that the brownish discoloration of the media was characteristic of a single species named *A. chromogenus,* but it is now known that a considerable number of species which differ among themselves in other characters may form this black pigment. These forms are frequently referred to as the chromogenus group of actinomycetes.

The formation of this pigment, according to Beijerinck, is due to the action of an enzyme, tyrosinase, on tyrosine, converting this substance to a pigment, melanin; this reaction is supposed to be the same one which causes the spontaneous darkening of potatoes when their cut surface is exposed to the air or when urine, in cases of melanuria, turns dark in color on standing. Skinner [24] found that this pigment was produced only in media which contain free or combined tyrosine, and no species produced it in any medium unless it did also in certain synthetic media with tyrosine. Another brown pigment, tinctorially and chemically different, is produced by a few rare species in tyrosine-free media. Another soluble pigment is also produced by some of the actinomycetes from free but not from combined tyrosine. This is a pink or red pigment which turns to melanin on prolonged standing or on being heated with sodium hydroxide.

The pigments produced by the actinomycetes, as was stated, are very striking and, as has been indicated, they are a definite indication of metabolism. However, the biochemical study of pigment production has only been started. Conn and Conn [5] show that numerous pH indicators other than the well-known red ↔ blue indicator of *S. coelicolor* are produced. The great variability in color produced in different media of the same pH shows that metabolism also is responsible for the kinds of pigments produced. One Streptomyces strain, for instance, was found to produce a bright yellow color only on media containing free or combined histidine. The chemical properties of a few of the pigments have been studied but much more work should be done.

It is commonly said that pigment production of aerobic actinomycetes is subject to extreme variation. This statement needs qualification. It is true that a strain inoculated into several media of slightly different composition will vary enormously as to color. And it is also true that the ability to form pigments may be gradually lost or lessened by cultivation, although this ability may in some cases be entirely or partially revived. But a given strain will for months at a time give exactly the same color production on the same medium carefully and accurately made up. Synthetic media are largely used for this. We have here the same problem of variation, better called degeneration, that we have with the dermatophytes. Because of this physiological degeneration it is doubtful that type cultures will be of any more value in identifying these aerobic actinomycetes physiologically than are type cultures of the dermatophytes morphologically.

Stanier [26] has made a study of the variations of Streptomyces, including sudden changes in pigment production. He noted that variants rarely occur in colonies developing from mycelium but frequently occur in colonies from conidia. These variations are of the type that occurs in many giant colonies of molds, yeasts, bacteria, and smut sporidia. These variants were manifested by differences in size of colonies, pigmentation (three pigments or lack of them in various combinations in one of the species studied), type of aerial mycelium, conidia or lack of them, tendency to autolysis, and tendency to further variation. That the production of variants is any more common, however, in the actinomycetes as a group than in other organisms is not evident to the present author, who has observed thousands of colonies of actinomycetes of several weeks' incubation and, although variant sectors are sometimes seen, they do not seem to occur more frequently than they do in colonies of molds and bacteria of equal age.

Most of the actinomycetes grow well on all the usual bacteriological culture media. Some of the pathogenic strains grow very poorly, and some have never been cultivated, but these are exceptions. For the most part they prefer an alkaline medium, and many species are sharply inhibited by relatively slight degrees of acidity. Jensen [8] has described an acidophilous species. For most soil species the limiting pH is 5.0. With most strains on most media there is a tendency for the medium to become more alkaline during their growth. They vary somewhat in their temperature requirements, but most varieties will grow almost equally well at room temperature and in the incubator. A few soil forms are distinctly thermophilic, growing readily at 60° C. Such forms have also been isolated from heating hay. In general, the upper limits are the same as for bacteria, about 42° C. Most forms are strictly aerobic, but one of the pathogenic forms is anaerobic. This is discussed elsewhere.

The biochemical activities of the actinomycetes (Streptomyces) have been extensively investigated by Waksman,[28] whose papers should be consulted for detailed information. A wide variety of organic substrates may be utilized by this group of microorganisms. The simple sugars are readily utilized without fermentation, the media generally becoming alkaline in reaction. Sucrose is rarely inverted and is not a good source of carbon. Nearly all are actively diastatic, breaking up starch with great rapidity. Many species also split cellulose and some split agar-agar. Proteins are digested by most species, gelatin, casein, and blood serum being liquefied. Egg albumen, on the other hand, is not digested by most varieties. Chitin is utilized by a number of species. The breaking down of proteins to amino acids may proceed rapidly; the conversion of the latter to ammonia takes place much more slowly and may completely fail with some species. Nitrates seem to be more readily utilized than ammonium salts, possibly because utilization of nitrates makes the medium more alkaline, whereas utilization of ammonia makes the medium more acid. The majority of species can reduce nitrates to nitrites, but not to ammonia or free nitrogen. Some species are hemolytic. A number of forms produce a rennin coagulation of milk. Fat-splitting enzymes may be demonstrated in a number of species. No work which bears critical chemical scrutiny shows any nitrogen-fixing ability. Higher hydrocarbons of the paraffin series are oxidized by several pathogenic and non-pathogenic species.

Actinomyces (*sensu stricto*). This genus is largely, if not exclusively, parasitic, living on tooth surfaces, in carious teeth, and in tonsillar crypts of man and probably of lower animals, and causing infections under exceptional conditions. Only one species, *Actinomyces bovis* may be recognized with certainty, although other species are named. The use of the specific name *Israeli* for the causative agent of common actinomycosis is incorrect unless it is shown that bovine and human actinomycosis are caused by different species. Present indications are that there is but one species. If Actinomyces is accepted as a generic name, *A. bovis* must be the type species. The outstanding characters, the intolerance of free oxygen, the rapidity with which the mycelium fragments into arthrospores, the failure to grow in the usual Sabouraud or other slightly acid media, make this genus quite different from the other actinomycetes. The most important genus medically, and the one first named and studied extensively, it has been much misunderstood. For many years, cultures labeled *A.* (or *Streptothrix*) *hominis* or *A. bovis* have been in culture museums and these aerobic and saprophytic species are often described in textbooks and in systematic treatises as the cause of actinomycosis. However, in recent years the correct idea, that the ordinary actinomycosis is caused by the bacteria-like anaerobic actinomycete, has been generally accepted. The medical aspects of this genus are discussed elsewhere. See Chapter III for methods of isolation and culturing this genus. The generic name Cohnistreptothrix has been used by Brumpt and other writers to mean the same as Actinomyces in this restricted sense and by Ørskov to include conidia-forming aerobic actinomycetes. It is invalid in either sense. Rosebury [22] has recently written an extensive review on *A. bovis*.

Nocardia. This generic term, often incorrectly used to include all the actinomycetes, has been retained by Waksman and Henrici [30] to include those aerobic species which fragment into arthrospores readily (but usually not so readily as Actinomyces) and also which do not form true conidia. Like in Actinomyces the arthrospores continue to divide by fission and species of Nocardia resemble Mycobacterium or Corynebacterium very closely. Many species, both pathogenic and non-pathogenic, are acidfast. They are more acidfast in tissue than in culture but they are partially so in culture media, especially in milk, much like some of the saprophytic Mycobacteria. Species of Nocardia can be readily isolated from soil and some of these are found to be pathogenic to animals. All the acidfast species seem to be able to utilize hydrocarbons and it is easy to isolate saprophytic species with enrichment media whose only carbon source is paraffin wax. Replicates of ten tubes of such media inoculated with 1 ml. of 1/10,000 or 1/100,000 dilutions of several Minnesota soils showed growth of Nocardia in most tubes, hence they must be very numerous in soils. Jensen [11] has made a study of Nocardia species in soils. The generic term Proactinomyces is sometimes used in the same sense as Nocardia. Shchepkina [23] has made the surprising observation that Nocardia was found as an endoparasite in cotton fibers. Not all species isolated from soil, however, are able to dissolve cellulose, although many of them do so. Pathogenic species of Nocardia are discussed in the following chapter.

Micromonospora. This is, as far as is known, a purely saprophytic genus. First named by Ørskov,[18] in 1923, to include those aerobic forms in which the conidia were borne singly, it remained practically unknown until Jensen,[9, 10] in 1930 and 1932, showed that many species were common in soil. More recently, Waksman, Umbreit, and Cordon [31] found that thermophilic Micromonosporae were common in composts and seemed to be active in organic matter decomposition there. They concluded that many of the thermophilic actinomycetes found by former workers in composts and self-heating straw and hay were species of Micromonospora. Still more recently Erikson [7] has found that Micromonospora species are common in a lake bottom where they apparently take part in the decomposition of cellulose and especially of chitin, during the seasons of the year that the mud is partially aerobic. Obviously this is a genus that will be met with in

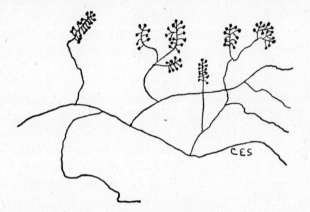

Fig. 133. *Micromonospora* sp. from lake bottom mud. Waksman's collection.

the literature in the future as it seems to be common and important, and to include species which are able to grow at high, medium, and low temperatures.

Streptomyces. Streptomyces has only recently [30] been created as a genus. Most of the non-medical literature is on this section of the inclusive genus Actinomyces, and it is under this latter generic name that most of the past literature will be found. It is very strange that such numerous and ubiquitous organisms remained for so long unknown to so many bacteriologists. It was only after Krainsky, Conn, and Waksman (1914–1918) had shown how numerous they were in the soil—they make up 20 to 50 per cent of the colonies that appear on agar plates poured from soil dilutions—that soil bacteriologists realized that they were common soil organisms. They are air (or dust) organisms as well, and any agar plate that is purposely or inadvertently left exposed to the air is likely to show several colonies of Streptomyces. Even so, bacteriologists who are familiar with many less common saprophytic contaminants are frequently heard to express the opinion that "actinomycetes are mostly pathogenic and are rare." These soil-inhabiting and air-borne Streptomyces are erroneously placed in many of our lists of pathogenic actinomycetes.

Streptomyces species, mostly of soil origin, are the basis of most of the monographic work on the actinomycetes, e.g., Drechsler,[6] Lieske,[14] Waksman,[27] Ørskov.[18] This genus is made up of strictly aerobic forms, which fragment little or not at all, which reproduce largely by conidia in chains, and which are not acidfast. The conidia are not formed on all media by all strains. Especially do they fail to form conidia on media rich in nutrients, but in poorer media, such as Czapek's, conidia usually form quickly with most species. These are the most mold-like actinomycetes and it is understandable that most mycologists, knowing only these organisms, see little reason to consider actinomycetes as bacteria.

As was stated, species of Streptomyces form an important part of the soil flora. They are more numerous in soils containing an abundance of organic matter than in poorer soils. The reaction of the soil seems to be the principal limiting factor, growth being inhibited by even slight amounts of acidity. They are, therefore, practically absent in sour waterlogged soils, as in acid bogs and high-moor peat. They are actually most numerous near the surface, but may extend to a greater depth than the bacteria, so that deeper in the soil they form a larger proportion of the total microbic population.

They do not fix atmospheric nitrogen, nor do they convert ammonia to nitrates. On the contrary, they reduce nitrates to nitrites, in which form nitrogen is said to be assimilated by them. But the reduction is not carried on to the formation of free nitrogen. They break down proteins to simpler compounds, so that directly or indirectly they are active in ammonification.

The soil Streptomyces are perhaps more important in their activity in decomposing the more complex carbohydrates, since practically all species break down starch, and many of them chitin and cellulose. Thus they are well adapted to initiate the decomposition of dead plant or animal matter, since they can attack the most complex and abundant of the organic compounds present: protein, starch, cellulose, and to some extent lignin. Chitin is also decomposed by soil Streptomyces, and the very large number of these chitinovorous actinomycetes is indicated [25] by the fact that several colonies of chitin-destroying actinomycetes develop on plates poured from soil dilutions of 1:1,000,000. The very slow and imperfect decomposition of plant matter in acid peat bogs may be due in part to the absence of large numbers of actinomycetes.

An important disease of potatoes is due to several species of Streptomyces. Potato scab is a disease of the tubers characterized by the production of warty excrescences or "scabs" on the surface, which eventually break down and slough off. For a more complete discussion of this disease the reader is referred to any standard book on plant pathology, e.g., Heald, or to an earlier but excellent work on potato scab by Lutman and Cunningham.[15]

There are several species now known to cause this disease. Different species differ in their invasive ability and they may produce

Fig. 134. Potato scab.

different types of scab on the same variety. There is considerable varietal difference in potatoes and some varieties of the host are more seriously parasitized by certain species or strains of the species of the parasite, hence not only rotation of crops but also of varieties is indicated.[3, 16] In general, in addition to rotation, treatment of seed potatoes with germicide, and use of certified scab-free seed potatoes, control consists in making the soil acid by the addition to the soil of sulphur or ammonium sulphate which is transformed to mineral acids by autotrophic bacteria. Fortunately the potato plant is more tolerant of acid than are the actinomycetes. This acidity helps control the disease but is not an absolute preventive. The best-known species, *Streptomyces scabies* (*Actinomyces scabies*), is sometimes used for all the potato scab actinomycetes. The specific name *chromogenus* is inadmissible for reasons given earlier.

Other Streptomyces have been isolated, causing spoilage of nuts in storage and earthy flavors in various food and dairy products.

Some of these organisms which secrete fat-splitting enzymes have been found to grow in butter with a definite production of acid, resulting in rancidity. Streptomyces have been found growing on rubber and decomposing it very slowly.

It is not possible to identify most of the species of Streptomyces which are isolated. Waksman's [27] keys and species descriptions, published several years ago, are the best available. This material has been condensed in a key in Bergey's *Manual*, Editions 1 to 5 inclusive, and in Waksman's *Principles of Soil Microbiology*.[29] The identification is based very largely on cultural characters and more particularly on pigmentation on media of precise composition. For these the student is referred to Waksman's monographic treatment [27] of the group. After using Waksman's methods several years, one of the authors is compelled to admit that he has been unable to identify more than a small fraction of hundreds of isolates he has obtained from soil. The fault lies not in the very careful and excellent description of Waksman, nor, it is believed, in the technique used, but in the fact that there are hundreds of "species" or "varieties" in soil and the chance of a person's isolating one that Waksman isolated is small. The most one can usually do is to place an isolate as "close to this or that" species. Actually identification of species is not an end in itself, and if one can know that he has a saprophytic Streptomyces species, he may well be satisfied and leave specific identification to specialists at the present stage of our knowledge of this group. Stanier's [26] finding with the variants of Streptomyces species that certain nutritional characteristics are much more stable characters than pigment production is very suggestive for further work on classification of this group, and probably a complete reinvestigation is in order. The question of the validity of the species concept for this group has been posed and, although we are not willing to go so far as to agree that Streptomyces cannot be effectively classified into species, possibly as much could be said for abandoning the species concept for this genus as for any group of microorganisms.

LITERATURE

The older literature on the taxonomy, morphology, and physiology of the actinomycetes will be found by consulting the monographs [6, 14, 18, 27] mentioned in the chapter. We have listed only the recent papers to which we have referred, and have omitted the older citations found in Henrici's first edition unless, because of bibliography or textual materials, there was special reason for their inclusion. It is felt that the material contained in these earlier papers is by now a part of our well-known information that does not need to be authenticated by citation of authority.

1. BADIAN, J., Über die zytologische Struktur und den Entwicklungszyklus der Actinomyceten (Polish-German summary), *Acta Soc. Bot. Polon.*, **13**, 105 (1936).

2. BREED, R. S., and H. J. CONN, The nomenclature of the Actinomycetaceae, *J. Bact.*, **4**, 585 (1919).

3. BRUYN, H. L. G. DE, Investigations on certain actinomycetes that cause potato scab (Dutch-English summary), *Tijdschr. Plantenziekten*, **45**, 133 (1939).

4. BUCHANAN, R. E., *General Systematic Bacteriology*, Williams and Wilkins, Baltimore, 1925.

5. CONN, H. J., and J. E. CONN, Value of pigmentation in classifying actinomycetes, *J. Bact.*, **42**, 791 (1941).

6. DRECHSLER, C., Morphology of the genus Actinomyces, *Botan. Gaz.*, **67**, 65; **67**, 147 (1919).

7. ERIKSON, D., Studies on some lake mud strains of Micromonospora, *J. Bact.*, **41**, 277 (1941).

8. JENSEN, H. L., Actinomyces acidolphilus n. sp. A group of acidophilus actinomycetes isolated from soil, *Soil Sci.*, **25**, 225 (1928).

9. ———, The genus Micromonospora Ørskov—a little known group of soil microorganisms, *Proc. Linnean Soc. N. S. Wales*, **55**, 231 (1930).

10. ———, Further observations on the genus Micromonospora, *Proc. Linnean Soc. N. S. Wales*, **57**, 173 (1932).

11. ———, Contributions to our knowledge of the Actinomycetales, II and IV, *Proc. Linnean Soc. N. S. Wales*, **56**, 345 (1931); **57**, 364 (1932).

12. KNAYSI, G., *Elements of Bacterial Cytology*, Comstock, Ithaca, N. Y., 1944.

13. KRASSILNIKOV, N. A., and T. A. TAUSSON, Variability of Proactinomycetes and Mycobacteria (Russian-English summary), *Microbiologiya*, **7**, 50 (1938).

14. LIESKE, R., *Morphologie und Biologie der Strahlenpilze*, Bornträger, Leipzig, 1921.

15. LUTMAN, B. F., and G. C. CUNNINGHAM, Potato scab, *Vermont Agr. Exp. Sta. Bull. 184*, 1914.

16. MICHEL, W., Versuche zur Schaffung einer einfachen Methode für die Prüfung des Verhaltens verschiedener Kartoffelsorten gegen Schorf, *Angew. Botan.*, **22**, 133 (1940).

17. NEWCOMER, E. H., and G. KENKNIGHT, Nuclei in Actinomyces, *Papers Mich. Acad. Sci.*, **25**, 85 (1939).

18. ØRSKOV, J., *Investigations into the Morphology of the Ray Fungi*, Levin and Muksgaard, Copenhagen, 1923.

19. PLOTHO, O. VON, Die chromatische Substanz bei Actinomyceten, *Arch. Mikrobiol.*, **11**, 285 (1940).

20. PUNTONI, V., Sulle relazioni fra il b. bifido e gli attinomiceti anaerobi tipo Wolff-Israel, *Ann. igiene*, **47**, 157 (1937).

21. ———, La classificazione degli attinomiceti (Microsyphonales Vuill.), *Third Intern. Congr. Microbiol., Rept. Proc.*, New York (1939), 195 (1940).

22. ROSEBURY, T., Parasitic actinomycetes and other filamentous microorganisms in the mouth, *Bact. Revs.*, **8**, 189 (1944).

23. SHCHEPKINA, T. V., Investigations and descriptions of cotton fibre endo-parasites (Russian-English summary), *Bull. acad. sci. U.R.S.S.* [Cl. Math. and Nat. Sci.], Ser. Biol., **2**, 164 (1940).

24. SKINNER, C. E., The "tyrosinase reaction" of the actinomycetes, *J. Bact.*, **35**, 415 (1938).

25. SKINNER, C. E., and F. DRAVIS, A quantitative determination of chitin de-stroying microorganisms in soil, *Ecology*, **18**, 391 (1937).

26. STANIER, R. Y., Agar decomposing strains of the Actinomyces coelicolor species group, *J. Bact.*, **44**, 555 (1942).

27. WAKSMAN, S. A., Cultural studies of species of Actinomyces, *Soil Sci.*, **8**, 71 (1919).

28. ———, Studies in the metabolism of the actinomycetes, *J. Bact.*, **4**, 189 (1919); **5**, 1 (1920).

29. ———, *Principles of Soil Microbiology*, Williams and Wilkins, Baltimore, 2nd ed., 1932.

30. WAKSMAN, S. A., and A. T. HENRICI, The nomenclature and classification of the actinomycetes, *J. Bact.*, **46**, 337 (1943).

31. WAKSMAN, S. A., W. W. UMBREIT, and T. C. CORDON, Thermophilic actino-mycetes and fungi in soils and in composts, *Soil Sci.*, **47**, 37 (1939).

CHAPTER XIII

ACTINOMYCOSIS

The subject of actinomycosis is difficult to present in a logical manner because of the large number of types of pathogenic actinomycetes and the multiplicity of diseases they cause on the one hand, and because of errors in identification on the other. Lebert is credited with the first report of the disease in man in 1857. In 1876 Bollinger[2] described the disease in cattle and in 1877 Harz named the organism *Actinomyces bovis*. A part of the material Bollinger studied was bovine actinobacillosis which is caused by a Gram-negative bacillus and at that time it was not differentiated from actinomycosis. The knowledge of the characteristics of *A. bovis* was based only upon its appearance in tissues until 1891 when Wolff and Israel[27] isolated it in pure culture, described it adequately, and showed that it was an anaerobe. Unfortunately, in this same year, Bostroem also attempted to obtain cultures and, using aerobic methods of cultivation, failed to grow *A. bovis* but isolated in a few of his cultures an aerobic actinomycete (Streptomyces) which he erroneously described as *A. bovis*. It is generally considered now that this organism was a chance contaminant. The Bostroem organism is of a type common in soil and vegetation and gave rise to the popular misconception that the pathogen occurs in nature on straws and that it is transmitted from such material to animals and man. Actually *A. bovis* has never been found on vegetation except in rare cases when the awns of grasses and similar material have been found as foreign bodies in lesions about the jaws. Even in these cases it is highly probable that the fungus was not present on the awns until they were contaminated in the oral cavity, where *A. bovis* is known to be commonly present.[8, 12, 15, 18, 23, 24, 28]

A. bovis is difficult to isolate and maintain in culture, but the Bostroem contaminant grows readily and is easily transferred in culture. As a consequence, few laboratories or culture collections have maintained cultures of *A. bovis*, but a strain of Bostroem's aerobic fungus, once deposited in a culture collection under the erroneous name, is maintained easily and remains indefinitely as a source of confusion.

Other clinical types of actinomycosis are caused by distantly related, or perhaps unrelated, actinomycetes (Nocardia spp.). One type of Madura foot, for example, is caused by *Nocardia madurae,* and this disease has been known since Carter's studies in 1861. A generalized actinomycosis, usually involving the central nervous system and caused by an acidfast actinomycete (*N. asteroides*) also has a history somewhat confused and obscured by the lapse of time and the mutability of the fungus causing it. *N. asteroides* was isolated by Eppinger from a brain lesion in 1890. In addition to these better known species there are several others and some named varieties which will be discussed later. Other types of infection with some clinical and histological resemblance to actinomycosis have sometimes been confused with it. Actinobacillosis [14] and Staphylococcic actinophytosis (botryomycosis) [7] are the most important of these.

For the reasons just given the name actinomycosis as sometimes used in the broad sense is almost meaningless. Even when it is used in a restricted sense to include only those diseases caused by actinomycetes it is still indefinite because of the multiplicity of species and of the types of disease which they cause. Strictly speaking actinomycosis should refer only to the disease which is caused by the anaerobe, *A. bovis,* and in which sulphur granules are characteristically, but not invariably, present. A mycosis caused by a species of Nocardia (aerobic and in some cases acidfast actinomycetes) would then, in the narrow sense, be called nocardiosis.

Actinomycosis in Lower Animals. Actinomycosis occurs in a variety of animals, both wild and domesticated. Moody has described lesions, clearly actinomycotic, in the bones of a fossil rhinoceros. The disease is known to occur in deer and moose, sometimes in epizootic form. It has been noted in practically all the domesticated animals, but mainly in the herbivorous species, and particularly in cattle. The disease in cattle occurs in all parts of the world, but is more frequent in certain areas. Thus in the United States more cases are observed in the slaughter houses of the Middle West than in the eastern or southern states. This apparent difference may be due to a more systematic search for the disease in some areas, however. It is annually a cause of considerable economic loss.

The disease is probably transmitted from animal to animal indirectly through contact with fodder contaminated by the infected animal. A number of authors have reported the presence of particles of hay or grain, especially the awns of barley, covered with a growth of Actinomyces, in the tonsils, the soft tissues about the teeth, or in the tongue of cattle and swine. It is probable that in such cases the vegetable particle acted as a foreign body about which the fungus grew. *Actinomyces bovis* has never been found on such material except when it is present in lesions. The organism does occur in the oral cavity as a saprophyte, however.

In cattle the disease occurs most frequently in the mouth parts, usually the tissues about the teeth and in the jaw bones. Lesions in the tongue, frequently called woody tongue on account of the induration of tissues, are usually those of actinobacillosis. Lignières and Spitz,[14] and Magnusson,[16] and others have pointed out this clinical differentiation.

Actinomycosis of the jaw bones, lumpy jaw, occurs through invasion of the tissues of the jaw bone by way of the peridental membrane. The organisms may extend from carious teeth or may be carried from the tooth or membrane surfaces into the soft tissues by hard food particles during chewing. By extension through the tissues between the tooth and the alveolar processes the jaw bone becomes involved. The disease may be confined to the periosteum in some cases, but usually involves the bone marrow itself. The growth of the parasite gives rise to very characteristic tissue changes. In the immediate vicinity of the organism the bony tissue is destroyed and an abscess is formed. Between these abscesses there is an overgrowth of bony tissue. As a result of these two processes there is formed a large swelling on the jaw bone, composed of new bone tissue which is honeycombed in all directions so that it has a spongy texture.

The abscesses in the bone finally break through to the exterior either into the mouth or on the skin surface, forming fistulae which discharge pus.

Primary lesions of the lungs and of the intestinal tract also occur in cattle but are not nearly so frequent as those of the mouth parts.

Clinical Appearance in Man. In man the disease has been known to involve all parts of the body, but it occurs as a primary lesion most frequently in the neighborhood of the face and neck. Second in frequency are primary lesions of the abdominal cavity, and third the cases primary in the lungs.

Cervico-facial actinomycosis in man usually originates in the mouth parts and many cases follow neglect of carious teeth, tooth extraction, jaw fracture, or other accident in which the organism present as a saprophyte in the oral cavity is introduced into the tissues. The jaw bone is not so frequently involved as in cattle. The infection spreads through the soft parts causing a brawny or board-like induration. Infection is usually somewhat more acute than in bovines, suppuration being more pronounced, and overgrowth of granulation tissue less so.

Abdominal actinomycosis occurs much more frequently in man than in cattle. A large proportion of cases apparently have their origin in the neighborhood of the appendix or cecum, and lead to the development of walled-off pericecal abscesses. Such cases are frequently operated upon for chronic appendicitis or appendiceal abscess, and show a pronounced tendency to drain pus for some time. A rather large number of cases involving the internal female genital organs are on record.[5] In at least some of these cases the primary lesion apparently was appendiceal. Primary abdominal lesions frequently result in secondary liver abscesses, and there are some cases of actinomycotic liver abscess in which no primary lesion in the abdomen can be demonstrated. Abdominal actinomycosis is possibly contracted by swallowing tonsillar granules containing the fungus, or infected material from carious teeth, which lodge in the appendix.

Primary pulmonary actinomycosis may develop when the fungus is inhaled. In some cases the pulmonary lesions are secondary to lesions of the mouth parts. Lesions of the lungs vary in character from a subacute bronchopneumonia to a chronic disease resembling tuberculosis with the development of cavities.

A few cases appear to be primary in the subcutaneous tissues. In some of the cases so reported one is led to question the diagnosis since the anaerobe was not isolated. Such cases may have been actually nocardiosis. In actinomycosis the skin lesions are usually secondary.

Any suppurative inflammatory reaction which stubbornly resists treatment, but tends to discharge continuously, should lead one to suspect the possibility of actinomycosis.

Diagnosis. The diagnosis of actinomycosis is established by finding the organism in the pus in the form of very characteristic sulphur granules (in German, Drusen), or in the form of Gram-positive branching hyphae or diphtheroid hyphal fragments. The granules vary greatly in size, the larger ones being distinctly visible to the naked eye. They have a radiating lobulated structure which is quite characteristic. Where much pus is available, they are best searched for by diluting the pus somewhat and straining through several layers of gauze. The larger granules will be caught on the gauze and may be removed for examination. With smaller amounts it is better to spread the diluted pus in a Petri dish and go over it with a hand lens. With still smaller amounts, a wet microscopic preparation can be made by placing the pus on a microscope slide under a cover slip for direct examination. If the pus is very thick it can be mixed with a drop of 10 per cent sodium hydroxide before the cover slip is put in place. Occasionally the granules may be encrusted with lime salts, in which case treatment with dilute acid is necessary to make their structure visible.

The granules vary in color, the smaller ones being rather translucent and indefinite in color, the larger ones yellowish or even brown. Occasionally there is an associated micrococcus which imparts to them a dark, almost black, color.

The granules are best observed in a microscopic preparation with the low-power microscope lens. The interior of the granules will not

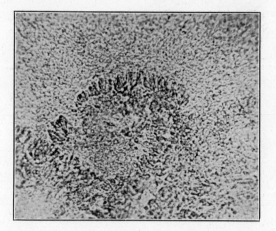

Fig. 135. Photomicrograph of a crushed, unstained granule from actinomycotic pus. The dark irregular lines mark the position of the highly refractile clubs bordering the lobules of the granule.

stand out sharply in unstained preparations, but the clubs at the periphery are quite refractile and will appear as irregular lines marking the borders of the lobules (Fig. 135). Such an examination merely proves the presence of a lobulated granule of the parasite. In human cases this will most probably, but not certainly, be Actinomyces. In bovine cases the identity must be proved by further examination. This may be done by making stained smears. To do this the granules are crushed between two slides and then spread in a thin film which is stained with Gram's stain. In actinomycosis branching hyphae or diphtheroid hyphal elements which are Gram-positive or contain Gram-positive material in beads in and on the cells are found. Usually the club structures are disintegrated by such a procedure, but occasionally they may be recognized in the stained smear where they take the counterstain.

The clubs are formed by the deposition of material upon the peripheral hyphae of the granule. They are not specific and similar material is deposited on other microorganisms which form similar granules. The commonest example is in actinobacillosis described by Lignières and Spitz. In this disease of cattle a Gram-negative bacillus, *Actinobacillus Ligniersi*, grows in clusters surrounded by a sheath of clubs which sometimes branch. The resemblance to actinomycotic granules is very close until a Gram-stained smear is ex-

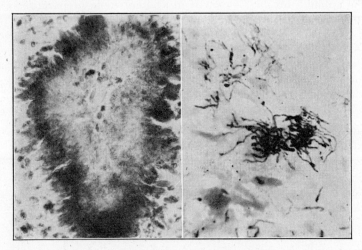

Fig. 136. Left, section of granule of *Actinomyces bovis;* right, Gram-stained smear of granule of *A. bovis.*

amined. There is a close clinical resemblance between the two diseases.

Magnusson [16] has made an extensive investigation of actinomycosis in cattle and swine, and has come to the conclusion that a considerable number of the cases which have been in the past diagnosed as actinomycosis are not caused by Actinomyces but by this bacillus.

A second bacterial disease in which club-bearing granules are conspicuously present is Staphylococcic actinophytosis.[7] This has been especially established by Magrou in observations of this disease which is usually known as botryomycosis and is most often seen in horses. This is a chronic inflammatory disease of the subcutaneous tissues associated with the presence of certain granules of lobulated structure which were formerly mistaken for a fungus, Botryomyces. Magrou showed that these granules are in reality small colonies of *Staphylococcus aureus,* surrounded by an acid-staining sheath of material very similar to that formed in actinomycosis. The disease occurs rarely in man. Some cases have been characterized by abscesses about the rectum, where the primary lesions apparently followed injury by fish bones.

Appearance in Culture. *Actinomyces bovis* is anaerobic or microaerophilic, difficult to isolate, fastidious in its nutritional requirements, and it must be transferred at intervals of ten days to a few weeks if a strain is to be maintained in culture. For isolation in culture a granule should be removed from pus promptly after its collection and freed of as much extraneous material as possible by rolling it across the bottom of a sterile Petri dish with a sterile needle. It should then be transferred to a deep culture tube containing melted agar, crushed with a sterile needle, and mixed with the agar. Dilution cultures should then be made from the original tube and the cultures incubated at 37° C. If preferred the material can be streaked on the surface of an agar plate which is then incubated anaerobically, with or without the addition of carbon dioxide.

If the material to be cultured is heavily contaminated the granules can be quickly washed in physiological salt solution before cultures are made, but delay in planting the material and exposure to air greatly decrease the viability of the fungus.

A. bovis will not grow on Sabouraud agar. Veal infusion agar containing 1 per cent glucose and adjusted to pH 7.4 is probably the most satisfactory medium for primary isolation. If deep tubes are used isolated colonies in the dilution tubes can be removed by means of a sterile Pasteur pipet having an internal diameter of 1 to 2 mm. and transferred to fresh agar in order to obtain a pure culture. Chopped meat broth and Brewer's thioglycollate semi-solid medium containing dextrose are also good media for *A. bovis* cultivation but purification of a mixed culture is rather difficult from these substrates.

In a deep culture tube of veal infusion agar or chopped meat broth the fungus grows in the form of a white or yellowish cuneiform colony (Fig. 132). In most cases there is a zone of optimum growth about 2 cm. below the surface of the agar. The colonies of *A. bovis* in a mixed culture can usually be differentiated from the lens-shaped colonies of cocci by examining with a hand lens. Broth medium is not clouded.

Microscopic examination reveals crooked, sometimes branching, diphtheroid elements which result from the dissociation of the fragile hyphae (Fig. 136). If a colony only 2 or 3 days old is examined it is easier to demonstrate the hyphal character of the growth. The hyphae are 0.5 to 1 micron in diameter and have a characteristic appearance because of the orientation of the branches and the strong tendency of the hyphae to break apart at the septa. Although most of the growth is at the hyphal tip as in other fungi there is some intercalary elongation of the cells which is responsible for the characteristic zigzag appearance. The organism is Gram-positive, but some cells destain except for particles and droplets of Gram-positive material.

Treatment and Prognosis. Actinomycosis is resistant to treatment, but the prognosis is fairly good in localized lesions of the cervico-facial area (so-called lumpy jaw). Systemic infections involving the abdominal and thoracic organs are usually fatal. The usual treatment consists of surgical drainage and administration of iodides and deep x-ray. Thymol has been reported as useful in a few cases. Recent reports indicate that the sulphonamides and penicillin are effective in the treatment of this mycosis.

Taxonomy. *Actinomyces bovis* is the correct name for the anaerobic organism which causes the common type of actinomycosis in which mycotic granules surrounded by "clubs" are usually present. At the present time it is usually considered that a single species is responsible for human and bovine actinomycosis. The name of the fungus was improperly used by Bostroem for a saprophytic contaminant, as already pointed out, and some later investigators have accepted Bostroem's usage. Misuse of the name has caused so much confusion that a number of authorities have adopted the designation *Cohnistreptothrix Israeli* in place of the older name. Reasons for retaining the old name are set forth in a number of papers.[8, 26]

It is unprofitable to discuss the taxonomy of Bostroem's organism because it is apparent from the literature that a considerable number of aerobic species of Streptomyces have been identified with it at one time or another. Some of these were in all probability air-borne contaminants which, once deposited in culture collections, were distributed under the erroneous name *A. bovis;* some may have been introduced into the isolation cultures from contaminated syringe needles, and some may actually have been pathogens of an unusual type. *Nocardia asteroides* will be discussed below.

Geographic Distribution. The distribution of the disease is worldwide in temperate and tropical climates. Sanford, whose map indicating a concentration of cases in the upper Mississippi Valley is often cited, did not claim that his survey of reported cases gave any indication of the distribution of the disease. His statement that it probably indicated, instead, where the disease had been properly searched for and diagnosed has been generally overlooked. The common conception that actinomycosis is more frequent in rural areas because farmers are exposed to the fungus on straw and hay (where actually it has never been found) is a striking example of a medical error arising from an early erroneous identification of a culture being perpetuated by repetition.

Habitat in Nature. From the excellent early studies of Wright [28] it has been known that *Actinomyces bovis* is present in carious teeth. Later studies of Lord,[15] Naeslund,[18] Emmons,[8] Slack,[23] and others have confirmed the early observations and shown that it is often present in tooth cavities, on the surface of teeth, and in the crypts of tonsils. Rosebury has recently reviewed most of the literature on this subject. Demonstration of the fungus and its isolation in pure culture from the oral cavity may be difficult because of the presence of other microorganisms. Emmons in an examination of several hundred tonsils found the fungus present in 30 to 40 per cent and isolated it in pure culture from about 10 per cent of the pairs of tonsils examined. The fungus is present in the granules which lie free in the crypts of tonsils. These are not cases of actinomycosis. There is no infection and the fungus grows saprophytically, exciting little or no host reaction. The granules invariably have a mixed bacterial flora consisting largely of Streptococci, fusiform bacilli, Leptotrichia, spirillae, and spirochetes. *A. bovis* may be inconspicuous or lacking, but in some granules it may be the principal organism present.

Strains of *A. bovis* isolated from the oral cavity in the absence of clinical actinomycosis are indistinguishable from strains isolated from the disease, and have been used in the production of experimental actinomycosis in animals. The pathogen exists commonly as a saprophyte in the oral cavity. It has never been isolated from soil and vegetation.

Actinomycetes in Mycetoma Pedis. Thirteen species of actinomycetes have been recovered from cases of mycetoma pedis (Madura foot) according to Gammel [9] and, in a number of cases reported since that review, other fungi have been described. Most of these are Hyphomycetes and were discussed in Chapter VII. The fungus of interest in the present discussion is *Nocardia madurae*, isolated and named by Vincent.

The granules of *N. madurae* as examined in pus from a case of Madura foot have in general the same structure as the sulphur granules from the lumpy jaw type of actinomycosis, consisting of a central basic staining portion composed of a dense meshwork of the fine filaments and a peripheral zone of acid-staining clubs. These bodies are much smaller and finer in structure than those in actinomycosis proper.

N. madurae may be readily cultivated on ordinary media and is aerobic. The growth on solid media is usually somewhat mealy or membranous and wrinkled, generally creamy white or grey in color, though at times cultures develop a crimson color. The aerial mycelium is very scant or lacking. There is no soluble pigment on any medium. Starch is digested, milk is peptonized, and gelatin is liquefied. The mycelium undergoes fragmentation in old cultures, but it is less fragile than *Actinomyces bovis*. No spirals are formed in the aerial mycelium and there are no spores.

Madura foot may occasionally, though very rarely, extend up the leg by way of the lymphatics, but does not tend to metastasize to other parts of the body and endanger life. On the other hand, it tends to progress steadily and does not respond to medication. The best treatment is amputation.

Other actinomycetes causing mycetoma pedis are *N. mexicana* (reported by González Ochoa [10] in several cases in Mexico), *N. somaliensis,* and *N. Pelletieri.* There are, besides these, many other species names in the literature, some based upon a single isolation. The validity of these names can be determined only by a critical comparison of many strains. These fungi are extremely variable, and a multiplicity of names is the inevitable result of describing as a new species each strain which differs in minor and variable characteristics.

Acidfast Actinomycetes. The acidfast actinomycetes form a group which is not of very great practical importance, because infections caused by them are rare but of great scientific interest since they form a distinct connecting link between the bacteria proper and the higher fungi.

A number of apparently different species of acidfast actinomycetes have been isolated from both domestic animals and man. They all bear a rather close resemblance to each other in their morphological, cultural, and pathogenic properties, tending to form mealy growths on culture media, with readily fragmenting mycelium, and forming pseudotubercles in the tissues.

The acidfastness of these forms is not so pronounced as that of the tubercle bacillus, i.e., they may be decolorized with acids in a shorter period of time; but it is distinct enough to demonstrate clearly the organisms in tissues or exudates. In general they are much more definitely acidfast in tissues and exudates than in cultures, but they tend to lose this property after continued cultivation.

They may be distinguished from the other pathogenic actinomycetes by the readiness with which they may be cultivated on artificial media, by their cultural characters, and particularly by their high virulence for laboratory animals. In the latter respect, however, there is considerable individual variation in strains and some strains isolated from fatal human cases may produce only local and self-limited lesions in experimental infections. Their relationship to the acidfast bacteria is indicated not only by their acidfastness. Several species, notably *Nocardia asteroides*, form a wrinkled mealy growth of yellowish orange color which bears a very close resemblance to that of the tubercle bacillus on solid media. The lesions of the natural infection may also closely simulate tuberculosis; the experimental infections are generally more acute than tuberculosis, producing more of a suppurative reaction and necrosis, with less granulomatous reaction. But the close relationship is most clearly indicated by the immunological reactions. Thus Nelson and Henrici found that with complement-fixation reactions the acidfast actinomycetes showed a closer relationship to the acidfast bacteria than they did to the non-acidfast actinomycetes. The possibility of cross allergic reactions between tuberculosis and infections caused by acidfast species of Nocardia, as manifested by intradermal skin reactions, has interested several investigators. Conclusions reached have been somewhat contradictory. Drake and Henrici[6] reinvestigated this problem in experimentally infected guinea pigs and rabbits. Using old tuberculin and a filtrate prepared from broth cultures of *N. asteroides* which they called asteroidin, as well as several fractions of the latter, they were not able to demonstrate any cross reactions to tuberculin.

Three species have been obtained from infections in animals: *N. farcinica* from cattle, *N. Caprae* from goats, and *N. Canis* from dogs.

N. farcinica produces a disease of cattle characterized by a spreading subcutaneous lymphangitis with localized abscesses, somewhat resembling glanders in horses, and designated "farcin du boeuf" by Nocard, who first described it and isolated the organism. It occurs in France and on the island of Guadeloupe in the French West Indies, but has also been reported from other parts of the world. The organism forms a pale yellow wrinkled growth on solid media, with a powdery aerial mycelium in older cultures. No change occurs in milk or gelatin. The organism is pathogenic for guinea pigs, cattle, and sheep but not for other animals.

N. Caprae, described by Silberschmidt, is very similar to the above; it differs in forming a more whitish growth on solid media, a more pronounced fragmentation of the mycelium, and in forming a pellicle of rosy color on milk. It is pathogenic for both rabbits and guinea pigs.

Several strains have been isolated from spontaneous infections in dogs which have been designated *N. Canis*, though none has been adequately described. One studied by Musgrave and Clegg appeared to be identical with *N. Caprae*.

One of the varieties which have been found in man, *N. asteroides*, is the best known. This species was discovered by Eppinger and named by him *Cladothrix asteroides*. The same organism has been found in a number of other cases since. On solid media it forms a wrinkled growth of mealy consistency varying from pale yellow to deep orange in color, depending upon the age of the culture and the composition of the medium. Aerial mycelium is rarely formed; when present it is white and very scant. Most strains readily dissociate into one producing a short white aerial mycelium and one forming a waxy, wrinkled growth closely resembling that of the tubercle bacillus. It does not liquefy gelatin or peptonize milk. The organism is very pathogenic to guinea pigs and rabbits, although some strains show reduced virulence.

An acidfast strain isolated from a human case by Ayoyama and Myamoto resembled *N. Caprae* in color. Another one isolated by Birt and Leishman gave a snow-white growth and peptonized milk. A fourth type obtained by Berestneff liquefied gelatin and was not pathogenic for laboratory animals.

Henrici and Gardner [13] isolated an acidfast actinomycete from a human case which resembled *N. asteroides* in forming a buff-colored mycelium, but with a very pronounced production of aerial mycelium, so that the growth was of a pronounced chalky white; and which differed from the other acidfast strains in being actively proteolytic, liquefying gelatin, producing in milk first a rennin coagulation and then peptonization, and giving a pronounced dark brown tyrosinase reaction. But as mentioned in a preceding chapter, these characters have not remained constant, save the white aerial mycelium and the darkening of protein-containing media. They named their organism *Actinomyces gypsoides*. It was very pathogenic for rabbits and guinea pigs.

In 1920 Henrici and Gardner were able to collect from the literature records of twenty-six cases in man. In all but three of these the infection was primary in the lungs or peribronchial lymph nodes. In the lungs there is produced a caseous bronchopneumonia with eventually softening and cavitation, but there is a pronounced tendency for the organisms to become distributed through the blood with the formation of abscesses in other viscera, especially the brain. A rather large proportion of the reported cases have died from brain abscesses, and in some of these the pulmonary lesions were not discovered until after death. There were two cases of primary peritonitis following a simple surgical exploration of the abdomen.

Infections with the acidfast actinomycetes are to be differentiated from tuberculosis. In pronounced pulmonary cases this is not easily done, and undoubtedly these infections have been mistakenly diagnosed as tuberculosis a number of times. In the sputum the organism readily undergoes fragmentation and, being acidfast, the fragments resemble tubercle bacilli very closely. They are more variable in length, and sooner or later long branched filaments will be found.

Although these forms grow readily on ordinary culture media, they grow more slowly than bacteria, and isolation from sputum by plating is difficult. By guinea pig inoculations pure cultures may be readily obtained. This would seem to be the procedure of choice for establishing the diagnosis. If inoculated intraperitoneally the animals generally die in less than a week, with very characteristic miliary white nodules over the peritoneal surfaces, especially in the omentum. The cultures retain their virulence for surprisingly long periods. Thus Musgrave and Clegg found subcultures of Eppinger's strain of *N. asteroides* fully virulent after twenty years.

N. asteroides undoubtedly is common in soils. Gordon and Hagan [11] isolated acidfast strains, some of which closely resembled that species and are without doubt identical with it, by placing paraffin-dipped rods in a soil suspension. The ability of this and related fungi to utilize paraffin makes this a highly selective method. Emmons isolated strains from soil by injecting a soil suspension intraperitoneally into guinea pigs.

LITERATURE

1. ALPERS, B. J., Abscess of the brain, *Arch. Otolaryngol.,* **29,** 199 (1939).
2. BOLLINGER, O., Ueber eine neue Pilzkrankheit beim Rinde, *Centr. med. Wissen.,* **15,** 481 (1877).
3. COLEBROOK, L. A., A report upon 25 cases of actinomycosis, with especial reference to vaccine therapy, *Lancet,* **200,** 893 (1921).
4. CORNELL, A., and H. B. SHOOKHOFF, Actinomycosis of the heart simulating rheumatic fever, *Arch. Internal Med.,* **74,** 11 (1944).
5. CORNELL, V. H., Actinomycosis of tubes and ovaries, *Am. J. Path.,* **10,** 519 (1934).
6. DRAKE, C. H., and A. T. HENRICI, Nocardia asteroides; its pathogenicity and allergic properties, *Am. Rev. Tuberc.,* **48,** 184 (1943).

7. DRAKE, C. H., M. T. SUDLER, and R. I. CANUTESON, A case of staphylococcic actinophytosis (botryomycosis) in man, *J. Am. Med. Assoc.*, **123**, 339 (1943).
8. EMMONS, C. W., The isolation of *Actinomyces bovis* from tonsillar granules, *Public Health Repts.*, **53**, 1967 (1938).
9. GAMMEL, J. A., The etiology of maduromycosis, *Arch. Dermatol. Syphilol.* (*Chicago*), **15**, 241 (1927).
10. GONZÁLEZ OCHOA, A., El micetoma por *Actinomyces Mexicanus* Boyd y Crutchfield, 1921, en Mexico, *Rev. inst. salubridad y enfermedades trop.* (*Mex.*), **3**, 303 (1942).
11. GORDAN, R. E., and W. A. HAGAN, A study of some acid-fast actinomycetes from soil with special reference to pathogenicity for animals, *J. Infectious Diseases*, **59**, 200 (1936).
12. HALL, W. E. B., Actinomyces in the tonsils, *Am. J. Clin. Path.*, **14**, 215 (1944).
13. HENRICI, A. T., and E. L. GARDNER, The acidfast Actinomycetes; with a report of a case from which a new species was isolated, *J. Infectious Diseases*, **28**, 232 (1921).
14. LIGNIÈRES, J., and G. SPITZ, Contribution à l'étude des affections connues sous le nom d'actinomycose, *Arch. parasitol.*, **7**, 428 (1906).
15. LORD, F. T., and L. D. TREVETT, The pathogenesis of actinomycosis, *J. Infectious Diseases*, **58**, 115 (1936).
16. MAGNUSSON, H., The commonest forms of actinomycosis in domestic animals and their etiology, *Acta Path. Microbiol., Scand.*, **5**, 170 (1928).
17. MATHIESON, D. R., R. HARRISON, C. HAMMOND, and A. T. HENRICI, Allergic reactions of Actinomycetes, *Am. J. Hyg.*, **21**, 405 (1935).
18. NAESLUND, C., Studies of Actinomycetes from the oral cavity, *Acta Path. Microbiol. Scand.*, **2**, 110 (1925).
19. NEGRONI, P., Cincuenta casos de actinomicosis y resultados de la vacunoterapia, *Rev. insto. bacteriol. dept. nacl. hig.* (*Buenos Aires*), **7**, 662 (1936).
20. NEGRONI, P., and H. BONFIGLIOLI, Morphology and biology of *Actinomyces Israeli* Kruse, 1896, *J. Trop. Med. Hyg.*, **40**, 226 (1937).
21. PINOY, E., Actinomycoses et mycétomes, *Bull. Inst. Pasteur.*, **11**, 929 (1913).
22. SCHNEIDER, L. V., and D. L. FINUCANE, Pulmonary actinomycosis complicated by pneumothorax treatment, *Diseases of Chest*, **7**, 1 (1941).
23. SLACK, J., The source of infection in actinomycosis, *J. Bact.*, **43**, 193 (1942).
24. SULLIVAN, H. R., and N. E. GOLDSWORTHY, A comparative study of anaerobic strains of Actinomyces from clinically normal mouths and from actinomycotic lesions, *J. Path. Bact.*, **51**, 253 (1940).
25. TOPLEY, W. W. C., and G. S. WILSON, *The Principles of Bacteriology and Immunity*, Wm. Wood, New York, 1929.
26. WAKSMAN, S. A., and A. T. HENRICI, The nomenclature and classification of the Actinomycetes, *J. Bact.*, **46**, 337 (1943).
27. WOLFF, M., and J. ISRAEL, Ueber Reincultur des Actinomycetes und seine Uebertragbarkeit auf Thiere, *Arch. path.* (*Virchow's*), **126**, 11 (1891).
28. WRIGHT, J. H., The biology of the microorganisms of actinomycosis, *J. Med. Research*, **8**, 349 (1905).

CHAPTER XIV

ANTIBIOTIC SUBSTANCES

De Bary in 1879 [5] emphasized the significance of the antagonistic relations occurring among the microorganisms. He noted that when two organisms were grown on the same substrate one overcame the other. This phenomenon has been designated as antibiosis. As early as 1897, Duchèsne [6] noted that certain Penicillia were capable of inhibiting the growth of various bacteria. In 1913, Vaudremer [22] demonstrated that *Aspergillus fumigatus* attenuated cells of *Mycobacterium tuberculosis*. The literature on the general field of microbial antagonisms has been adequately reviewed by Waksman.[23]

PENICILLIN

Seldom has there been such an avid interest shown in a new therapeutic agent as that displayed in penicillin. The now classic paper of Fleming published in 1929 [8] on the discovery of a substance which displays antibacterial properties was at first unnoticed and all but forgotten except by a few alert and imaginative workers. Attempts made by Fleming and a few others to interest the medical profession and the microbiologists in carrying out further studies on this antibacterial agent met with general apathy or indifference. It was not until the work of Dubos on gramicidin and tyrocidine (tyrothricine) awakened the scientific interest in the possibilities of therapeutic agents of microbial origin that the great majority of investigators learned a promising drug of mold origin had been described many years previously. Fleming had, in the course of routine laboratory examination of staphylococcal plates, noted that a contaminating Penicillium had settled to form a colony and that the bacterial colonies were being lysed. He also observed that when the mold, which he identified as *Penicillium rubrum* (later classified as *P. notatum* Westling), was cultivated in broth it endowed the cultural medium with antibacterial properties. He further determined that the broth filtrate displayed bacteriostatic and bactericidal action only toward certain organisms. Because it seemed to be relatively non-toxic to animals, Fleming suggested that it be used therapeutically in the control of certain bacterial diseases. Clutterbuck, Lovell, and Raistrick [3] in their studies of various mold metabolic products investigated certain chemical properties of the antibacterial substance of Fleming produced by *P. chrysogenum*. From that time on, except for occasional papers by Fleming, Reid,[17] or MacLean,[14] penicillin was generally unnoticed until the investigation of its chemotherapeutic properties by the Oxford University group of workers under the able leadership of Florey demonstrated its useful possibilities. Since that time innumerable investigators have studied methods of its production, its pharmacology, its chemistry, and its medical applications. Prominent among those studying methods of production have been the workers at the Northern Regional Research Laboratory under the leadership of Coghill.

Very little has been published about the chemistry of this compound. According to Abraham and Chain,[1] the barium salt of penicillin is said to have an empirical formula of $C_{24}H_{32}O_{10}N_2Ba$, with a molecular weight of 645, or $C_{23}H_{30}O_9N_2Ba$. Catch, Cook, and Heilbron [2] have suggested that the formula of the strontium salt is $C_{24}H_{34}O_{11}NSr$. Meyer, *et al.,* [15] from their studies with the ammonium salt, suggest the formula of $C_{14}H_{19}NO_6$ or $C_{14}H_{17}NO_5 + H_2O$ for penicillin. Thus the agreement is fairly good. Abraham and Chain suggest that there may be present a ketonic, two acetylable, and one latent carboxylic group. Catch and his associates suggest that while penicillin titrates as a monobasic acid, it may be more enolic in character. It is soluble in such solvents as ether, acetone, esters, and dioxane; moderately soluble in chloroform; and slightly soluble in benzene and carbon tetrachloride. In water, it is soluble to the extent of about 0.5 per cent.

This chemotherapeutic agent generally displays a selective action toward bacteria, being more active against the Gram-positive than the Gram-negative organisms. At present it has been reported to be of value when used against staphylococcic, hemolytic streptococcic, anaerobic streptococcic, pneumococcic, and gonococcic infections. It has also been found to be of, as yet undetermined, value against syphilis, actinomycosis, and bacterial endocarditis. It is beneficial, but its true worth against these diseases has not been fully established. It is of questionable value in cases of ruptured appendix, liver abscesses, urinary tract infections, and rat bite fever due to *"Streptobacillus moniliformis."* Penicillin is of no value in infections caused by most Gram-negative bacteria, tuberculosis, acute rheumatic fever, infectious mononucleosis, coccidomycosis, malaria, blastomycosis, histoplasmosis, and certain other diseases. See Herrell [13] for a list of susceptible and unsusceptible organisms. An impressive host of investigators has studied the clinical use of this drug.

The Oxford or Florey unit has been generally adopted as the standard of denoting the antibacterial potency of penicillin. It has been defined as "that amount of penicillin which when dissolved in 50 ml. of meat extract broth just inhibits completely the growth of test strain of *Staphylococcus aureus*." [9] Because the serial dilution method used by Fleming was not altogether satisfactory, an agar cup plate method of assay similar to that which had been used by Reddish [16] and Ruehle [19] was employed by the Oxford workers. An agar plate which has been inoculated with the test organism is first prepared. Small glass or porcelain tubes are set on the agar. The sample to be tested is then placed in these cylinders and the plate is incubated. The drug diffuses out into the medium and the development of the test organism is inhibited, clear zones being produced around the tubes. In general, there is a correlation between the potency of the sample and the size of the clear zones, within certain limits. The Oxford group have defined the unit of antibacterial activity as that amount of penicillin which when dissolved in 1 cc. of water gives the same inhibition as the original standard. They found experimentally that an inhibition zone 24 mm. in diameter was thus obtained. The very fact that so many modifications of the original serial dilution and the agar cup methods have been proposed indicates that an absolutely satisfactory method of assay has yet to be devised. Until a chemical method of assay is developed, there will no doubt be many more modifications suggested. Foster and Woodruff [10] have discussed the merits and faults of the various assay methods.

A number of organisms have been found capable of producing penicillin. In general, they belong to the *P. notatum-chrysogenum* group although organisms of the Aspergillus genus have been reported to form antibiotic substances with properties very similar to if not identical with those of penicillin. The organism used for the commercial production of this chemotherapeutic agent depends on the method of production.

Four methods of producing penicillin have been proposed. The earlier preparations of penicillin were produced by surface cultures. *P. notatum* NRRL 1249.B21 strain has been most generally used for the production of the antibiotic by this method. Spores of the mold are used to inoculate a layer of culture medium, usually 1.5 to 2 cm. in depth. The mold can be grown in flasks or bottles which are incubated at 22° to 25° C. A thin pellicle begins to appear some twenty-four hours after inoculation; a definite white growth is present by the third day; and the growth is green by the fifth. The pH of the medium which is about 3.5 to 4.5 at the beginning does not rise until about the fourth or fifth day. The production of penicillin increases as the pH rises to 7. As the medium becomes alkaline the antibiotic content is lowered so it is imperative that the penicillin be harvested from about the seventh to the eleventh day, depending on when its content is at a maximum.

As already indicated in an earlier section, the investigators at the Northern Regional Research Laboratory have had considerable experience with submerged fermentations, e.g., gluconic acid production. Therefore, studies were carried out by these workers to see if penicillin could be made by this method. It was found that *P. notatum* 832 was better suited for this type of production than the strain used for the surface culture method. It is necessary to aerate and agitate the culture medium with absolutely sterile air in order to obtain submerged growth of the mold. In the vat or rotary drum fermenters, the mold develops as small pellets, although it may grow in a filamentous form if the agitation has been quite vigorous. The obvious advantage of the submerged growth method over the surface growth method is the saving in time and labor. The penicillin can be harvested in from three to seven days.

A third method of producing the antibiotic that has been proposed is the growth of the mold on bran. After sterilization and inoculation, the bran may be spread thinly in trays or placed in rotary drums. According to Coghill,[4] this method presents several difficulties, of which two are the difficulty of sterilizing the bran and the difficulty of dissipating the heat produced by the mold in the fermentation, both weaknesses being due to the poor heat transfer property of the substrate.

The fourth method of producing penicillin that has been proposed is the circulation of the culture medium through a column of wood shavings (as in the manufacture of vinegar) or pebbles.

With all these methods, one of the important causes of failure to develop a good yield of penicillin is bacterial contamination. If contamination occurs either through inadequate sterilization of the culture medium or by the introduction of unsterile air, particularly in the submerged growth method, the entire batch may be ruined. Hence, pure cultures must be used and aseptic precautions rigidly observed. Certain organisms are said to possess penicillinase, an enzyme capable of destroying the antibiotic. In most other fermentations, contaminations merely lower the yields, but in the penicillin fermentation the growth of undesirable bacteria may completely destroy the antibiotic. Since this drug may be inactivated by metals such as copper, lead, cadmium, zinc, and to a lesser degree by nickel, mercury, and uranium,[1] such substances must not be present in the equipment used to produce or process it.

The methods used in purifying penicillin have not been made available to the public as yet. However, according to Coghill[4] present-day methods are but variants of those originally reported by the Oxford University group of workers. These investigators purified penicillin by first adjusting the pH of the broth to a point between 2.0 and 3.0 and extracting the penicillin (which behaves like an organic acid) with a solvent such as ether, chloroform, or amyl acetate. Since the drug is highly unstable at this pH, this procedure must be carried out at as low a temperature and in as short a period of time as possible. The penicillin, now in the organic solvent, is extracted with a solution of sodium bicarbonate. By repeating this process, shuttling the antibiotic between solvents and buffer solutions of the appropriate pH, the penicillin can be obtained in purer form. Since penicillin is unstable in aqueous solutions, the preparations must be frozen and dried from this state, lyophilized, in much the same manner that our dried plasma is prepared. Present-day preparations of the drug are a pale yellow to a dark brown powder containing from 100 to 500 units per milligram. They generally are mixtures of sodium salts of some of the organic acids originally present in the culture medium and have a sodium penicillin content of about 8 to 30 per cent. The preparations are rigorously tested for strength, sterility, toxicity, and pyrogens.

It has become apparent recently[21] that most of the samples of penicillin preparations are mixtures of at least two and sometimes three distinct chemical entities. In the United States they have been designated as penicillins F, G, and X, and as I, II, and III in England. They often occur in widely differing proportions in various samples. Schmidt, Ward, and Coghill[21] point out that, because of this, a given sample of penicillin may display apparently different antibacterial properties depending on the test organism used. Pure sodium penicillin G has recently been chosen as the international standard, of which 0.6 μg. corresponds to one international unit. For further details on penicillin, see Herrell[13] or Waksman.[24]

STREPTOMYCIN

It has been noted that penicillin is primarily active against the Gram-positive group of organisms. Schatz, Bugie, and Waksman[20]

TABLE 5

SOME ANTIBIOTIC SUBSTANCES FROM MOLDS AND ACTINOMYCETES

Organism	Antibiotic Agent	Chemical Nature	Biological Activity
Aspergillus clavatus (also Penicillium patulum, P. expansum, P. claviforme)	Clavacin (clavatin, claviformin, patulin)		Various bacteria; fungi; highly bactericidal; toxic.
A. flavus	Aspergillic acid		Various bacteria; toxic.
A. flavus (also A. giganteus, A. parasiticus)	Flavicin (flavatin, flavicidin, aspergillin, gigantic acid, parasiticin)	Resembles penicillin.	Resembles penicillin.
A. fumigatus	Fumigacin (helvolic acid)	$C_{33}H_{44}O_8$	Gram + bacteria; bactericidal; highly toxic.

Organism	Substance	Structure	Activity
A. fumigatus	Fumigatin		Slightly active against various bacteria; Gram+ bacteria; inactive in vivo; low toxicity.
A. flavus-Oryzae group	Kojic acid		Gram− bacteria; toxic.
Chaetomium cochliodes	Chaetomin		Gram+ bacteria.
C. iodinium	Iodinin		Streptococci; inactivated by quinones.
C. violaceum	Violacein	Violet-black pigment.	Gram+ bacteria.

TABLE 5

SOME ANTIBIOTIC SUBSTANCES FROM MOLDS AND ACTINOMYCETES *(Continued)*

Organism	Antibiotic Agent	Chemical Nature	Biological Activity
Gliocladium sp. (also *A. fumigatus, Trichoderma sp.*)	Gliotoxin	Sulphur-containing ring compound.	Various bacteria; bactericidal.
Micromonospora sp.	Micromonosporin		Gram + bacteria.
Nocardia gardneri	Proctinomycin	Organic base.	Gram + bacteria; bacteriostatic; toxic.
Penicillium citrinum (also *A. candidus*)	Citrinin		Slightly bacteriostatic against Gram + bacteria; toxic.
P. cyclopium (also *P. puberulum*)	Penicillic acid	$CH_3C(:CH_2)COC(OCH_3):CHCOOH$	Various bacteria.
P. notatum-chrysogenum group	Notatin (penatin, penicillin B, etc.)	Glucose oxidase.	Various bacteria in presence of glucose.

P. puberulum	Puberlic acid	Dibasic acid, quinol structure.	Slightly active against Gram + bacteria.
P. puberulum	Puberulonic acid		Slightly active against various bacteria.
P. spinulosum (also *A. fumigatus*)	Spinulosin	6-Hydroxyfumigatin.	Slightly active against various bacteria.
Streptomyces albus	Actinomycetin	Protein-like in nature.	Bacteriolytic.
S. antibioticus	Actinomycin	Nitrogen-containing ring compound.	Gram + bacteria; also slightly active against Gram − bacteria; bacteriostatic; toxic.
S. lavendulae	Streptothricin	Organic base.	Various Gram − bacteria; some Gram + bacteria; limited toxicity.

have recently found that *Streptomyces griseus* produces a substance which possesses activity against the Gram-negative group of organisms. Because it is apparently non-toxic, as is penicillin, in amounts used therapeutically, interest has been focused on this antibiotic. Chemically, streptomycin behaves as an organic base (penicillin acts as an organic acid). Unlike penicillin, it is insoluble in ether or chloroform but soluble in water and dilute acid solutions. Feldman and Hinshaw [7] have concluded from their studies that this new antibiotic may be of value in the treatment of tuberculosis. Fordyce R. Heilman has demonstrated by both *in vitro* and *in vivo* experiments that this drug may have possible use in the treatment of diseases caused by the Gram-negative organisms such as *Pasteurella tularensis* [11] and organisms of the Klebsiella genus.[12] Robinson, Smith and Graessle [18] have reported on further studies of the chemotherapeutic properties of streptomycin.

MISCELLANEOUS ANTIBIOTIC SUBSTANCES

The dramatic chemotherapeutic usefulness of penicillin has stimulated a number of workers to study antibiotic substances produced by other fungi. Already an imposing list of these antibiotic agents has been investigated. For the most part, these substances have proved to be of toxic nature to experimental animals. However, further investigations may very well lead to new chemotherapeutic agents. Streptomycin was such an antibiotic isolated and studied after penicillin was discovered, and now shows useful possibilities. It might be pointed out that the organism which produces the penicillin of Fleming also produces a second antibiotic principle, evidently an oxidase which produces hydrogen peroxide in the presence of glucose. It is unfortunate that the term penicillin B has sometimes been used for it and some confusion may possibly arise. Table 5 lists some of the other antibiotic substances that have been isolated from certain molds and actinomycetes.

LITERATURE

1. ABRAHAM, E. P., and E. CHAIN, Purification and some physical and chemical properties of penicillin; with a note on the spectrographic examination of penicillin preparations by E. R. Holiday, *Brit. J. Exptl. Path.*, **23**, 103 (1942).
2. CATCH, J. R., A. H. COOK, and I. M. HEILBRON, Purification and chemistry of penicillin, *Nature*, **150**, 633 (1942).
3. CLUTTERBUCK, P. W., R. LOVELL, and H. RAISTRICK, Studies on the biochemistry of microorganisms; the formation from glucose by members of the

Penicillium chrysogenum series of a pigment, an alkali-soluble protein and penicillin—the antibacterial substance of Fleming, *Biochem. J.*, **26**, 1907 (1932).

4. COGHILL, R. D., Penicillin—Science's Cinderella, *Chem. Eng. News*, **22**, 588, (1944).

5. DE BARY, A., Die Erscheinungen der Symbiose, 1879 (cited by Waksman [24]).

6. DUCHÈSNE, E., Contribution à l'étude de la concurrence vitale; antagonisms entre les moisissures et les microbes, Thesis, Lyon, 1897 (cited by Waksman [24]).

7. FELDMAN, W. H., and H. C. HINSHAW, Effects of streptomycin on experimental tuberculosis in guinea pigs; a preliminary report, *Proc. Staff Meetings Mayo Clinic*, **19**, 593 (1944).

8. FLEMING, A., On the antibacterial action of cultures of a Penicillium, with special reference to their use in the isolation of *B. influenzae*, *Brit. J. Exptl. Path.*, **10**, 226 (1929).

9. FLOREY, H. W., and M. A. JENNINGS, Some biological properties of highly purified penicillin, *Brit. J. Exptl. Path.*, **23**, 120 (1942).

10. FOSTER, J. W., and H. B. WOODRUFF, Microbiological aspects of penicillin; methods of assay, *J. Bact.*, **46**, 187 (1943).

11. HEILMAN, F. R., Streptomycin in the treatment of experimental tularemia, *Proc. Staff Meetings Mayo Clinic*, **19**, 553 (1944).

12. ————, Streptomycin in the treatment of experimental infections with microorganisms of the Friedländer group (Klebsiella), *Proc. Staff Meetings Mayo Clinic*, **20**, 32 (1945).

13. HERRELL, W. E., *Penicillin and Other Antibiotic Agents*, Saunders, Philadelphia, 1945.

14. MACLEAN, I. H., A modification of the cough plate method of diagnosis in whooping cough, *J. Path. Bact.*, **2**, 472 (1937).

15. MEYER, K., E. CHAFFEE, G. L. HOBBY, M. H. DAWSON, E. SCHWENK, and G. FLEISCHER, On penicillin, *Science*, **96**, 20 (1942).

16. REDDISH, G. F., Methods of testing antiseptics, *J. Lab. Clin. Med.*, **14**, 649 (1931).

17. REID, R. D., Some properties of a bacterial-inhibitory substance produced by a mold, *J. Bact.*, **29**, 215 (1935).

18. ROBINSON, H. J., D. G. SMITH, and O. E. GRAESSLE, Chemotherapeutic properties of streptomycin, *Proc. Soc. Exptl. Biol. Med.*, **57**, 226 (1944).

19. RUEHLE, G. A. A., and C. M. BREWER, United States food and drug administration methods of testing antiseptics and disinfectants, *U.S.D.A. Circ. 198*, 1931.

20. SCHATZ, A., E. BUGIE, and S. A. WAKSMAN, Streptomycin, a substance exhibiting antibiotic activity against gram-positive and gram-negative bacteria, *Proc. Soc. Exptl. Biol. Med.*, **55**, 66 (1944).

21. SCHMIDT, W. H., G. E. WARD, and R. D. COGHILL, Penicillin VI. Effect of dissociation phases of *Bacillus subtilis* on penicillin assay, *J. Bact.*, **49**, 411 (1945).

22. VAUDREMER, A., Action de l'extrait filtré d'*Aspergillus fumigatus* sur les bacilles tuberculeux, *Compt. rend. soc. biol.*, **74**, 278, 752 (1913).

23. WAKSMAN, S. A., Antagonistic relations of microorganisms, *Bact. Revs.*, **5**, 231 (1941).

24. ————, *Microbial Antagonisms and Antibiotic Substances*, Hildreth, New York, 1945.

INDEX

Absidia, 84, 90
Acervulus, 96
Acetaldehyde, 318, 326, 330, 343
Acetobacter aceti, 223
Achorion, 160
Acid, *see* Hydrogen-ion concentration
Acid tolerance, of actinomycetes, 51, 362
  of fungi, 50, 215
Actinobacillosis, 376
Actinobacillus Lignieresi, 376
Actinomyces, 351, 353, 363; *see also* Nocardia, Streptomyces
Actinomyces bovis, 52, 73, 350, 371, 379
  cultures of, 377
  habitat of, 373, 379
  isolation of, 58, 60, 377
  taxonomy of, 351, 363, 378
A. chromogenus, 361
A. Israeli, 363
Actinomycetaceae, 353
Actinomycetales, 351
  key to genera of, 353
Actinomycetes, acidfast, 364
  acid tolerance of, 51, 362
  classification of, 349, 353
  conidia of, 349
  isolation of, 59, 377
  morphology of, 354
  phylogeny of, 350, 353
  physiology of, 358
  pigments of, 360
  sexuality in, 358
  variations of, 361
Actinomycosis, 371; *see also* Mycetoma, Nocardia
  diagnosis, 374
  distribution, 378
  granules in, 374
  in animals, 372
  maxillary, 373

Actinomycosis (*Continued*)
  systemic, 374
  treatment, 378
Adenosine diphosphate, 324, 333
Adenosine triphosphate, 324, 333
Adenylic acid, 324, 333
Adenylic acid system, 324, 325, 333
Aeciospores, 17
Alcohol, utilization by yeasts, 65, 282; *see also* Industrial Alcohol
Alcoholic fermentation, 323
  enzymes involved in, 331
  phosphate, role of, 324
Ale, 278, 340
Aleuriospores, 8
Algae, relations to fungi, 1, 31
Alkalinity, preference of actinomycetes for, 51, 362
  preference of dermatophytes for, 51
Allescheria Boydii, 213
Alternaria, 39, 113
  in dairy products, 252
  in raw cotton, 255
  in soil, 258
  in wool, 257
  on wood, 257
Alternaria tenuis, 252
Amanita muscaria, 129
A. phalloides, 129
Aminobenzoic acid, 219, 322
Amylase, 238, 250, 335, 337, 339
  production, in aluminum pots, 239
    in rotating drums, 239
    on trays, 238
  uses of, 239
Amylo process, 337
Anaerobic actinomycetes, *see Actinomyces bovis*
Ang-quac, 229
Antheridium, 10, 29
Anthomyces, 299
Apophysis, 85